Butterflies of Surrey
Revisited

Front cover photograph
Purple Emperor male, Bookham Common
Ken Willmott

ISBN 978-0-9556188-4-0

British Library Cataloguing-in-Publication Data.
A catalogue record for this book is available
from the British Library

Surrey Wildlife Atlas Project

First published 2013
by Surrey Wildlife Trust
School Lane, Pirbright, Woking, Surrey GU24 0JN

Produced by Flipside, Cranleigh

Butterflies of Surrey Revisited

Ken Willmott

Malcolm Bridge

Harry E. Clarke

Francis Kelly

and members of Surrey & SW London branch of Butterfly Conservation

SURREY WILDLIFE TRUST

CONTENTS

SPECIES ACCOUNTS

INTRODUCTION

IN 1995 Surrey Wildlife Trust published *Butterflies of Surrey* by Graham Collins, the first of a series that reached number 13 in 2012 with *Smaller Moths*. That original volume was a one-author work of 87 pages; it sold out long ago and the time has come for a revisit. Much has changed since 1995: Surrey has lost Pearl-bordered and Small Pearl-bordered Fritillaries, Duke of Burgundy and the Wall, while Glanville Fritillary has been controversially introduced in the Farnham area. Of our current 42 resident or regular migrant species, 24 have declined in abundance since 2000.

This 2013 volume is neither a revision nor a second edition. It is a new book that expands the scope of the original volume, takes advantage of additional and more diverse data as well as improved technology, and is based on records up to 2012. The writers, photographers and those providing editing skills are all members of Butterfly Conservation's Surrey & SW London branch. Equally important contributors are those who walked weekly transects, and other recorders, who have built up a rich body of data.

The main section of the book is occupied by the species accounts. Here the authors have followed a standard template for each species, but they have been encouraged to expand the content to include their personal observations and specialist knowledge, particularly on aspects of the butterfly life cycle, behaviour, or the complex issue of conservation.

Each species account has a distribution map, abundance and flight-period charts, plus a featured transect table. Comparisons are drawn between the years before 2000 and the period 2000-2012. Although the accounts concentrate on the vice-county of Surrey, particularly with respect to species status and habitat, this guide will be of interest to butterfly enthusiasts of all experience levels, everywhere.

Features cover geology, ecology, the weather, gardening, photography and day-flying moths. There are guides to important sites that represent Surrey's key habitats of downland, heathland and woodland, describing where and when to go, and what you may see. The appendices include a wealth of statistics and other data.

The production of this book follows the wettest year (2012) in England since 1917, with butterflies in their lowest numbers since the start of the Butterfly Monitoring Scheme in 1976. We take comfort from their remarkable, proven capacity to bounce back from adversity. The butterfly journey from egg to larva (caterpillar) to pupa (chrysalis) to flying adult is well known, but no less magical for that. Enjoy the beauty of these amazing creatures, and the countryside in which they live.

Francis Kelly, editor, August 2013

PS: March 2013 was the coldest in south-east England since 1962, and 4th-coldest in records dating back to 1910. Butterfly emergence was set back by three to four weeks. July 2013 was the 2nd-sunniest July and 3rd-sunniest month in records going back to 1929. It ended six months of below average temperatures and butterflies took full advantage.

BUTTERFLY CONSERVATION

www.surreybutterflies.org *www.butterfly-conservation.org*

Butterfly Conservation (BC), founded in 1968, is a registered charity with approaching 20,000 members. Surrey & SW London is one of over 30 UK branches and has nearly 900 members.

BC has the following recording schemes:

BNM: Butterflies for the New Millennium: monitors distribution, leading initially to the *Millennium Atlas* in 2001 (1995-1999 records), and then to the quinquennial *State of UK's Butterflies* reports in 2006 (2000-2004) and 2011 (2005-2009).
Data available via National Biodiversity Network Gateway *data.nbn.org.uk*

UKBMS: UK Butterfly Monitoring Scheme, begun in 1976, features over 1,000 transect walks that monitor trends of abundance and flight periods. *www.ukbms.org*

WCBS: Wider Countryside Butterfly Survey, rolled out in 2009 between BC, Centre for Ecology & Hydrology, and British Trust for Ornithology. Supplements BMS transect records. Covers random 1km squares, usually visited biannually. *www.ukbms.org/wcbs.aspx*

BBC: Big Butterfly Count, run by BC, encourages records from the general public over three weeks in July/August.

Butterfly Conservation, Manor Yard, East Lulworth, Wareham, Dorset, BH20 5QP

EDITORIAL TEAM

KEN WILLMOTT (FRES), chief author: born Sutton 1949; has devoted a lifetime to butterfly study and conservation. BC Surrey branch Conservation Adviser; voluntary adviser to National Trust Surrey properties and Forestry Commission, Chiddingfold Forest. Received 2008 Marsh Lepidoptera Award for services rendered since being BC founder-member in 1968. Retired from the printing industry in 2000. Lives in Leatherhead.

MALCOLM BRIDGE, County Recorder 2001-2013: born Halifax 1942; began teaching in West Yorkshire; headteacher for 22 years, in Putney and then Roehampton. A youthful interest in butterflies and moths remained on hold until 1996 when he joined Butterfly Conservation and became active in the Surrey and SW London Branch. Oaken Wood manager from 2003. Lives in Crystal Palace.

HARRY E. CLARK: born Bristol 1956; with a background in mathematics, has spent his career in IT; currently an Information Security consultant. A love of the countryside and interest in butterflies started when he was a boy. Lives in Effingham.

FRANCIS KELLY, editor: born Manchester 1951; was a racing journalist, culminating in 26 years as production editor of the Racing Post from its launch in 1986. A lifelong interest in natural history turned towards butterflies when he joined Butterfly Conservation in 2004. Lives in Woking.

WRITERS

KEN WILLMOTT
Malcolm Bridge
Gay Carr
Harry E. Clarke
Ian Cunningham
Peter Curnock
Geoff Eaton
Harry Eve
David Gradidge
Barry Hilling
Alan Hunt
Howard Street
Mike Weller

PHOTOGRAPHERS

BH Barry Hilling
FK Francis Kelly
GE Geoff Eaton
GW Geoff Woodcock
HC Harry E. Clarke
HS Helen Sterne
HT Helen Tickner
JFK Jovita Kaunang
KW Ken Willmott
MB Malcolm Bridge
MW Martin Wills

EDITOR ....Francis Kelly
Chief adviser ....Ken Willmott FRES
Chief sub-editor ....Geoff Eaton
County Recorder ....Malcolm Bridge
Design & Production ....Francis Kelly
Graphics ....Helen Tickner
Maps & Charts ....Harry E. Clarke
Picture editor ....Barry Hilling ARPS
Proof-reader......................Roger Hawkins

ACKNOWLEDGEMENTS

Surrey County Council: Surrey Wildlife Trust gratefully acknowledges the generous financial support given by SCC towards the costs of producing this book.

Transect walkers and other recorders: without whom a book of this kind would not be possible. In particular: Richard Donovan, transect coordinator for Surrey branch.

Butterfly Conservation (www.butterfly-conservation.org): national organisation whose regional branches include Surrey & SW London (www.surreybutterflies.org).
In particular: Richard Fox, Ian Middlebrook, Zoë Randle.

UK Butterfly Monitoring Scheme (www.ukbms.org): operated by the Centre for Ecology & Hydrology (CEH) and Butterfly Conservation. In particular: Marc Botham.

Graham Collins: wrote the original *Butterflies of Surrey* in 1995. We have been grateful to build on his work.

Gail Jeffcoate: County Recorder 1995-2000;
member of BC's National Conservation Committee.

Alistair Kirk: Surrey Biodiversity Information Centre manager, and project manager for the atlas series.

Jeremy Thomas: one of Europe's foremost butterfly experts. Observations and comments attributed to [Jeremy] Thomas in the species accounts refer to *The Butterflies of Britain & Ireland*, Thomas & Lewington (2010).

Vice-counties of England & Wales

1 West Cornwall with Scilly
2 East Cornwall
3 South Devon
4 North Devon
5 South Somerset
6 North Somerset
7 North Wiltshire
8 South Wiltshire
9 Dorset
10 Isle of Wight
11 S Hampshire
12 N Hampshire
13 West Sussex
14 East Sussex
15 East Kent
16 West Kent
17 SURREY
18 South Essex
19 North Essex
20 Hertfordshire
21 Middlesex
22 Berkshire
23 Oxfordshire
24 Buckinghamshire
25 East Suffolk
26 West Suffolk
27 East Norfolk
28 West Norfolk
29 Cambridgeshire
30 Bedfordshire
31 Huntingdonshire
32 Northamptonshire
33 E Gloucestershire
34 W Gloucestershire
35 Monmouthshire
36 Herefordshire
37 Worcestershire
38 Warwickshire
39 Staffordshire
40 Shropshire
41 Glamorgan
42 Breconshire
43 Radnorshire
44 Carmarthenshire
45 Pembrokeshire
46 Cardiganshire
47 Montgomeryshire
48 Merionethshire
49 Caernarfonshire
50 Denbighshire
51 Flintshire
52 Anglesey
53 S Lincolnshire
54 N Lincolnshire
55 Leicestershire with Rutland
56 Nottinghamshire
57 Derbyshire
58 Cheshire

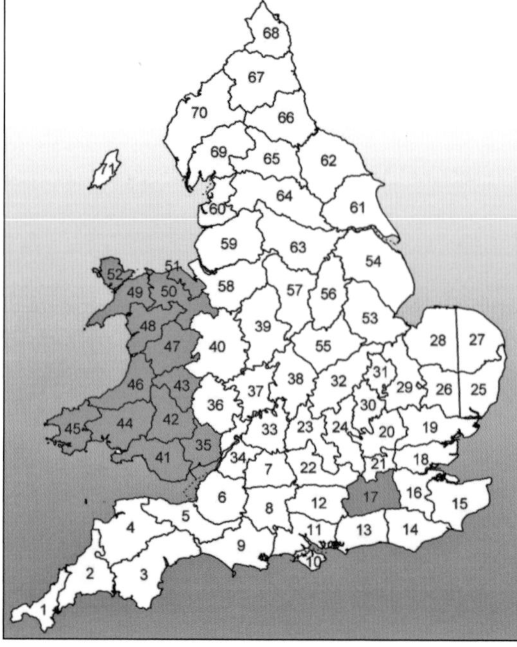

59 S Lancashire
60 W Lancashire
61 SE Yorkshire
62 NE Yorkshire
63 SW Yorkshire
64 MW Yorkshire
65 NW Yorkshire
66 Durham
67 S Northumberland
68 N Northumberland
69 Westmoreland with Furness
70 Cumberland
71 Isle of Man

WALES
35 & 41–52 (pink)

SCOTLAND
72–112 (not shown)

Counties by total species *including regular migrants and established introductions*

46 Dorset
Hampshire
45 Somerset & Bristol
Sussex
Wiltshire
43 Gloucestershire
42 **SURREY**
Cornwall (VC1 36, VC2 36)
Devon
Isle of Wight
Wales (Sth 42, Nth 36)
41 Berkshire
Buckinghamshire
Kent
40 Oxfordshire
39 Cumbria
Lincolnshire
West Midlands *(Hereford, Shrops, Staffs, Worcs, Birmingham, Black Country)*
38 Bedfordshire
37 Cambridgeshire & Essex
36 Lancashire
Northamptonshire
Warwickshire
Yorkshire
Norfolk
35 Herts
North East England: *(Northumberland, Durham, North Teesside)*
34 Scotland
Ireland (ROI 34, NI 25)
East Midlands *(Notts, Leics, Rutland, Sth Derbys)*
33 Suffolk
29 Middlesex
28 Cheshire *(Peak District 28)*
19 Isle of Man
3 Shetland

Surrey vice-county (10km squares)

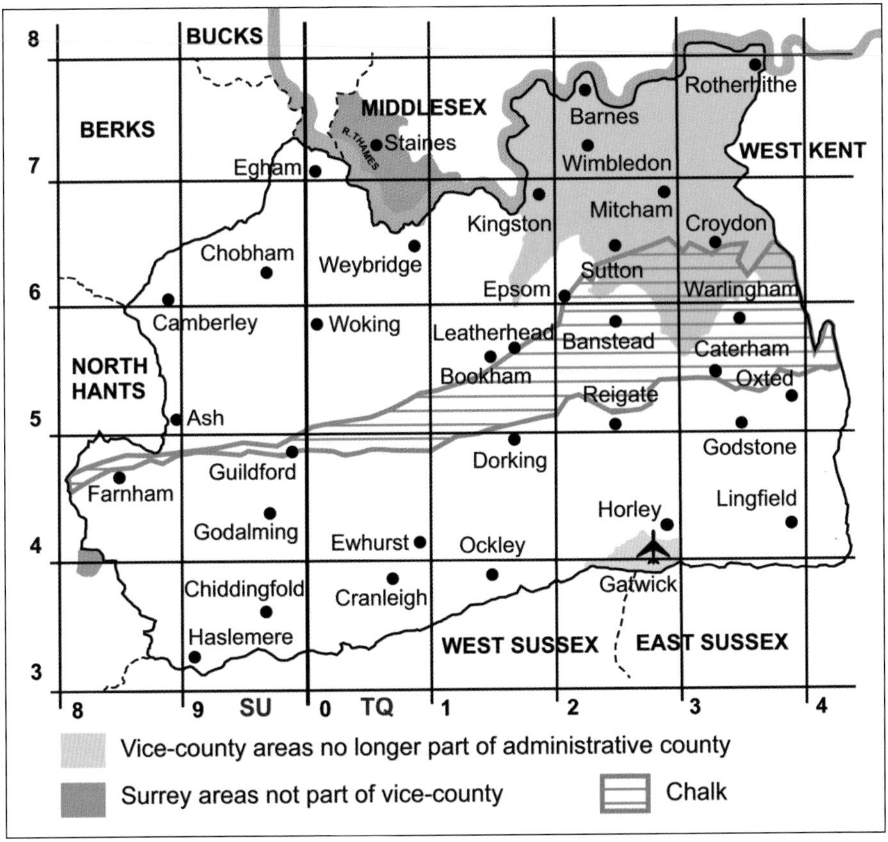

Vice-county areas no longer part of administrative county

Surrey areas not part of vice-county

Chalk

WATSONIAN vice-counties were introduced in 1852 by Hewett Cottrell Watson, and continue to be used for consistent biological recording, independent of local government reorganisations. Surrey is VC17.

The original administrative county of Surrey extended to the River Thames as far east as Rotherhithe.

Non-Surrey areas *inside* VC17:

1889 County of London created: modern London boroughs of Lambeth, Southwark & Wandsworth removed from Surrey; Croydon made into a county borough exempt from county administration.

1965 Kingston, Merton, Richmond, Sutton & Croydon become London boroughs.

1974 Gatwick Airport and some surrounding land transferred to West Sussex.

Surrey areas *outside* VC17:

1895 Dockenfield (western boundary) gained from Hampshire.

1965 Staines & Sunbury transferred from Middlesex to Surrey, becoming the new district of Spelthorne in 1974.

GEOLOGY OF SURREY

Dr Geoff Eaton
Department of Earth Sciences, The Natural History Museum, London

THE variety and distribution of Surrey's butterflies are controlled essentially by habitat. However, habitat, of which vegetation is a key aspect, is strongly influenced by the underlying soil and ultimately the rocks from which that soil is derived. This relationship is acknowledged here with respect to several butterfly species.

THE geological map of Surrey shows a series of sub-parallel bands of variable width aligned roughly east to west across the county. These bands represent different rock units in the solid geological succession that outcrop (i.e. are exposed) at the surface. By convention this succession is divided into groups of rock formations. These solid rocks define the Surrey landscape and represent more than 90 million years of earth history from c. 140 Ma (million years ago) within the Early Cretaceous geological time period (145-100 Ma) through the Late Cretaceous (100-66 Ma) to c. 44 Ma within the Paleogene Period (66-23 Ma).

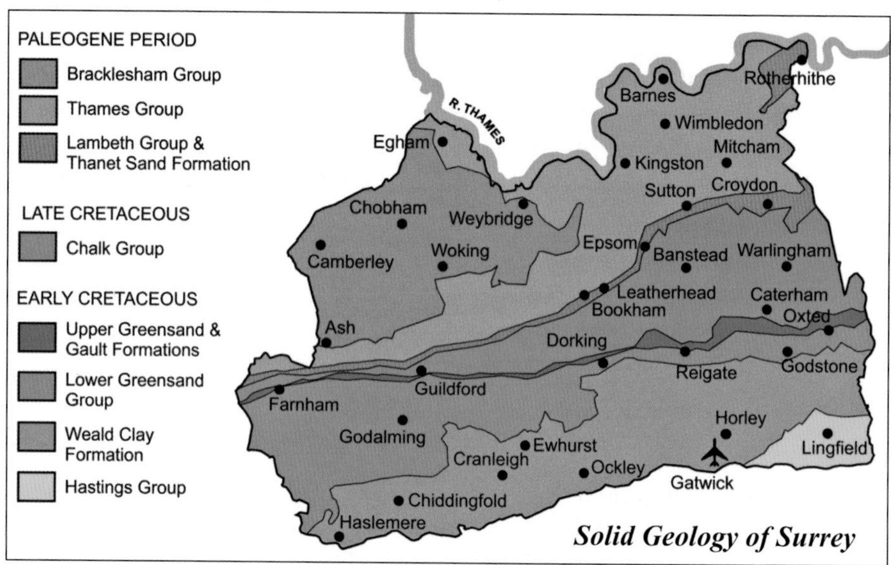

Solid Geology of Surrey

Early Cretaceous rocks yield the oldest-known fossil flowering plants and bees, and it may be tempting to suggest that butterflies might have been flying at about the same time. However, the oldest fossil butterflies occur in younger rocks of Paleogene age. In contrast, fossil moths have been found in much older rocks of Early Jurassic age (see time chart for age details).

All of Surrey's exposed rock formations dip (i.e. slope down) to the north, and generally at a very low angle. As a result of this, the oldest (Early Cretaceous) formations outcrop in the south of the county and form the Surrey Weald, while the youngest (Paleogene) formations outcrop in the north of the county in the London

(Thames) Basin. These two areas are separated by the North Downs formed of the Late Cretaceous Chalk Group. This simple alignment of the rocks belies the fact that Surrey partially covers two significant geological structures: the northern half of the gently-arched dome of the Weald Anticline in the south, and the southern half of the shallow bowl of the London Basin Syncline adjacent to the north. Both of these folded structures were formed during the early part of the Neogene Period (23-2.6 Ma).

In addition to the solid rock succession there are much younger superficial deposits (also referred to as "Drift") that have accumulated within the last 2.6 million years, in the Quaternary Period. These deposits have a complex, irregular distribution across the whole county, and although they are described briefly at the end of this account, they are not shown on the Surrey map. However, the British Geological Survey's maps of Surrey show both the solid geological succession and the superficial deposits. For the benefit of readers who may wish to delve deeper into Surrey's geology, selected publications that influenced this account are listed separately in the references.

Time chart

Geological ages, events and selected oldest fossil records: Jurassic Period to the present.

Quaternary Period	
	years ago: thousands
End of the "Ice Age"	10
Modern man	200
	years ago: millions
Primitive man	2.3
Neogene Period	***23-2.6***
Formation of Weald Anticline	
Paleogene Period	***66-23***
Butterflies	50
Cretaceous Period	***145-66***
Mass extinction (incl. dinosaurs)	
Bees	100
Flowering plants	125
Jurassic Period	***201-145***
Birds	150
Moths	195

Early Cretaceous Rocks

EARLY Cretaceous rocks outcrop in the south of Surrey, and the oldest, the non-marine, sand-dominated Hastings Group, occur in the extreme south-east around Lingfield. Most of Surrey's southern margin is occupied by the younger Weald Clay Formation that was deposited in the non-marine environment of the floodplain of a meandering river system. In a subtropical climate with lush vegetation, dinosaurs walked here and left their footprints and ultimately their remains to be fossilised for our wonder and amazement. The Weald Clay produces a belt of fairly flat country with a heavy soil that supports extensive woodland. Chiddingfold Forest, close to the Sussex border in the south-west, provides an ideal habitat for the Purple Emperor, White Admiral, Silver-washed Fritillary and our precious Wood White. Also, large stands of blackthorn associated with this soil type may support the elusive Brown Hairstreak, as at Holmwood Common, south of Dorking, and at Felland Copse, South Earlswood.

The succeeding Lower Greensand Group (Atherfield Clay, Hythe, Bargate, Sandgate and Folkestone Formations) forms a line of hills lying south of the North Downs. This is the Greensand Ridge, which is not as prominent and persistent as the Downs, but does include the highest point in Surrey: Leith Hill (294m), south-west of Dorking. The Lower Greensand Group consists predominantly of shallow marine sandstones and owes its name to the green mineral, glauconite. This mineral, which is associated with marine sedimentation, may impart a greenish hue to fresh rock, but the colour is lost on weathering. In the west of Surrey the Lower Greensand outcrop widens considerably and gives rise to extensive areas of sandy heathland, such as Thursley and Witley Common (Sandgate and Folkestone Formations), that provide a suitable habitat for the Grayling and the Silver-studded Blue.

The two youngest Early Cretaceous formations, the Gault and Upper Greensand, are also of marine origin. The stiff clays of the Gault outcrop in an easterly widening belt between the Greensand Ridge and the North Downs; the heavy ground is largely given over to cultivation and pasture. The outcrop of the Upper Greensand generally merges into the scarp face of the Downs.

Late Cretaceous Rocks

THE Late Cretaceous Chalk Group forms the most prominent and persistent feature of the Surrey landscape, the North Downs. The Late Cretaceous Period witnessed rising sea-level and an increasingly arid climate. As shorelines retreated and the hinterland diminished, sediment input into the Late Cretaceous sea was greatly reduced. This was the depositional setting for the Chalk, a unique limestone composed mostly of calcareous coccoliths – the fragmentary fossil remains of a particular group of minute, marine, planktonic algae.

The limestones of the Chalk Group produce an alkaline soil that supports typical downland vegetation. However, the presence of superficial deposits covering the Chalk, for example sands and gravels, may result locally in a more acid soil. These various soil types support a diverse, often exclusive flora that readily attracts a wide variety of butterflies. Only on the Downs will you see the Adonis Blue and the Silver-spotted Skipper, and here will be your best chance of seeing Dingy and Grizzled Skippers, Chalkhill and Small Blues, Marbled White and Dark Green Fritillary.

Paleogene Rocks

THE Chalk is succeeded by rocks of Paleogene age in the London Basin. The oldest Paleogene rocks occupy a narrow band of country from Farnham in the west to beyond Croydon in the east, and include the Thanet Sand Formation and the Lambeth Group (Upnor, Woolwich and Reading Formations). Although predominantly sands and clays, this relatively complex rock sequence reflects deposition in shallow marine, estuarine and lagoonal, and river floodplain environments.

The overlying Thames Group represents a significant phase of marine sedimentation and includes the basal, sand-dominated Harwich Formation and the London Clay Formation. The outcrop of the London Clay occupies much of the remainder of northern Surrey. It is largely covered by the London suburbs in the north-east of the county, but elsewhere it provides a wide range of natural habitats on a heavy clay soil. For example, the densely wooded areas of Bookham Common, west of Leatherhead, are ideal for woodland butterflies; of the key species previously noted in the Chiddingfold Forest (Weald Clay), only the Wood White is absent from Bookham. The Common's more open areas support large stands of blackthorn, making this another locality for the Brown Hairstreak.

The London Clay is succeeded by the mainly sandy Bracklesham Group (Bagshot, Windlesham and Camberley Sand Formations). A marine depositional environment is indicated by fossil evidence and the presence of glauconite. This group occupies much of the higher ground in the north-west of Surrey where the acid sandy soils give rise to heathland habitats that support the Grayling and Silver-studded Blue. Typical locations are Horsell Common, Woking, and Chobham Common.

Following deposition of the Bracklesham Group during the mid-Paleogene Period, there is little evidence of further sedimentation for more than 40 million years until the Quaternary Period. This long interval of geological time includes the later part of the Paleogene and the entire Neogene Period.

Superficial Deposits

IN Surrey superficial deposits were laid down during the last 2.6 million years, in the Quaternary Period. They include clays, silts, sands and gravels, and represent river terrace deposits, alluvium, and periglacial deposits. The last named were associated with the development of permafrost in areas marginal to ice sheets that advanced across Britain during the "Ice Age". The most extensive of these progressed as far as the northern area of the London Basin, but did not reach Surrey. Periglacial deposits are often poorly sorted; they generally accumulated as a result of the destructive action of water on existing sediments when subjected to the effects of freeze-thaw in a very cold climate. They include "Head" deposits that occur mainly in valleys, and "Clay-with-flints" and the Netley Heath Beds; all of these can be found on the North Downs. The end of the "Ice Age", as defined by the retreat of the last ice sheet, occurred about 10,000 years ago.

SURREY'S rocks have a remarkable story to tell: of ancient sediments deposited mainly beneath the sea, over a time period measured in tens of millions of years that witnessed the acme and decline of the dinosaurs, the end-Cretaceous extinction event, and the rise of the mammals that led ultimately to us. All this may appear remote and in the past, but the link between the seemingly ever-constant rocks and the ephemeral beauty of our butterflies, albeit via soil type and the diversity of plant life, is immediate and in the present. Think on this when you next climb the scarp face of the Downs on a perfect summer's day in search of the Adonis Blue or Silver-spotted Skipper.

■ SINCERE thanks to **Prof Richard Fortey**, Department of Earth Sciences, The Natural History Museum, London, and **Richard Ellison**, British Geological Survey, Keyworth, Nottingham, for their critical reading of this chapter.

BUTTERFLY ECOLOGY

Harry E. Clarke

BUTTERFLIES require a variety of resources for survival but many of these are under threat from climate change and habitat loss. Climate change is the likely reason why Surrey butterflies now emerge just over a week earlier compared with 1990.

Butterflies are ectothermic, meaning that they are dependent on external air temperature, wind speed and solar irradiation. To fly they must raise their body temperature to at least 18-28ºC, which they achieve by basking in the sun, mostly with open wings. Species like Brimstone and Grayling bask with closed wings, but tilted in relation to the sun. Some species, such as Red Admiral, Peacock and Painted Lady, also shiver their flight muscles.

Butterflies need places to roost. For example, the Common Blue requires long grass where it can roost head-down. Hibernators require a specific overwintering site, which may differ from roosting sites.

Females are fussy about where they lay their eggs as they look to maximise the larva's chances of developing to adulthood. The larval foodplant may be present but possibly overgrown or too exposed. For example, the White Admiral prefers honeysuckle in dappled shade rather than full sun; the Large White prefers larger cabbage plants than the Small White does, but will also lay smaller batches of eggs on the leaves of nasturtium or garlic mustard.

Often only plants at the edge of a patch are chosen, or those in a short sward. Plants high in nitrogen are preferred, with females laying near to the fresher terminal leaves where nitrogen levels are highest. Pupation can occur some distance from the foodplant, as in the Peacock and Small Tortoiseshell. Some Lycaenidae larvae stay close to their foodplants and their ant hosts, which can take them into a chamber.

Butterflies have associations with plants and other animals. While the evolution of the Lepidoptera is closely related to that of flowering plants, butterflies use only a small number of these as their larval hosts. Skippers (Hesperiidae) use grasses (Poaceae), legumes (Fabaceae) and members of the rose family (Rosaceae). Whites and Yellows (Pieridae) use cabbages (Brassicaceae) and legumes. Blues, Hairstreaks and Coppers (Lycaenidae) use mainly legumes, with the exception of the tree- and scrub-feeding Hairstreak species, and the Small Copper (dock family). Browns (Satyrinae) feed predominantly on grasses, while other nymphalids, such as Small Tortoiseshell and Peacock, will use plants from other families, e.g. stinging nettles. The families and subfamilies of Surrey's butterflies are listed on page 213.

Adults need nutrients to provide energy for flying, mating and egg-laying. The requirements for males and females can differ. The main food source is nectar, but honeydew is also used. Some males obtain additional minerals from mud puddles, urine, or even mammal faeces. The Purple Emperor is well known to be attracted to strange smells, including fermenting sap from wounded trees.

During copulation, in addition to sperm, the male passes a nuptial gift of nutrients to

Green-veined Whites (spring brood): male (right) passes up to 25% of his body weight to the female during mating. **BH**

the female, to aid in egg-development and egg-laying (Wiklund *et al.*, 1993). The size of the nuptial gift varies between species from 1% of the male's body weight, up to 25% for the Green-veined White.

Some species, notably among the Lycaenidae, have a strong association with ants in either the larval and/or the pupal stages. In this symbiotic relationship, ants receive sweet liquids exuded from specialised glands on the larvae, which in return receive some protection from flies and wasps.

Males use different strategies to find a mate. Butterflies such as the Orange-tip patrol to find a female. Others use a perch, which may be resource-based, such as a nectar source or foodplant (e.g. Small Tortoiseshell); lek-based, such as a master tree used by the Purple Emperor; or a bare patch of raised earth used by the Wall. Males of some species use both sexual strategies, adjusting according to the number of unfertilised females available at the time.

A female lays many eggs, from 160 by the Brown Hairstreak up to 750 by the Large White, but only a small fraction of these will reach adulthood. Bad weather or lack of suitable foodplants can limit the number of eggs laid. Some larvae will starve or fall victim to another larva (Orange-tip is a well-known cannibal), to parasitoids, or to predators such as birds and other invertebrates.

The main parasitoids of butterflies are from the orders of Diptera (flies) or Hymenoptera (wasps). The flies include the families of Tachinidae and Bombyliidae; the wasps include the superfamilies of Ichneumonoidea and Chalcidoidea (parasitoids of eggs such as those of Purple and White-letter Hairstreaks).

Butterflies use different techniques to survive the winter months. Migrants such as Painted Lady and Clouded Yellow head south. The others enter diapause, which is usually triggered by a combination of temperature, particularly at night, and daylight length. British butterflies overwinter in every stage, according to the species: e.g. Brown Hairstreak as egg, Meadow Brown as larva, Orange-tip as pupa and Brimstone as adult.

Although some butterfly populations will eventually die out if numbers are greatly reduced, some, such as the Small Copper, survive well in a small population structure. The mixing of genetic material between populations is important, but the butterfly's ability to move from one colony to another varies between species and appropriate habitat management. At one end of the spectrum is the Painted Lady, which can migrate huge distances; at the other end are less mobile species like the Small Skipper, for which even minor barriers such as tall hedges may reduce dispersal. Habitat management for such a species should be close to the remaining population.

Large habitats with potential for a metapopulation structure are better than smaller ones, which can become isolated. Corridors with suitable nectar sources are important. Sedentary species, with limited choice of larval foodplants, such as the violet-feeding Fritillaries, are at greater risk than vagrants such as the Brimstone.

TRENDS

THERE can be major differences between distribution and abundance trends. Factors such as the weather may affect abundance on particular sites, while habitat change can reduce distribution. For example, the Chalkhill Blue and White Admiral are abundance winners in 2000-2012, but both have declined in overall distribution. Most of those declining in distribution are habitat specialists: e.g. Adonis Blue, Dark Green Fritillary, Small Blue. ■ See table on page 215.

Winners *2000-2012 Surrey transect abundance has increased by > 10%.*

Chalkhill Blue	+466%	Grayling	+73%	Small Heath	+23%
White Admiral	+252%	Silver-studded Blue	+58%	Grizzled Skipper	+22%
Purple Hairstreak	+117%	Dingy Skipper	+28%	Orange-tip	+19%
Small Blue	85%	Small Copper	+27%	Dark Green Fritillary	+15%

Losers *2000-2012 Surrey transect abundance has decreased by > 10%.*

White-letter Hstreak	–92%	Gatekeeper	–46%	Brown Hairstreak	–31%
Essex Skipper	–76%	Silver-spotted Skip	–43%	Wood White	–31%
Peacock	–75%	Red Admiral	–39%	Meadow Brown	–30%
Small Tortoiseshell	–71%	Comma	–38%	Silver-washed Frit	–26%
Small/Essex Skipper	–62%	Brimstone	–37%	Speckled Wood	–25%
Green-veined White	–56%	Common Blue	–34%	Small White	–21%
Large White	–49%	Large Skipper	–31%	Holly Blue	–14%
Ringlet	–49%	Brown Argus	–31%	Adonis Blue	–14%

DISTRIBUTION MAPS

Harry E. Clarke

SYMBOLS, shown at tetrad level (2km sq)

● STABLE recorded 2000-12 and also before
▲ GAIN recorded 2000-12 but not before
O LOSS recorded before 2000 but not since
\+ pre-1982 record at hectad (10km sq) level only

Green high counts (upper quartile)
Small low counts (lower quartile)
Red greatest loss (upper quartile)

Upper and lower quartiles are calculated on the maximum count of any single visit since the beginning of 2000. For losses prior to 2000, the maximum count for all years is used.

NB: some apparent losses will be due to under-recording away from hotspots rather than a genuine loss (e.g. Purple Hairstreak map on page 76). Conversely, a gain could represent increased recording or genuine expansion.

SOURCES

Biological Records Centre: 1970-82:
data used in the *Atlas of Butterflies in Britain and Ireland,* (Heath *et al.*, 1984)

UK Butterfly Monitoring Scheme (UKBMS) Surrey dates 1986->

Butterflies for the New Millennium (BNM) Surrey dates 1989->

Recording for Surrey generally began in 1989. Records are submitted to the County Recorder, usually by members of Butterfly Conservation, stored in a Levana database, and copied to Butterfly Conservation.

Wider Countryside Butterfly Survey (WCBS) Surrey dates 2007->

Big Butterfly Count (BBC) Surrey dates 2010->

DATA

Quality: has varied over the years. Earliest records were at hectad level and usually recorded only presence rather than numbers. Later records were submitted at tetrad level. Current records are recorded at monad (1km sq) level or better. Misidentification can be a problem and we have attempted to eliminate obvious errors. Some will inevitably remain, for which we can only apologise.

Selection: includes records whose supplied grid reference is within the vice-county boundary. Only a small part of some tetrads is within the boundary. For some species there can be an apparent loss of a tetrad on the county boundary. In all cases, individual records need to be viewed in the light of all available information for the species.

Coverage: there are records from every tetrad. However, as shown on the records richness map (page 21), there is uneven coverage, with hotspots such as Denbies Hillside and Box Hill particularly well covered. Records are generated almost entirely by volunteers and the general public, and we encourage readers to submit their data via *www.surreybutterflies.org* or directly to the County Recorder.

TRANSECTS

THE UK Butterfly Monitoring Scheme (UKBMS) was launched in 1976 with 34 sites, and now over 1,000 sites are monitored using the transect method. The methodology and development of transect monitoring for butterflies have been reviewed in detail elsewhere (Pollard and Yates, 1993). In brief, a fixed-route walk (transect) is established at a site and butterflies are recorded along the route on a regular (weekly) basis under reasonable weather conditions for a number of years. Transect routes are chosen to sample evenly the habitat types and management activity on sites. Care is taken in choosing a transect route as it must then remain fixed to enable butterfly sightings to be compared from year to year. Transects are typically about 2-4km long, taking between 45 minutes and two hours to walk, and are divided into sections corresponding to different habitat or management units.

Butterflies are recorded in a fixed-width band (typically 5m wide) along the transect each week from the beginning of April until the end of September yielding, ideally, 26 counts per year. Transect walks are undertaken between 10.45am and 3.45pm and only when weather conditions are suitable for butterfly activity: dry; wind speed maximum Beaufort scale 5; temperature minimum 13°C if there is at least 60% sunshine, or 17°C if overcast.

The first records for Surrey were from Banstead Downs in 1986. In 1988 three other sites were added: Denbies Hillside, Hackhurst Down and White Down. By 1990 13 sites were providing data, which grew to 36 sites by 2000, peaking at 53 sites in 2008. Over the years 67 Surrey sites have provided data (see pages 200-201), some for only a few years, but Banstead Downs has been walked consistently for the last 27 years. Denbies Hillside has provided 25 years of data, and Hackhurst Down 24 years (no data for 2007), which provides excellent monitoring of the state of butterflies at those sites.

Single species (as opposed to normal "all species") transects have been increasingly established in recent years. While such transects must follow the standard methodology, the focus on a single (or small number of) species reduces both the time required and the number of weekly counts, e.g. Fairmile Common for Silver-studded Blue.

UK BMS annual abundance index: transect records are only a sample of the total population, thus providing an index rather than an absolute total. If counts are made in suitable weather for all 26 weeks the index may be the same as the total records, but is subject to statistical adjustment. If there are missing weeks or walks in unsuitable weather, the index consists of real counts plus statistically-estimated values where there is sufficient data from the site and other sites.

Featured transect

FOR each species we feature the transect with the highest recent counts.

Black square: year's highest count; **Dash**: no sightings; **Empty square**: not walked.
The BMS annual abundance index is shown. **NI**: no index calculated.

Individual transects are not an ideal way to monitor certain species. We have used records from all transects to compile tables for: Glanville Fritillary, Purple Emperor, and White-letter, Purple and Brown Hairstreaks.

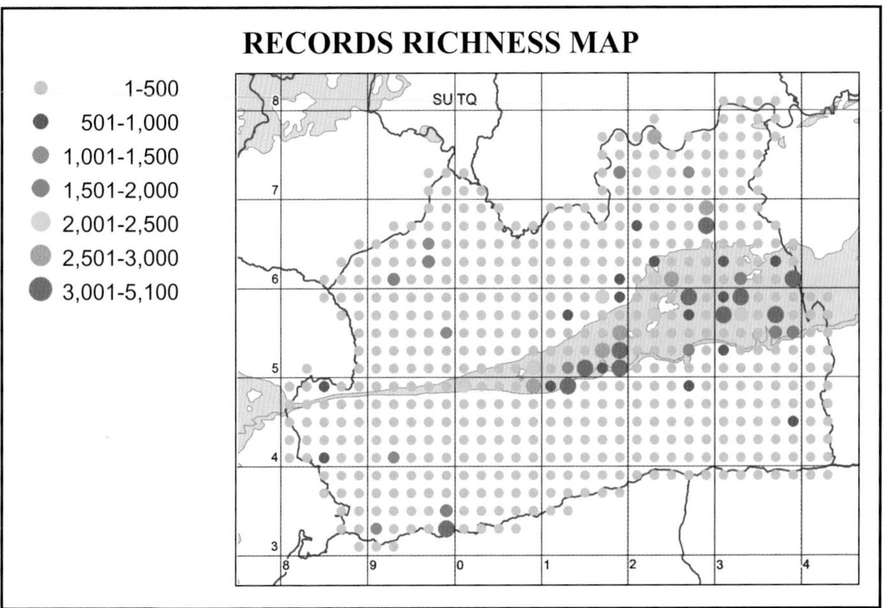

ABUNDANCE TREND CHART

FOR each species, the total abundance index over all Surrey transects is divided by the total number of transects with an index, to produce an average annual abundance index. To take into account missing indices for a site, the sum of all counts for that year is used, provided the count is greater than a quarter of the average index for the site. For the migrants Red Admiral, Painted Lady and Clouded Yellow, all records are used to calculate the index.

The average annual abundance index was plotted for 1990-2012, and a straight line using least squares was fitted through the data to calculate the trend. Some species (e.g. Dark Green Fritillary) were recorded at only a few sites in the early years, so a later start year has been used. A species is noted as increasing or declining only where the standard deviation is sufficiently small. Where the data is very variable or there is only a small trend, the species is noted as stable.

FLIGHT WEEKS CHART & TABLE

FOR each week, the total count from all Surrey transect walks is divided by total walks to produce an average weekly count. In the chart, this is further averaged across the periods 1990-99 and 2000-12.

PHENOLOGY TREND

TO study the effect of climate change from 1990 to 2012, the average peak flight period of the first hatching is calculated for each year. This works for migrants, hibernators, and those with multiple broods. A straight line using least squares is fitted through the data to calculate the trend to the nearest half-week, which is shown in the statistics box.

Small Skipper *Thymelicus sylvestris* **Ken Willmott**

Surrey status: still common and widespread but declining.
Flies: late June, July, with smaller numbers into August.
Trends: in decline, due to inappropriate grass-cutting, grazing and other disturbances. Needs more-regular separation from Essex Skipper for accurate monitoring.
Wingspan: 27-34mm.
Identification: one of five golden Skippers, together with Essex, Lulworth (not in Surrey), Large and Silver-spotted. The Small Skipper is a bright orange-fulvous colour with narrow black margins to its wings; underside paler. Male has black sex brand in middle of forewings; antenna-tip underside is orange.
Confusion species: Small Skipper is so easily confused with the slightly smaller Essex Skipper that transect counts are often combined as a single *Thymelicus* species, or "Smessex". Males are distinguished by the size and angle of the sex brand. Otherwise, check colour of antenna-tip underside.
Habitat: grassland sites where the foodplant is allowed to mature into flowering clumps.

Surrey 2000-12	407	(73%) of 558 tetrads, loss 8%
● **STABLE** 344		High counts ......green
▲ **GAIN** 63		Low counts ......small
O **LOSS**................98		Greatest loss ....red

Map combines records for Small Skipper and records that did not differentiate between Small and Essex. There are individual and combined charts for abundance and flight trends.

SMALL | **SMALL/ESSEX**

Surrey abundance trend (Small): Average annual transect index; Trend 1997-2012

Surrey abundance trend (Small/Essex): Average annual transect index; Trend 1990-2012

Small Skipper male on oxeye daisy, showing curved sex brand. **BH**

Top transect: Richmond Park.
Other key sites: Ashtead Common, Chiddingfold Forest, Epsom Downs, Ranmore Common.
Life cycle: univoltine; winters as larva within a silken cocoon without feeding prior to hibernation. Awakes in April to feed on the tender new grass; pupates in a light silken structure.
Larval foodplants: almost restricted to Yorkshire-fog grass, at least in Surrey. I have seen a female lay in the sheath of Timothy grass.

KEY DIFFERENCES BETWEEN SMALL & ESSEX SKIPPER

Antenna-tip underside

Small: orange, pointed, occasionally has dusting of black scales that does not end abruptly.

Essex: jet-black, ends abruptly at base of antenna "club".

Black sex brand on male's forewing

Small: long, thick, curved, oblique to veins.

Essex: shorter, thinner, straight, parallel to veins.

SMALL

Surrey flight weeks

35 30 25 20 15 10 5 0

Apr May Jun Jul Aug Sep

Average weekly transect count

—1997-99, —2000-12

SMALL/ESSEX

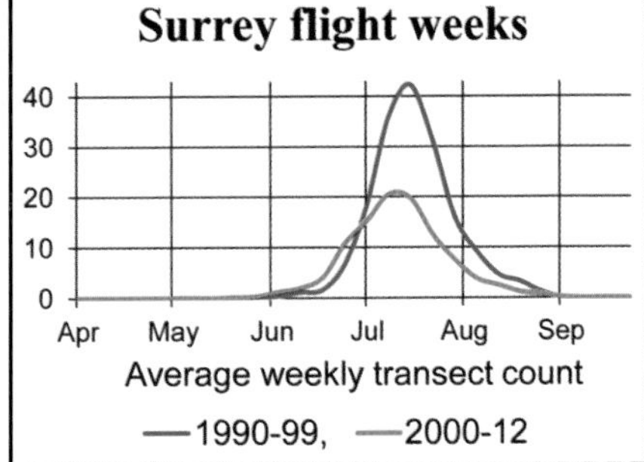

Small Skipper *continued* — **Ken Willmott**

SMALL SKIPPERS can form large colonies where the primary larval foodplant, Yorkshire-fog grass, grows in uncut, ungrazed grassland. They are often accompanied by Essex Skippers, which disrupts accurate monitoring.

Males tend to search for females and, unlike the Large Skipper, rarely wait for females to enter their territory. The female typically lays 2-6 eggs in the opening of a loosely-closed sheath. Isolated clumps of Yorkshire-fog can attract several females and I have found 23 eggs in a single sheath, separated in groups of 3, 4 and 16.

Most butterflies coat their eggs with a glutinous substance that adheres to the chosen surface; not the Small Skipper! It relies on the pressure of the closed sheath to contain the eggs before the emergent larva secures itself further by spinning a silken cocoon, attaching it to the grass for hibernation. If you find the eggs, handle carefully or they will easily drop out.

Small Skipper, showing antenna-tip orange underside, lays into Yorkshire-fog. **KW**

In spring the developing larva constructs a dwelling from fresh grass blades. Like the other Skippers that build similar tubes, Small Skippers have an anal comb for ejecting their faeces some distance from their abode, thus maintaining hygiene and avoiding possible bacterial infections. After moulting four times, the larva pupates low down at the base of its grass clump, spinning a flimsy cocoon from where it emerges after 2-3 weeks.

Smaller colonies can be found along roadside verges and tracks within woodland, such as in Chiddingfold Forest. With the continuing creation of open space on Bookham Common in recent years, the Small Skipper has created a metapopulation structure – as one formerly suitable habitat disappears a new one develops within reasonable range. In one area, where summer cattle-grazing has been established for a number of years, Small Skipper has decreased markedly, and several colonies have been lost to scrub invasion.

In 2012 for the first time I observed a Small Skipper lay on Yorkshire-fog in my Leatherhead garden and soon found an egg batch on another stem. Yorkshire-fog is not abundant here and the nearest substantial grassland area is distant. This suggests that the Small Skipper can readily disperse from deteriorating habitat to establish new colonies.

Flight weeks ▲High transect counts △Middle ^Low

Apr					May				Jun				Jul					Aug				Sep			
1	8	15	22	29	6	13	20	27	3	10	17	24	1	8	15	22	29	5	12	19	26	2	9	16	23
								^	△	△	△	▲	△	▲	▲	▲	△	△	△	^	^				

Small Skipper

weekly transect counts

Richmond Park TQ190730

Raymond Garrett

WEEK		2000	2001	2002	2003	2004	2005	2006	2007	2008	2009	2010	2011	2012
3 June	10								-	-			1	-
10	11								1	-			2	-
17	12								4	-			1	-
24	13								**94**	5			**4**	1
1 July	14								19	9			1	3
8	15								8	**18**			1	**14**
15	16								-	11			-	9
22	17								-	-			-	4
29	18								2				-	1
5 August	19								-	1			-	-
Abundance index									124	52			9	32
Weeks recorded									**6**	**5**			**6**	**6**

Small/Essex Skipper

weekly transect counts

Richmond Park TQ190730

Raymond Garrett

WEEK		2000	2001	2002	2003	2004	2005	2006	2007	2008	2009	2010	2011	2012
3 June	10					-	-	-	-	-		-	1	-
10	11				-	-	-	-	-	-		-	6	-
17	12					2	2	-	15	-	40	7	9	-
24	13				115	125	130		-	31	**202**	41	31	-
1 July	14				269	**195**		**129**	**114**	77	186	**74**	**32**	4
8	15				**327**	66	**185**		71	309	93	51	12	47
15	16				90	85		71	73	**439**	23	20	18	**63**
22	17					100	28	56	6	103	14	3	1	**63**
29	18					64	19		4		5	-	-	31
5 August	19					3	-	-	1	14	1	-	-	4
Abundance index					884	640	NI	NI	266	NI	NI	NI	NI	214
Weeks recorded					**4**	**7**	**5**	**3**	**7**	**6**	**8**	**6**	**8**	**6**

Phenology trend	**1997-2012**		earlier by one week	
Small/Essex	**1990-2012**		earlier by 1.5 weeks	
Best transect day 2000-12	Jul 10, 2010		Roundshaw Downs	156
Small + Small/Essex	Jul 15, 2008		Richmond Park	450
Transects abundance	**1997-2012**	loss 83%	**2000-2012**	gain 22%
Small/Essex	**1990-2012**	loss 71%	**2000-2012**	loss 62%
UK transects abundance	**1976-2012**	loss 73%	**10-year trend** loss 66%	
UK 4,361 10k squares	**2005-09** 1,422 = 32%		**10-year trend** loss 3%	

Essex Skipper *Thymelicus lineola*

Ken Willmott

Surrey status: probably still common and widespread, but under-recorded due to similarity to Small Skipper.

Flies: late June to early August, emerging a little later than Small Skipper.

Trends: declining for the same reasons as the Small Skipper.

Wingspan: 26-30mm.

Identification: another of the golden Skippers and difficult to separate from the Small Skipper. Essex is a little smaller; male sex brand is less distinct and straight rather than curved; antenna-tip underside is black in Essex, orange in Small. Fresh Small Skippers occasionally have a dusting of black scales on the underside of the antenna, which does not end abruptly as in Essex. The dark outer margin of the forewing is more variable than that of the Small Skipper.

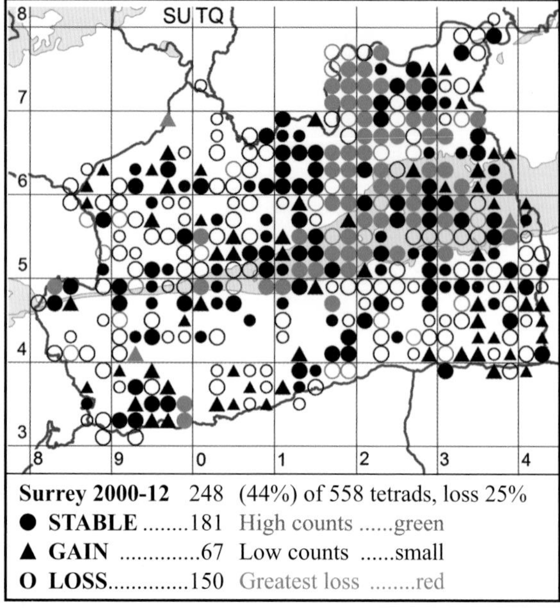

Map and charts show records for Essex Skipper only. See Small Skipper for combined records.

Confusion species: see Small Skipper for summary of differences.

Habitat: grassland with light scrub; wider, sunny verges along woodland rides.

Top transect: Richmond Park.

Other key sites: Ashtead Common, Chiddingfold Forest, Epsom Downs, Ranmore Common.

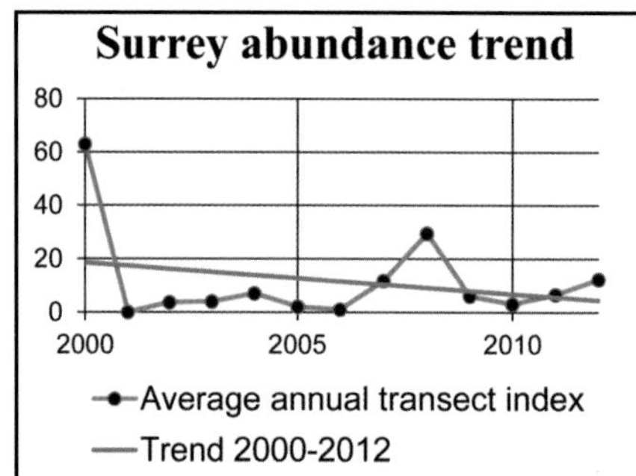

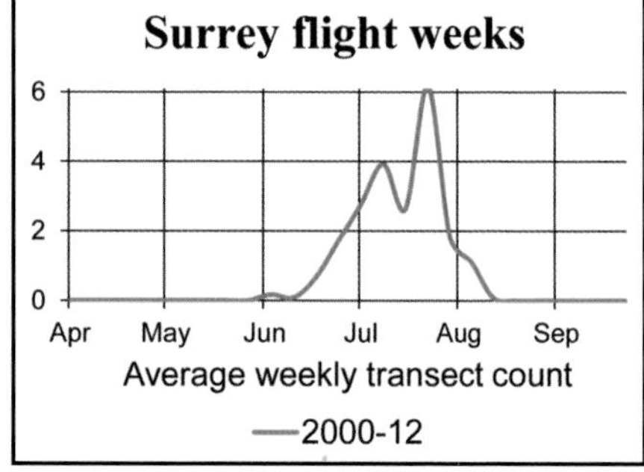

Essex Skipper showing antenna-tip black underside (above) and thin male sex brand (right). **FK**

Life cycle: univoltine; eggs, unlike those of the Small Skipper, do not hatch until the following spring, although the larva becomes fully formed within the egg shell (pharate). The larva makes a flimsy structure from a few strands of silk, eventually using the wider grass blades to construct a tubular dwelling. It moults four times before pupating around mid-June; adult emerges after 2-3 weeks.

Larval foodplants: cock's-foot, creeping soft-grass, false-brome and other grasses with tighter leaf-sheaths than those used by the Small Skipper.

Phenology trend	**2000-2012**	earlier by two weeks	
Best transect day 2000-12	Jul 10, 2008	Richmond Park	66
Transects abundance	**2000-2012** loss 76%		
UK transects abundance	**1977-2012** loss 64%	**10-year trend** loss 91%	
UK 4,361 10k squares	**2005-09** 687 = 16%	**10-year trend** gain 8%	

Flight weeks ▲High transect counts △Middle ^Low

Apr					May				Jun				Jul					Aug				Sep			
1	8	15	22	29	6	13	20	27	3	10	17	24	1	8	15	22	29	5	12	19	26	2	9	16	23
									^	^	△	△	▲	▲	△	▲	△	△	^						

Essex Skipper *continued*

Ken Willmott

THE Essex Skipper was unknown in Britain before 1889 when three specimens were captured at Hartley Wood, St Osyth, Essex. They were first thought to be aberrations of Small Skipper, but were separated as a distinct species after the slight differences were noted, especially the antenna-tip black underside.

The capture of this "new" species was recorded by Hawes (1890). Other enthusiasts reviewed their collections and announced its presence among their Smalls! The species had been separated in Europe many years previously and was now found to be locally common in Essex, Suffolk and nearby counties. The Essex name is attributed to South (1906).

Essex and Small Skippers fly in the same habitats, so careful inspection is needed for correct identification. A good time to check the antenna-tip underside is early evening, when the butterflies are settling down to roost and not as likely to fly off at the critical moment.

Small and Essex females can be separated by their different egg-laying activities. Slow-flying, diligent Small females are conspicuous as they lay in sheaths of Yorkshire-fog. The Essex Skipper lays flatter-shaped eggs lower down the stem of grasses with a tighter leaf sheath. The female is virtually hidden from view during this activity.

Larvae can be found in wider-blade grasses during late May and early June. The two species are green but have different head patterns – Essex is striped brown and white, Small is plain green.

Male Essex Skippers are said to patrol in search of females, but may also use perching until temperatures are warm enough to fly efficiently. They may also use the perching strategy early and late in their season in order to save energy when there are fewer females available.

Essex Skipper — weekly transect counts

Richmond Park TQ190730 — **Raymond Garrett**

	WEEK	2000	2001	2002	2003	2004	2005	2006	2007	2008	2009	2010	2011	2012
17 June	12								2	-			4	-
24	13								10	4			13	-
1 July	14								10	19			**14**	1
8	15								**17**	**66**			7	13
15	16								-	40			-	**22**
22	17								-	4			-	6
29	18								10				-	5
5 August	19								-	11			-	1
12	20								-	-			-	1
Abundance index									46	178			36	48
Weeks recorded									**5**	**6**			**4**	**7**

Silver-spotted Skipper *Hesperia comma* **Malcolm Bridge**

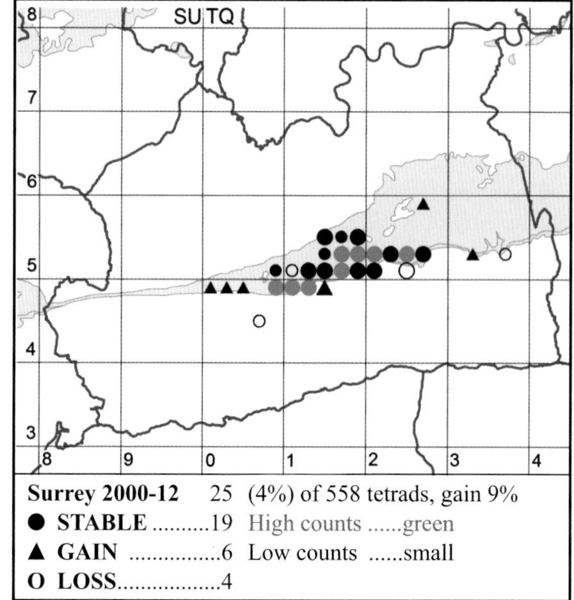

Surrey status: nationally rare but thriving on the North Downs from Hackhurst Down (above Gomshall) in the west to Reigate/Wingate Hill in the east.
Flies: late July to early September.
Conservation: protected from sale; BC 2010 Red List: near-threatened.
Trends: has recovered from 1970s low point.
Wingspan: male 29-34mm, female 32-37mm.
Identification: small, orange-brown; eponymous underwings are largely olive-green and marked with conspicuous silver-white spots, more strongly in the female. It was once called the Pearl Skipper.
Confusion species: Large Skipper, which is slightly bigger and flies from early June, is worn and in reduced numbers by the time the Silver-spotted Skipper is flying.
Habitat: south-facing downland.
Top transect: Box Hill, Dukes.
Other key sites: Colley Hill, Denbies Hillside, Hackhurst Down, Headley Heath.
Life cycle: univoltine; winters as egg. Larva hatches in March and lives in a nest of silk and leaves; pupates in a silk cocoon. Male finds a sunny perch to await the arrival of a female, whose creamy-white eggs are laid singly. Adult lifespan is about six days.
Larval food plant: sheep's-fescue grass.

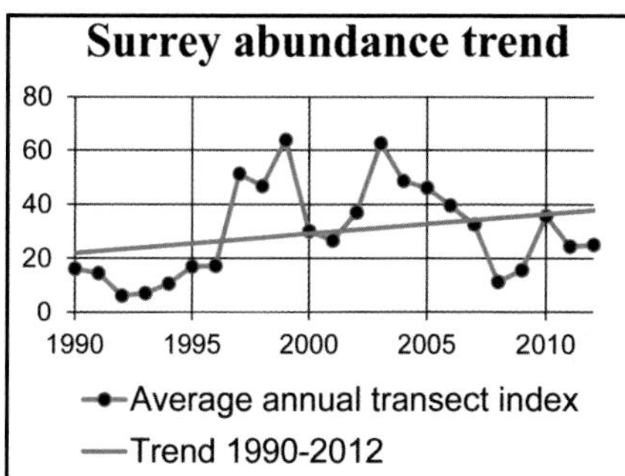

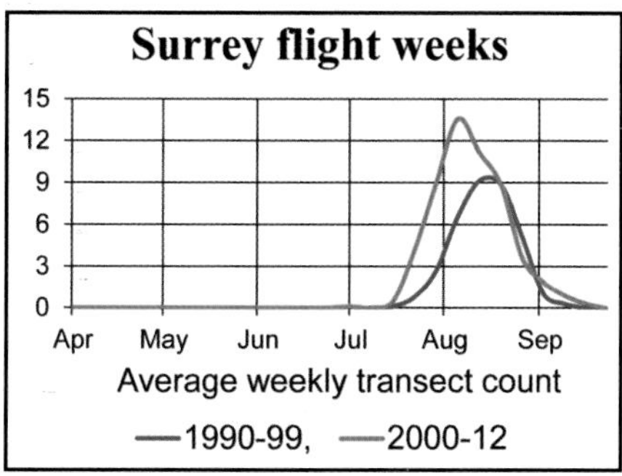

Silver-spotted Skipper *continued*

Malcolm Bridge

THE Silver-spotted Skipper needs warmer (20°C+) weather than any other British butterfly. It has attracted the interest of leading entomologists, academic and amateur, and is regarded as an exemplar species of population dynamics. There is some uncertainty about its dispersal capabilities. It is now considered (and its eastern outpost at Quarry Hangers supports this contention) that it can disperse over a range of 6-8km, and a study in West Sussex suggests that more than 10km has been achieved.

Current thinking is that the species occurs in a number of small colonies, which collectively form a metapopulation. Gail Jeffcoate *et al.* (2000) suggested that Surrey holds two adjacent metapopulations, west and east, divided at Dorking by the Mole Gap. The species is well monitored by several transects and the two sites that support the largest numbers are in the geographical centre of the main colonies – Box Hill and Denbies Hillside.

Ideal habitat is a thin-soiled, south-facing chalk down that includes areas of short, sparse sward and numerous nectar sources. Eggs are generally laid in patches in which about 40% of the ground is bare, 45% has sheep's-fescue and the remainder is composed of flowers. However, during the past two decades, the butterfly has taken advantage of warmer years and will now lay on fescues on less southerly aspects and on plants with as little as 20% of their edges abutting bare ground. This greater tolerance of breeding habitat has roughly doubled the area available for egg-laying.

In a major survey in the summers of 2001-2002, a Leeds University team lead by Rob Wilson found well-established populations in areas of unimproved grassland all along the scarp slope of the North Downs from Newlands Corner in the west to Wingate Hill, Reigate, in the east. In areas exposed to excessively heavy grazing, populations are small or absent (Hackhurst Down). Essentially, areas where sheep's-fescue grows to 2-6cm are likely to support populations.

On the shallower dip slope of the North Downs, with less development of bare ground, there is evidence of populations at Fetcham Downs, Norbury Park, Mickleham Downs, and many of the slopes north of Box Hill. Further east, Silver-spotted Skippers have been recorded at Park Downs, Banstead, and below Banstead Woods. Several eggs were found

Phenology trend	**1990-2012**	earlier by one week	
Best transect day 2000-12	Aug 19, 2003	Colekitchen	99
Transects abundance	**1990-2012** gain 73%	**2000-2012** loss 43%	
UK transects abundance	**1979-2012** gain 854%	**10-year trend** loss 55%	
UK 4,361 10k squares	**2005-09** 42 = 1%	**10-year trend** gain 35%	

Flight weeks ▲High transect counts △Middle ^Low

Apr					May				Jun				Jul					Aug				Sep			
1	8	15	22	29	6	13	20	27	3	10	17	24	1	8	15	22	29	5	12	19	26	2	9	16	23
															^	△	△	▲	▲	▲	△	△	△	^	

Silver-spotted Skipper pair, male on left, Brockham Quarry. **HT**

■ *Comparison photo: page 33*

at Quarry Hangers, near Caterham, 6km east of any habitat that was occupied in 2000.

Wilson (2003) speculated that, given continued good management, the species could colonise areas further to the east such as Farthing Downs, Happy Valley and Riddlesdown, where grazing is creating suitable habitat.

The Silver-spotted Skipper is nationally rare. The North Downs holds a significant percentage and it is also found in isolated areas of the South Downs, south Chilterns, north Dorset, and Hampshire. The declines of the last century, most marked during the 1960s and 1970s, have been arrested and some encouraging signs of recovery noted, helped by three consecutive warm summers in 1995-97. In the *Millennium Atlas* it is noted that the butterfly is still absent from much of its former range, and sites more than 10km from any refuge site have not been recolonised. A landscape approach to future conservation strategy is recommended.

Thomas noted that the outlook for this butterfly is encouraging, with more than 250 colonies of Silver-spotted Skipper in England, roughly five times as many as during the nadir of the 1970s.

Silver-spotted Skipper weekly transect counts

Box Hill, Dukes TQ185510 **Peter Creasey**

WEEK		2000	2001	2002	2003	2004	2005	2006	2007	2008	2009	2010	2011	2012
15-Jul	16	-								2		-	-	
22	17	-							-	10	-	15	1	-
29	18	-							11	**13**	-	23	18	
5 August	19		**1**						17		**39**	**35**	**19**	**31**
12	20								**22**	1	12	27		24
19	21									2	5		10	
26	22	-							-	1	-	-	-	5
2 September	23								-	-	-	-	-	1
Abundance index			5						63	33	66	NI	57	90
Weeks recorded			**1**						**3**	**6**	**3**	**4**	**4**	**4**

Large Skipper *Ochlodes sylvanus*

Ken Willmott

Surrey status: common but in smaller numbers than the more colonial grassland Skippers, Small and Essex.
Flies: late May to mid-August.
Trends: reduced numbers on transects.
Wingspan: male 29-34mm, female 31-36mm.
Identification: our largest Skipper is dark brown with orange patches, which are more conspicuous in the slightly bigger female. The paler underside, tinged with green in fresh examples, has faint square spots. Male's upper forewings have a strong sex brand.

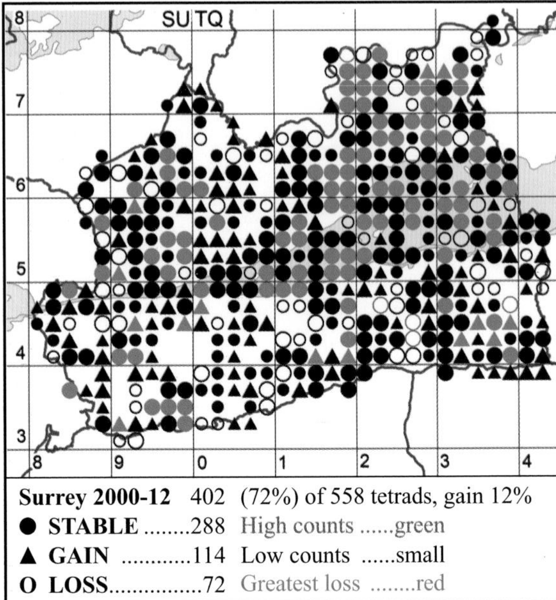

Confusion species: Small and Essex are both plain on the upperside. The main confusion is with the more strongly-marked Silver-spotted Skipper on downland in August, when worn Large Skippers may still be on the wing. Although their habitat niches are different, the two species can overlap where short turf meets taller, ungrazed grassland, at scrub and wood edges for example.
Habitat: longer swards, e.g. uncut meadows (surviving along edges, if cut); wider, sunny rides and clearings in woodland (has recently colonised a north-south ride on Bookham Common that had been significantly widened); heathland (with purple moor-grass); ungrazed downland (particularly scrub edges and the bottom of slopes); unkempt farmland. Also visits gardens, where it will occasionally breed in sunny, uncut areas.

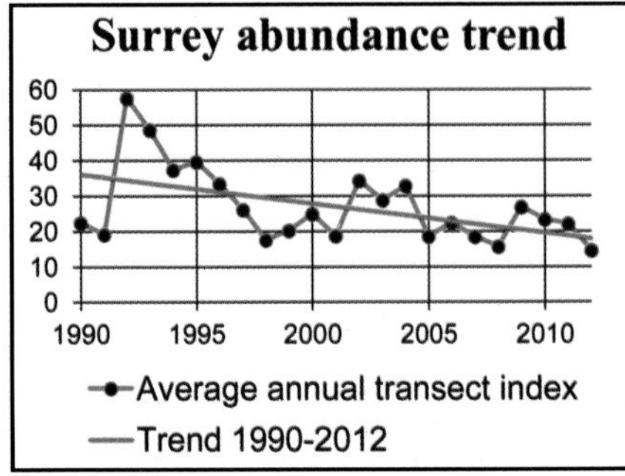

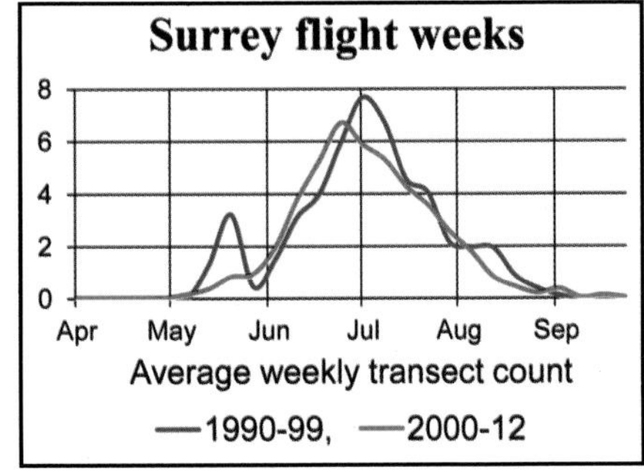

Above: Mating pair (female above). **HC**

Top right: Large Skipper. **BH**
Right, for comparison: Silver-spotted Skipper female on knapweed. **GW**

Top transects: Hutchinson's Bank, Ashtead Common, Brentmoor Heath, Chobham Common, Epsom Common.
Life cycle: univoltine; winters as larva after four moults. In September the larva closes the ends of its tubular dwelling to form a hibernaculum. It emerges the following March, according to temperature, and changes its skin twice more before pupating in May.
Larval foodplants: grasses with wide blades to accommodate larval abodes, such as cock's-foot and purple moor-grass.

Phenology trend	**1990-2012**	earlier by one week	
Best transect day 2000-12	Jun 24, 2003	Wandsworth	54
Transects abundance	**1990-2012** loss 50%	**2000-2012** loss 31%	
UK transects abundance	**1976-2012** loss 21%	**10-year trend** loss 18%	
UK 4,361 10k squares	**2005-09** 1,442 = 33%	**10-year trend** loss 8%	

Large Skipper *continued*

Ken Willmott

THE Large Skipper is a fast flier that can disappear in a blur, especially a male defending its territory. He will soon return, often to the same perch of perhaps a dead seed-head or a bramble leaf. Thus the mate-location strategy is perching, to await a passing female.

Rather than wait in vain when the female population is low, male perchers of other species can switch to patrolling (the strategy of seeking females), usually at the start or end of the emergence period. I have yet to record this change in the Large Skipper.

The female flies slowly among the grasses, almost hovering, until she selects a suitable wide blade. She alights on the upperside and bends her body underneath to lay a solitary egg. I once found two eggs in close proximity, probably deposited by the same female.

The tiny larva emerges after almost three weeks and constructs a tubular dwelling from a grass blade, emerging to feed both by day and by night. As the larva grows, so does the size of its tubular dwelling, which then consists of more than a single grass blade. The larva has an anal comb-like structure that it uses to eject frass some distance after reversing down its tube.

The larva moults six times, a number equalled in Britain by only Heath and Glanville Fritillaries. The pupa is encased within a much stronger grass structure, closed at both ends with silk, but weak enough to allow the newly emerged butterfly to escape.

Emergence is determined by weather conditions, especially temperature. In the notably poor spring of 2012 my first sightings were: June 13 (downland), June 17 (clay). In the more clement spring of 2009 my respective first records were May 20 and May 30.

Populations can be small and survive in discrete areas if undisturbed. One such site in Leatherhead, no more than 30 square metres in the immediate surrounds of an electricity pylon, was always unscathed when the surrounding meadow was cut every July. Even pylons can be moved and the site is now part of a business park. Nearby is Leatherhead's sole surviving piece of ancient woodland, Teazle Wood, with its own population of Large Skippers. In 2012 this wood was purchased by local residents as a nature reserve.

Conservation work on Bookham Common has included the widening of a particular north-south ride. As soon as the grasses began to invade the almost bare earth (3+ years), pioneering Large Skippers located the now sunny, open ride. Females laid on grasses at the edge of the formerly-shaded footpath and in the gaps between the regenerating scrub.

Flight weeks ▲High transect counts △Middle ^Low

Apr					May				Jun				Jul					Aug				Sep			
1	8	15	22	29	6	13	20	27	3	10	17	24	1	8	15	22	29	5	12	19	26	2	9	16	23
					^	^	△	△	△	△	▲	▲	▲	▲	▲	△	△	△	△	△	^	^			

Large Skipper male, showing sex brand. **FK**

Large Skipper weekly transect counts
Hutchinson's Bank, New Addington TQ380617 **Martin Wills**

	WEEK	2000	2001	2002	2003	2004	2005	2006	2007	2008	2009	2010	2011	2012
20 May	8	-	-	-	-	-	-	-	1	-	-	-	5	-
27	9	-	-	-	1	-	-	-	1	-	2	-	7	-
3 June	10	-	-	-	1	1	-	-	5	2	3	-	**11**	1
10	11	3	-	4	11	-	**4**	1	7	-	4	3	10	1
17	12	8	2	**11**	**22**	2	2	6	**8**	**8**	**6**	3	10	**8**
24	13	6	4	**11**	12	2		**11**	4	3	**6**	**25**	8	3
1 July	14	**13**	4		6	**4**	1	5	1	6	**6**	13	4	6
8	15	8	**9**	2	6	3	3	3	-	3	3	9	7	1
15	16	4	-	6	6	**4**	-	2	-	3	1	1	1	3
22	17	-	4	2	1	2	-	3	-	1	2	4	4	1
29	18	1	5	1	1	3		-	-	2	1	1	-	1
5 August	19	3	-	4	-	1		-	-	-	1		-	-
12	20	-	-	-	-	-					-	-	-	-
19	21	-	-	-	-	-					-	-	-	-
26	22	1	-	-	-	-				-	-		-	-
Abundance index		47	28	49	67	25	NI	32	26	28	34	53	70	25
Weeks recorded		**9**	**6**	**8**	**10**	**9**	**4**	**7**	**7**	**8**	**11**	**8**	**10**	**9**

Dingy Skipper *Erynnis tages*

Malcolm Bridge

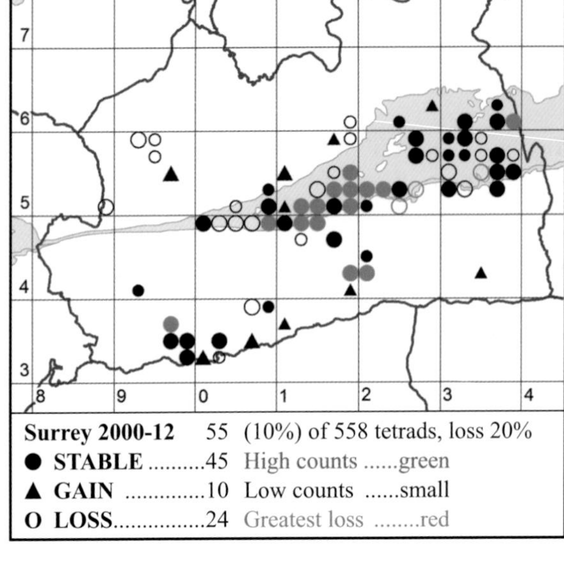

Surrey status: once locally common, especially along the North Downs; declined throughout the 20th century but now stabilised, at a lower level, on the Chalk and a few other localities.

Flies: mid-April to June, peaking in May; occasional partial second brood from mid-July.

Conservation: UK Biodiversity Action Plan priority species; BC 2010 Red List: vulnerable.

Trends: rapid decline in range and abundance now stabilised. Thomas noted that probably few colonies contain more than 100 adults, even in better years.

Wingspan: 27-34mm.

Identification: moth-like; upperside mainly brown-grey with an indistinct pattern of darker patches and lighter areas. Fresh specimens can be richly dark but worn ones provide the clue to the unfortunate name provided by the Aurelians in the 18th century. Male has pale-brown forewing costal fold containing androconial scales. Spends long periods basking on bare ground, with wings spread flat and pressed against the warm soil. Rests with wings wrapped around dead flower or grass head, becoming difficult to spot. The only British butterfly not to close its wings vertically above its body at rest.

Confusion species: Burnet Companion (see page 187), a day-flying moth, is similar in size and colour. Against possible expectations, the moth is the more attractive insect with

Surrey abundance trend

35 30 25 20 15 10 5 0

1990 1995 2000 2005 2010

—•— Average annual transect index

— Trend 1990-2012

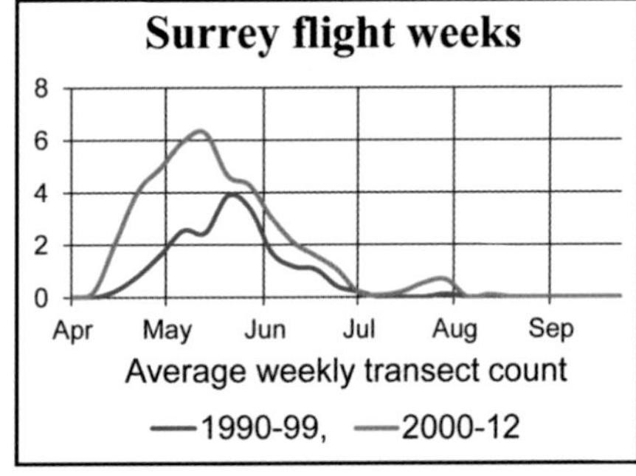

orange-yellow hindwings traversed by two brown bands. Both species prefer the Chalk but the moth also inhabits grasslands such as Richmond Park and Wimbledon Common.

Habitat: downland; also a few woodland rides and brownfield sites.

Top transects: Denbies Landbarn B, Hutchinson's Bank, Nore Hill, Box Hill, Quarry Hangers, Headley Heath.

Life cycle: usually univoltine; winters as fully grown larva. Darting male waits for a passing female, whose pale green-yellow eggs turn orange after a few days on plants in warm, sheltered spots with bare soil. Few, if any, are laid on ant mounds or in very short sward. Eggs hatch after some two weeks and the larva immediately spins two or three leaflets together to form a small tent. As it grows, nests are spun within which the grey-green larva shelters and feeds. Some eight months later, the following spring, the larva pupates within its hibernaculum. Occasionally there is a partial second brood in late summer.

Dingy Skipper pair, male above. **HS**

Larval foodplants: bird's-foot-trefoil; also horseshoe vetch (downland), greater bird's-foot-trefoil (heavier soils).

NATIONALLY, regionally and locally, many Dingy Skipper colonies have been lost in recent decades. The "improvement" of traditional grasslands, formerly species-rich, has eliminated larval foodplants. Also, reduced woodland management and the cessation of coppicing have restricted the butterfly to a few favourable rides and glades.

Despite these losses the Dingy remains Britain's most widely-distributed Skipper but it becomes relatively common only in southern counties and along parts of the Welsh coast. Its absence from many suitable sites is not fully understood but habitat fragmentation probably played a part in its declining fortunes.

Phenology trend	**1990-2012**	earlier by 2 weeks	
Best transect day 2000-12	May 11, 2005	Denbies Landbarn B	53
Transects abundance	**1990-2012** gain 116%	**2000-2012** gain 28%	
UK transects abundance	**1976-2012** loss 28%	**10-year trend** gain 49%	
UK 4,361 10k squares	**2005-09** 547 = 12%	**10-year trend** loss 5%	

Dingy Skipper *continued* **Malcolm Bridge**

Goss (1902) considered the Dingy Skipper to be distributed throughout Surrey, and common, sometimes abundant, on the North Downs. Worms (1950) listed it from Esher and the commons of Wimbledon and Mitcham, where there have been no records in recent decades.

Gail Jeffcoate *et al.* (2000) noted that this species prospers on the south-facing slopes of the North Downs, and acknowledged small colonies on the western heaths and within Chiddingfold Forest.

A Dingy Skipper "sighting" at Ham Riverlands in 2010 demanded a confirmatory visit, on a lovely mid-May day. Several areas with bird's-foot-trefoil along the southern edge of the old Thames floodplain produced small, brown, lively insects, which revealed themselves on settling to be Burnet Companions. It does appear that the Dingy Skipper remains absent from suburban south London.

Dingy Skipper — weekly transect counts

Denbies Landbarn B TQ135499 — **Gail Jeffcoate, Robert Cramp**

	WEEK	2000	2001	2002	2003	2004	2005	2006	2007	2008	2009	2010	2011	2012
8 April	2				1	-	-		1		-	-	-	1
15	3			-	7		-	-	3	-	11	-	2	
22	4			8	18	-	-	-	**10**	1	23	20	24	
29	5			13		1	29	10	8	2	**50**		**36**	23
6 May	6				**38**	31	**53**	15	8	20	17	**35**	11	26
13	7			19	10	**38**	47	**36**	5	**48**		30	11	
20	8			**22**	2	27	14		1	17	7	16	10	14
27	9			12	1	17	10	14	-	3	4	15	-	**29**
3 June	10				1	10	8	3	-	8	5	10	-	3
10	11			2	-	2	3	2		-	1	1	-	-
17	12			-	-	-	1	-	-	-	-	3		-
24	13			-	-	-	-	-	-	-	-	-	-	-
1 July	14			-	-	-	-	-	-	-	-	-	-	
8	15			-	-	-	-	-	-	-	-	-	-	-
15	16			-	-	-	-	-	4	-		-	-	
22	17			-	-	-	-	-	5	-	-		1	-
29	18				2	1	-	-	3		-		-	-
Abundance index				101	NI	127	166	107	50	96	112	150	104	NI
Weeks recorded				**6**	**8**	**8**	**8**	**6**	**10**	**7**	**8**	**8**	**7**	**6**

Flight weeks ▲High transect counts △Middle ^Low

Apr					May				Jun				Jul					Aug				Sep			
1	8	15	22	29	6	13	20	27	3	10	17	24	1	8	15	22	29	5	12	19	26	2	9	16	23
	^	△	△	▲	▲	▲	▲	▲	△	△	△	△	^	^	^	△	△		^						

Grizzled Skipper *Pyrgus malvae*

Malcolm Bridge

Surrey status: local spring speciality, mainly on the North Downs.

Flies: mid-April to June, peaking in May; rare second brood in July.

Conservation: UK Biodiversity Action Plan priority species; BC 2010 Red List: vulnerable.

Trends: fighting back after period of decline.

Wingspan: 23-29mm.

Identification: white flecks on dark background, with conspicuous barred fringe; paler underside has white markings on grey-brown background. Male has pale-brown forewing costal fold containing androconial scales; female has shorter, plumper abdomen.

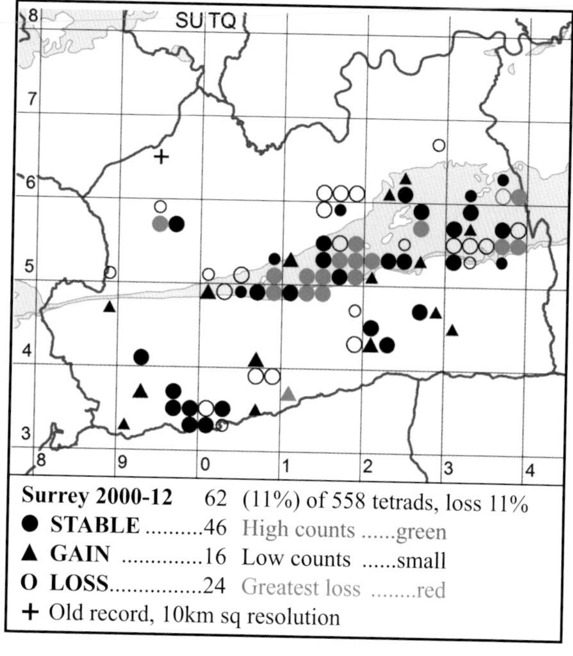

Surrey 2000-12 62 (11%) of 558 tetrads, loss 11%
● **STABLE** ....46 High counts ......green
▲ **GAIN** ....16 Low counts ......small
O **LOSS**................24 Greatest loss ....red
+ Old record, 10km sq resolution

Variations/aberrations: individuals with forewing spots merged into bars are encountered in Surrey; ab. *taras* has the bars coalescing into a central block; ab. *brunnea* has brown ground colour rather than black.

Confusion species: Dingy Skipper is plainer. My confusion species on downland in May is a large micro-moth, *Pyrausta nigrata* (large being a relative term because this moth is clearly smaller than a Grizzled Skipper). The moth's dark-brown wings, each traversed with a white, irregular bar, always oblige me to follow its flight until its true identity can be confirmed.

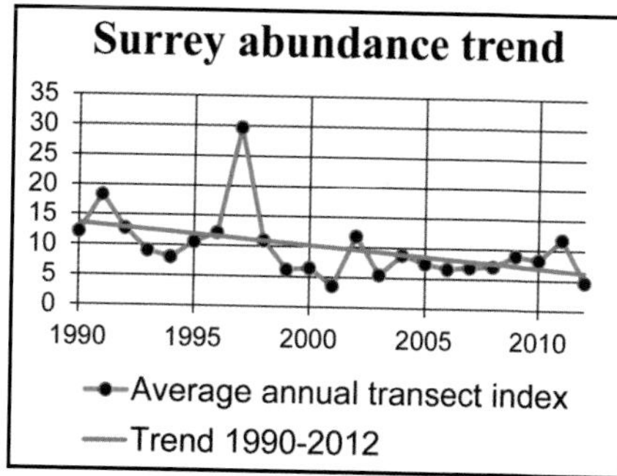

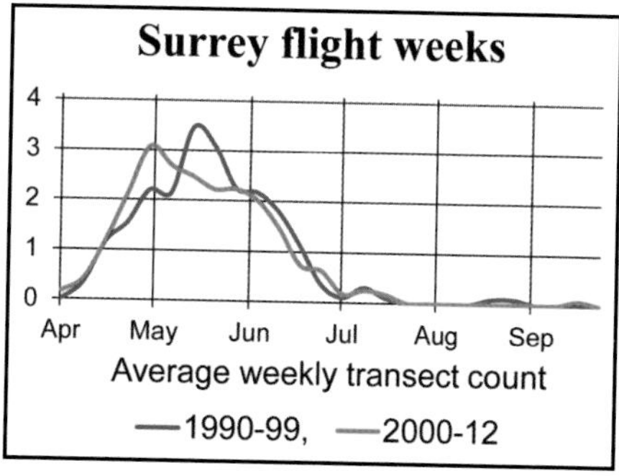

Grizzled Skipper *continued*

Malcolm Bridge

Habitat: mainly downland and, much less so, open woodland in the south of the county.

Top transects: Headley Heath, Hutchinson's Bank, Denbies Landbarn, Quarry Hangers, Witley, Nore Hill.

Life cycle: usually univoltine; rare, partial second brood; winters as pupa. Males joust over females, whose bun-shaped eggs are laid singly, usually on the underside of a leaf of a range of rosaceous plants. After about 10 days the larva emerges and feeds under a covering of silk, which it spins along the midrib of the leaf upperside. Feeding damage in the form of distinctive blotches can betray its presence.

Over the next two months, usually June and July, the growing larva constructs more-substantial shelters by spinning across the width of the leaf. As the silken strands dry, they contract with sufficient force to draw the leaf edges together, creating a secure shelter from which the larva emerges to feed. When fully grown, it crawls down to ground level, spins a loose cocoon, and pupates for about nine months.

Grizzled Skipper: upperside (male) **BH**
underside (female) **HS**

Phenology trend	**1990-2012**	earlier by one week	
Best transect day 2000-12	Apr 25, 2011	Headley Heath	12
Transects abundance	**1990-2012** loss 54%	**2000-2012** gain 22%	
UK transects abundance	**1976-2012** loss 31%	**10-year trend** gain 63%	
UK 4,361 10k squares	**2005-09** 320 = 7%	**10-year trend** loss 17%	

Flight weeks ▲High transect counts △Middle ^Low

Apr					May				Jun				Jul					Aug				Sep			
1	8	15	22	29	6	13	20	27	3	10	17	24	1	8	15	22	29	5	12	19	26	2	9	16	23
^	△	△	△	▲	▲	▲	△	▲	△	△	△	△	^	△	^									^	

THE Grizzled Skipper's main decline in Surrey has been in woodland. The loss of most of Surrey's working woods (not woodland cover), and the reduction in open rides, have probably been the key factors. Goss (1902) noted that the Grizzled Skipper was generally distributed and common in some of the woods in Surrey, but rare in the London suburbs. Collins (1995) found it restricted but fairly common.

Gail Jeffcoate *et al.* (2000) warned that the Grizzled Skipper was declining and its future was uncertain as suitable habitat becomes increasingly scarce. Since then lost tetrads have been balanced by new ones and the decline in abundance has been reversed.

Abandoned railway lines, of which Surrey has few, have provided good habitat for this species in parts of its range, and I continue to search for it along sections of the old line between Guildford and Horsham, now part of the South Downs Link. Brownfield sites on the Weald Clay also provide suitable conditions and some of the brickwork sites straddling the Surrey-Sussex border, both abandoned and working, support colonies.

Though tiny, territorial males are aggressive and their rapid flight makes following their movement extremely taxing, although they usually return to the point of departure. Females, in contrast, although less often seen are easy to watch as they flutter low over the ground searching out potential egg sites. It seems that a warm, wet July yields the largest number of adults in the following spring.

Larval foodplants: wild strawberry, agrimony, creeping cinquefoil; less often tormentil, wood avens, dog-rose, bramble, salad burnet.

Grizzled Skipper — weekly transect counts

Headley Heath TQ195533 — **Donna Dawson, Gordon Flower**

	WEEK	2000	2001	2002	2003	2004	2005	2006	2007	2008	2009	2010	2011	2012
15 April	3	-			-	-	-	-	-	-	2	-	7	-
22	4	-			-	-	1	-	1	-	2	3	**12**	-
29	5	-	-		3	1	4	3	**5**	1	**5**	6	6	-
6 May	6	**3**	-		**4**	6	**5**	**4**		2	4	**8**	8	2
13	7	**3**	-		1	**8**	3	2	-	3		5	9	-
20	8	1	**3**		1	6	2	1	-	**5**	4	5	3	2
27	9	1	1		-	3	3	2	-	3	3	1	2	**6**
3 June	10	-	-		1	1	2	**4**	1	2	2	3	2	
10	11	-	1		1	-	2	-	-	-	1	3	-	-
17	12	-	-		-	-	-	-	-	-	-	2		-
24	13	-	-		-	-	-	-	-	-	-	-	-	-
1 July	14	-	-		-	-	-	-	-	-	-	-	-	-
8	15				-	-	-	-	-	-	-	1	2	-
15	16		-		-	-	-	-	-	-	-	-	2	-
Abundance index		8	5		12	25	22	15	11	16	28	37	54	12
Weeks recorded		**4**	**3**		**6**	**6**	**8**	**6**	**3**	**6**	**8**	**10**	**10**	**3**

Wood White *Leptidea sinapis* — Ken Willmott

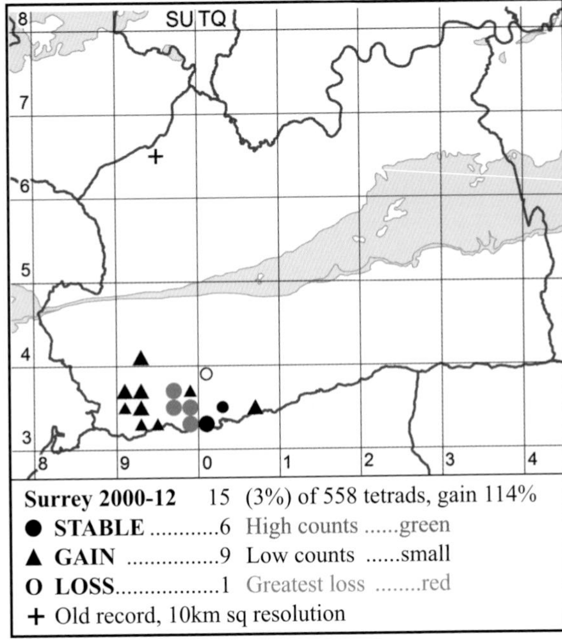

Surrey status: the county's rarest butterfly, reliably found only within several Forestry Commission properties in the Chiddingfold complex. Along with three adjacent tetrads in West Sussex, this is virtually the only population in the south-east region.

Flies: late April to June; mid-July to mid-August.

Conservation: protected from sale; UK Biodiversity Action Plan priority species; BC 2010 Red List: endangered.

Trends: vulnerable after massive declines. Surrey survival depends on forestry management maintaining open areas and wide sunny roadside verges within the Chiddingfold complex. Occasional appearances elsewhere are possible introductions. The abundance-trend chart is derived exclusively from the Oaken Wood transect apart from one record at Witley in May 2005.

Wingspan: 30-42mm.

Identification: sexually and seasonally dimorphic. The slow, meandering flight is distinctive and the rounded forewings can be seen when the butterfly settles. It never opens its wings to bask in the sun, but the male's black patch is clearly visible in flight, more so in the summer brood. Underside is delicately dusted with black/grey scales on a creamy-yellow background. Male has white patch on antennae undertip. In later brood, male's apical patch of black scales increases; female's decreases to almost pure white.

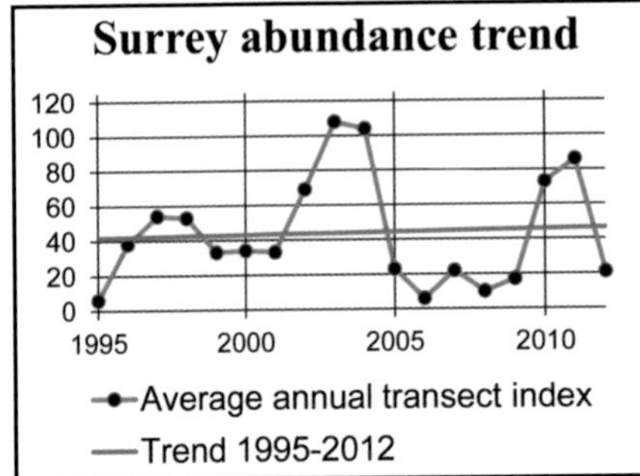

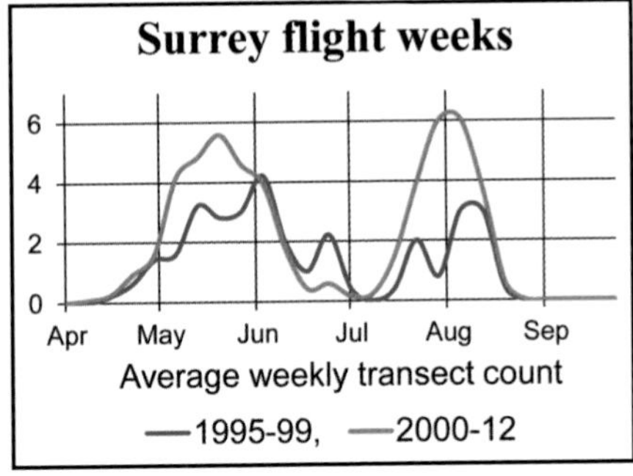

Wood Whites courting, male on left. **KW**

Confusion species: Green-veined and Small Whites, and female Orange-tip in the spring, are stronger fliers and will settle with wings open. Small White underside is creamy-yellow and more thinly dusted with black scales.

Habitat: in Surrey a butterfly of open woodland with wide, sunny rides and roadside verges, often associated with conifer plantations. Also found in open, scrub-mixed meadows within woodland, particularly where its larval foodplants prosper.

Key site: Chiddingfold Forest, of which BC's Oaken Wood reserve is a part. A colony established in the 1990s at a disused brickworks in Hambledon (SU973377), about 4km north of the core site, was lost to development in 2012.

Life cycle: bivoltine; sometimes emerges in late April (2011 was a particularly early year), but usually May; second brood emerges mid-July; winters as pupa.

Although most May eggs develop to produce a summer brood, I located a 23mm larva feeding on bird's-foot-trefoil on July 30, 1977, with second-brood Wood Whites on the wing and females already laying. I believe that the summer brood could be partial in some years. During the 1980s it was scarce, or even absent, in some parts of the Chiddingfold complex.

Eggs hatch in 10-15 days. The spring larvae take about a month to mature and the resulting pupae just a week if producing a July adult. Second-brood pupae that overwinter from spring or summer females take 7-10 months to hatch. Although they are difficult to find, I have succeeded in locating a wild pupa close to ground level on the stem of a well-eaten bird's-foot-trefoil plant. In contrast, during his early research, BC's Martin Warren found wild pupae within taller vegetation and at a higher elevation.

Larval foodplants: common and greater bird's-foot-trefoil, bitter-vetch, meadow vetchling, tufted vetch.

Wood White *continued*

Ken Willmott

THERE has been some debate about the emergence of the second brood and whether this occurs only in southernmost localities. Certainly in Surrey a second brood has never completely failed and in most years can be quite strong, equalling the numbers in the first brood.

South (1906) recognised an occasional second brood and illustrated remarkably different first- and second-brood males. He even gave a name to the summer generation – var. *diniensis*. He also provided evidence that the summer brood in July is sometimes partial, with numbers depending on the clemency of spring and summer weather.

Wood White laying on greater bird's-foot-trefoil. **KW**

There were dramatic declines in Surrey populations during the 1980s and some complete failures in former Chiddingfold sites. Then came the 1987 Great Storm, followed by another in 1990 while the Forestry Commission were still clearing the initial disastrous windfall debris. Wood White populations decline in woodland that becomes dominated by 50% or more shade, so the sudden opening up of the woodland structure by the forces of nature favoured its fortunes.

Time has passed and Corsican pine plantations grow taller and are beginning to cast their cold shadow. At a Chiddingfold verge favoured by Wood Whites I spent a remarkable 20 minutes with a female that deposited eggs on four different foodplants – greater bird's-foot-trefoil, bitter-vetch, meadow vetchling and tufted vetch, within a 25-metre stretch. This is now threatened by a nearby conifer plantation that within five years will shade out the verge and its plants. Conservation recommendations would be to remove the front 2-3 rows of pines and stack the resulting timber on the plantation side of the road, which receives the least amount of sunshine. This would leave the most important verge and bank undisturbed and unshaded by the maturing conifers.

The Forestry Commission does extensive work to help retain the Wood White as a Surrey resident. Every winter alternate roadside verges are cut in 50m stretches. Woodland clearings are also partially cut to maintain open space and to scuff the ground for vetches to seed successfully in the spring. A small percentage of Wood White pupae may be lost in the process but, without the cut, the larval and adult food sources would eventually be swamped by woody growth and therefore inaccessible to females searching for egg sites. Each year pupae can survive the winter in the remaining uncut verges.

To date, judging by single-species transect counts at peak emergence periods, numbers are stable. It is more usual with a bivoltine species for the second brood to be larger as it does not have to endure the rigours of winter and is not exposed to its predators for such

Wood White female on greater stitchwort. **GE**

a lengthy period. Surprisingly, despite the record-breaking wet spring and summer, both 2012 broods were virtually equal in numbers.

The Wood White's ability to disperse and find new breeding areas is good, especially if there are spells of unbroken sunshine and cloudless, warm days during its flight periods. Male flight is then relentless in search of females. Mated females continuously seek larval foodplants and are able to find new areas of abundance created by forestry operations during the previous winter. On such suitable days for prolonged flight, patrolling males go through a prolonged courtship. I have witnessed over 100 of these encounters but have yet to see a successful mating result from such a lengthy process (10+ minutes). Upon discovery by a passing male, the female abandons egg-laying, nectaring or flight, and settles with closed wings, to be joined by the eager male. He settles directly opposite, so they sit head to head. He touches her with his antennae and proboscis (tongue), which initiates a response. She rapidly flashes open her wings, stimulating a similar response from the male. Eventually the female escapes to continue her activities, sometimes still pursued by the male.

Although I have found numerous mating pairs I have seen the actual coupling event only a few times, and it was quick with no lengthy courtship: male discovers freshly emerged female; both are eager to reproduce their kind. In one pair the female had still not fully expanded her wings after emergence from the pupa.

Elsewhere in Britain the Wood White has strongholds in the clay woodlands of the East Midlands, often associated with conifer plantations and remnant deciduous high forest. Northamptonshire and Bedfordshire woodlands with wide, sunny roadside verges are particularly favoured, but even there it is local and vulnerable. The Wyre Forest and Forest of Dean are important sites, and there are coastal colonies on the undercliffs between Sidmouth in Devon and Lyme Regis in Dorset. A colony persists at Wicken Wood in the north-east of Buckinghamshire on the Northamptonshire boundary.

Wood White *continued*

Ken Willmott

Wood White

weekly transect counts

Oaken Wood, Chiddingfold SU990338

John Buckley

	WEEK	2000	2001	2002	2003	2004	2005	2006	2007	2008	2009	2010	2011	2012
8 April	2	-		-	-	-	-		-		-	-	1	
15	3	-		-	-	-		-	-	-	1	-	2	
22	4	-		-	1	-			-	-	-	-	10	
29	5	-	-	1	3	1	1	-	1	-	1		10	1
6 May	6	-	-	2	16	12	2	-	**9**	-	**2**	-	6	1
13	7	1	-	8	9	14	6		3	1		4	**12**	
20	8	**10**	-	3	15	11	9	2	5	-	1	9	5	1
27	9	4	-	6	8	11	**11**	-	-	-	1	7	2	**5**
3 June	10	4	4	11	5	9	6	1	-	-	-	5	2	
10	11	5	2	1	-	7	1	-	-	-	-	4	-	1
17	12	-	1	-	1	1	-	-	-	-	-	2	-	-
24	13	-	1	-	-	4	-	-	-	-	1	-	1	-
1 July	14	-	-	-	-	-	-	-	-	-	-	-	2	
8	15	-	-	-	1	-	-	-	-	-	1	1	-	
15	16	-	-	-	6	1	-	-	-	-	1	6	4	
22	17	-	2	1	15	5	1	1	-	3	1	**14**	4	-
29	18	-	5	7	**18**	**15**	4	2	1	-	**2**	12	6	-
5 August	19	4	**9**	**16**	6	10	2	**3**	-	1	1	6	**12**	3
12	20	2	**9**	12	4	3	1	1	1	**4**	**2**	3	2	1
19	21	-	-	1	-	-	1	-	-	-			3	2
Abundance index		34	33	69	108	101	45	11	22	10	17	NI	86	21
Weeks recorded		**7**	**8**	**12**	**14**	**14**	**12**	**6**	**6**	**4**	**12**	**12**	**17**	**8**

Phenology trend	**1995-2012**	earlier by 2 weeks
Best transect day 2000-12	Aug 2, 2003	Oaken Wood 18
Transects abundance	**1995-2012** gain 11%	**2000-2012** loss 31%
UK transects abundance	**1979-2012** loss 84%	**10-year trend** loss 59%
UK 4,361 10k squares	**2005-09** 63 = 1.4%	**10-year trend** loss 23%

Flight weeks Wood White — ▲High transect counts △Middle ^Low

Apr					May				Jun				Jul					Aug				Sep			
1	8	15	22	29	6	13	20	27	3	10	17	24	1	8	15	22	29	5	12	19	26	2	9	16	23
	^	^	△	△	△	▲	▲	▲	△	△	^	△	^	^	△	△	▲	▲	△	△					

Clouded Yellow *Colias croceus* — Geoff Eaton

Surrey status: unpredictable migrant; visits a variety of habitats.

Flies: most abundant in late summer.

Trends: nationally there are indications that this migrant has become more common and widespread since the 1970s, probably as a result of climate change. Surrey's last reasonable year was 2009; records since have been poor.

Wingspan: male 52-58mm, female 54-62mm.

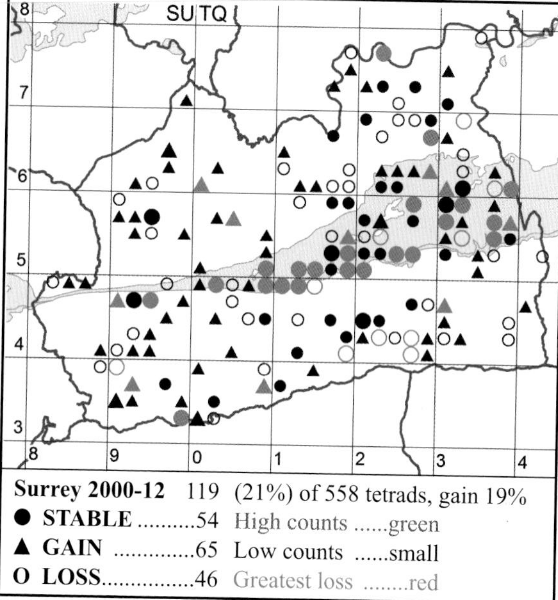

Map note: *records are inevitably volatile because the Clouded Yellow is an irregular migrant that can appear anywhere, most commonly on the Downs.*

Identification: rich, golden yellow with black edging; central black spot on forewing, and a larger, central orange spot on hindwing. Underside is a paler yellow, with a central black spot on the forewing and a distinctive almost mystical symbolic "8" in the middle of the hindwing. The female shows yellow spots within the black margin of the forewing, but their development is variable. This difference is difficult to appreciate because the Clouded Yellow usually settles with wings closed, but may be revealed if the butterfly flexes its wings while taking nectar. This feature can also be seen by transparency when the butterfly is viewed against the light. Both male and female butterflies may open their wings during mating.

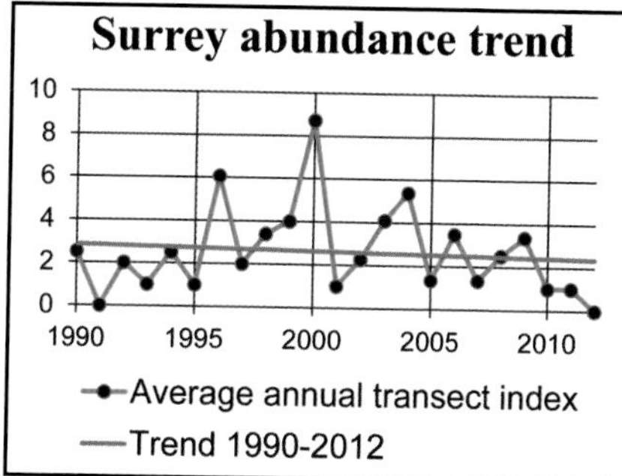

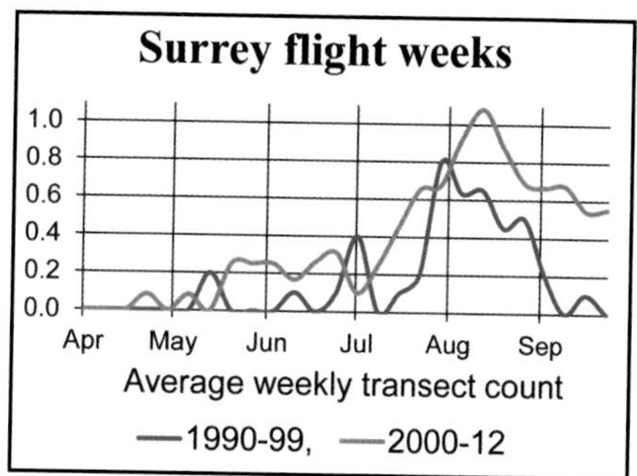

Clouded Yellow *continued*

Geoff Eaton

Variations/aberrations: most familiar variation is the pale form *helice*, which occurs in a small percentage of females. The base colour of the upperside typically ranges from white to grey and this variation is similar overall to the much rarer migrants, Pale and Berger's Clouded Yellow, but there are detail differences.

Confusion species: when viewed obliquely at rest the Clouded Yellow can take on the appearance of one of the common Whites, but normally the yellow colouring is distinctive. The Brimstone, our only other yellow butterfly, is paler and its wings display a unique outline and lack the black margin.

Habitat: may be seen passing through almost any habitat, including gardens, but favours flower-rich areas where the larval food plants thrive. In southern England there appears to be a preference for downland.

Clouded Yellow, McLaren Park. **GE**

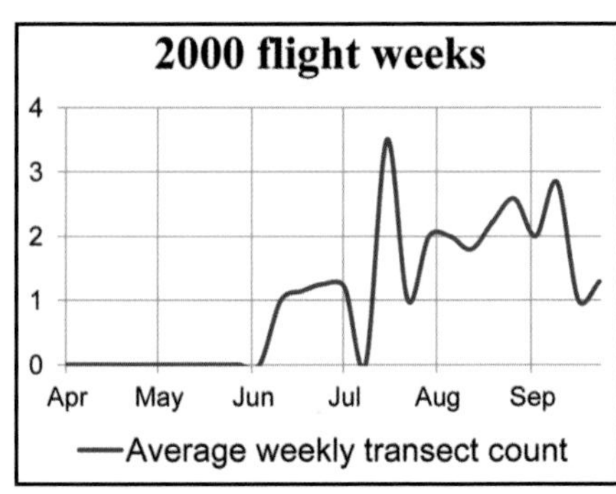

Top transect abundance indexes in 2000: London Wetland Centre 38, Headley Warren 28, Denbies Landbarn 19, Denbies Hillside 19, Ribblesdown Quarry 17, Sheepleas 15, Mitcham Common B 11, Oaken Wood 9.

Other key sites: Newlands Corner, Papercourt, McLaren Park.

Life cycle: early migrants usually arrive in May or June, although butterflies have been seen earlier in the year; summer migrants may arrive from July to September. Local adults, derived from earlier migrant egg-laying, are on the wing throughout the summer, when they supplement and usually outnumber the summer migrants. A second local generation may appear in late September or October and even fly into November.

Eggs are usually laid singly on the upper side of leaves. Initially they are pale yellow or white, but turn pinkish-orange before hatching after about a week. Larval growth is dependent on temperature and weather conditions, and maturity is reached in three to six weeks. The well-camouflaged chrysalis is formed low in ground vegetation. Adults emerge after about three weeks, and may survive for perhaps a month.

Larval foodplants: mainly lucerne and clovers; also bird's-foot-trefoil.

Clouded Yellow female at moment of take-off from hawkbit. **MW**

CLOUDED YELLOWS reach our shores in most years, but it is their occasional arrival in great numbers, and subsequent successful breeding, that define so-called "Clouded Yellow years". These occur on average perhaps once in a decade.

In its homeland around the Mediterranean and into western Asia, the Clouded Yellow is continuously brooded with three or four generations per year. It does not hibernate at any stage of its life cycle (a characteristic shared with that other great traveller, the Painted Lady); instead, larvae continue to feed through the winter period. Since the late 1990s there have been indications that a few larvae overwinter successfully in sheltered locations along the south coast, e.g. in the Bournemouth area (Skelton, 1999). However, the majority still succumb to our cold, damp winters.

The preferred habitat in southern England seems to be downland. In Surrey there is a clear concentration of records along the line of the North Downs, but the distribution map confirms that this butterfly may be seen anywhere in the county.

The weekly transect counts for the London Wetland Centre, Barnes (LWC), demonstrate the extreme variability in the number of Clouded Yellows recorded from year to year. In 2000, the last acknowledged Clouded Yellow year, there were early summer records here in June and early July, followed by consistent records from mid-July to early September. There were sightings from 25 other Surrey transects, six of them into double figures. But in 2001 the Surrey transect count was zero, and only five UK transects had more than one record.

Since then, 2002-2006 and 2009 were considered good years, but at the LWC the only significant years were 2006 and 2009, when June sightings were followed by consistent later records. The other years to 2012 provided only single records or none at all.

The LWC is some 15km north of the North Downs, and it is interesting to compare the data from the downland site at Denbies Landbarn B, near Dorking (selected years only). Here there are August/September records in 2002, 2003 and 2009, while 2004 provided an early June record followed by consistent sightings through much of August. Year 2006 provided just one sighting in late July (in marked contrast with the LWC), while 2007 yielded a single record in early May.

Clouded Yellow *continued* **Geoff Eaton**

Bearing in mind the unpredictability of this butterfly, a reasonable year for the Clouded Yellow in Surrey might begin with sporadic migrant records in late spring or early summer. Later migrants and an emerging local population could be expected in high summer, with a possible second local generation persisting well into autumn.

An example of this persistence is provided by 2009 data from McLaren Park, Woking, where I observed Clouded Yellow behaviour in an extensive area of managed grassland with a range of plants, including clover and bird's-foot-trefoil. Adult butterflies were seen first in early August, and despite widespread mowing and the first autumn frosts in October, they were recorded consistently from mid-September and throughout October, with a final sighting early in November.

Numbers were low, with no more than three individuals distinguished on any one occasion. In the cooler weather, males still patrolled their regular haunts with a fast, powerful flight. They also made long flights over the areas of mown grass and on settling adopted an angled position relative to the sun, reminiscent of the Grayling. Females were more secretive and concealed themselves deep in the remaining grassy vegetation, but were sometimes seen when disturbed by other butterflies, e.g. Small Copper.

An interesting feature of male behaviour was the selection of yellowing foliage (especially creeping thistle) as a preferred resting site in dull weather. The Clouded Yellow is strikingly bright and instantly noticeable; yellowing foliage may provide some degree of camouflage cover. Their apparent liking for yellow daisy-type flowers as a nectar source could serve a similar purpose. As at the LWC, there were no records from McLaren Park in 2010-2012.

The maximum weekly count in the transects discussed is six (LWC, 2000, 2006). Although migrating butterflies often congregate along the coast when they first make landfall, once they move inland they disperse and are not seen together in significant numbers. Francis Kelly's record of c. 20 Clouded Yellows nectaring on bird's-foot-trefoil west of Papercourt Lake, Send, near Woking in mid-September 2006 presumably represented a local emergence. In 2009, from August 9 to September 26, the same field yielded 3+ individuals favouring lucerne.

Phenology trend	**1990-2012**	NA (irregular migrant)	
Best transect day 2000-12	Sep 4, 2000	Headley Warren	8
Transects abundance	**1990-2012** loss 17%	**2000-2012** loss 88%	
UK transects abundance	**1979-2012** gain 367%	**10-year trend** loss 98%	
UK 4,361 10k squares	**2005-09** 1,143 = 26%	**10-year trend** loss 1%	

Flight weeks ▲High transect counts △Middle ^Low

Apr					May				Jun				Jul					Aug				Sep			
1	8	15	22	29	6	13	20	27	3	10	17	24	1	8	15	22	29	5	12	19	26	2	9	16	23
			^		^		△	△	△	^	△	△	^	△	△	△	△	▲	▲	▲	▲	△	▲	△	△

Clouded Yellow

weekly transect counts

London Wetland Centre TQ228770 **Richard Bullock**

	WEEK	2000	2001	2002	2003	2004	2005	2006	2007	2008	2009	2010	2011	2012
3 June	10	-	-	-	-	-	-	1	-	-	**2**	-	-	-
10	11	1	-	-	-	-	-	-	-	-	-	-	-	-
17	12	-	-	-	-	-	-	-	-	-	-	-	-	-
24	13	2	-	-	-	-	-	-		-	-	-	-	-
1 July	14	2	-	-	-	-	-	-	-	-	-	-	-	-
8	15		-	-	-	-	-	-	-	-	-	-	-	-
15	16	**6**	-	-	-	-	-	-	-	-	1	-	-	-
22	17	1	-	-	-	-	-	**6**	-	-	1	-	-	-
29	18	2	-	1	-	-	-	3	-	-	1	-	-	-
5 August	19	3	-	-	-	-	-	1	-	-	1	-	-	-
12	20	**6**	-	-	-	-	-	-	-	-	-	-	-	-
19	21	5	-	-	-	-	-	-	1	-	-	-	-	-
26	22	4	-	-	-	-	-	-		-	-	-	-	-
2 September	23	1	-	-	-	-	-	-	-	-	-	-	-	-
9	24	4	-	-	-	-	-	2	-	-	-	-	-	-
16	25	-	-	-	-	-	-	1		-	-	-	-	-
23	26	-			1	-	-	2	-	-	-	-	-	-
Abundance index		38		1	1			18	NI		7			
Weeks recorded		**12**		**1**	**1**			**7**	**1**		**5**			

Clouded Yellow

weekly transect counts

Denbies Landbarn B TQ135499 **Gail Jeffcoate, Robert Cramp**

	WEEK	2000	2001	2002	2003	2004	2005	2006	2007	2008	2009	2010	2011	2012
6 May	6				-	-	-	-	1	-	-	-	-	-
10 June	11			-	-	1	-	-		-	-	-	-	-
29-Jul	18				-	-	-	1	-	-	2	-	-	-
5 August	19			-	1	**5**	-	-	-	-	2	-	-	-
12	20			1	**2**	**5**	-	-	-	-	**3**	-	-	-
19	21			1	-	1	-	-		-	1	-	-	-
26	22			-	-	-	-	-	-	-	-	-	-	-
2 September	23			1	-	-	-	-	-	-	-	-	-	-
9	24			-	-	-	-	-	-	-		-	-	-
16	25			-	-	-	-	-	-	-	-	-	-	-
23	26			1	**2**	-	-	-	-	-	1	-	-	-
Abundance index				5	5	12		1	1		10			
Weeks recorded				**4**	**3**	**4**		**1**	**1**		**5**			

Brimstone *Gonepteryx rhamni*

Harry E. Clarke

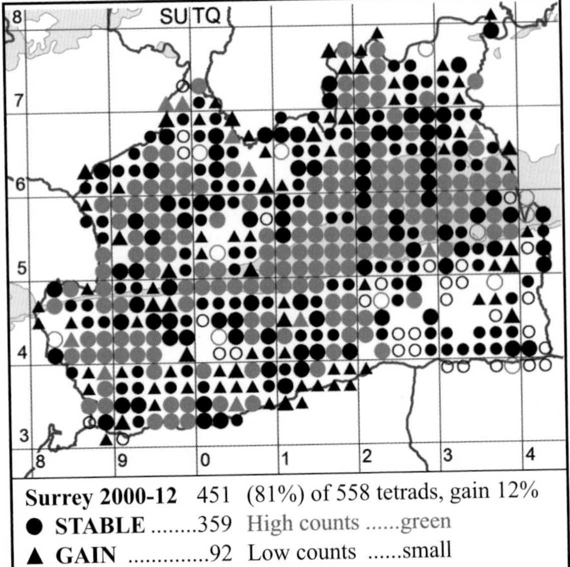

Surrey status: common and widespread, depending on presence of larval foodplants.
Flies: mid-March to September.
Trends: stable.
Wingspan: 60-74mm.
Identification: distinctive leaf-shape to both fore- and hindwings; male lemon-yellow, female pale greenish-white; small orange spots on both fore- and hindwings; underside has greenish tinge and prominent veins; head and antennae rustic red-brown; wings closed when at rest or feeding.
Confusion species: at a distance female may be mistaken for Large White, but wing shape and lack of black markings separate them. Male's patrol flight is high and conspicuous, unlike the low, fast flight of the Clouded Yellow.
Habitat: woodland, hedgerows, heathland, downland, fens and marshes, and especially damp carr woodland.
Top transects: Hutchinson's Bank, Juniper Hill, Park Downs, Pewley Down, Sheepleas.
Life cycle: univoltine hibernator. Eggs laid singly from mid-April to early July on the underside of a buckthorn leaf, or close to buds. During the first two instars the green larva rests along the midrib of the upperside of the leaf and eats down through the upper layers leaving characteristic perforations. In later instars the larva eats the whole leaf and

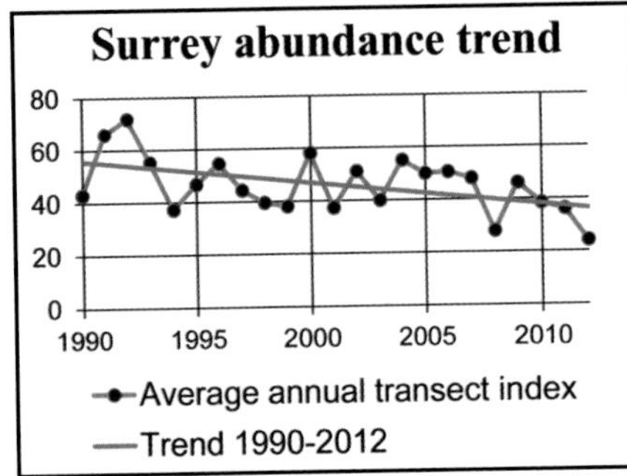

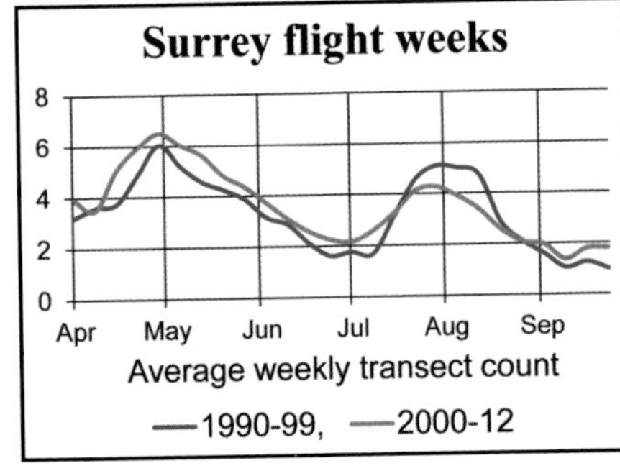

Brimstone male on dandelion. **GE**

rests on the leaf edge or along the stalk. Paradoxically, the larvae are less affected by parasites than those that hide; however, warblers seem to be significant predators, especially during the later stages of development.

Pupation mostly occurs away from the foodplant, usually on the underside of a leaf or stem in low vegetation, but occasionally on a buckthorn leaf. Emerges mid-July to mid-August, and the previous year's adults sometimes fly with fresh ones. Brimstones fly during the heat of the day, but settle down to roost by late afternoon.

Larval foodplants: buckthorn on calcareous soils; alder buckthorn on acidic soils.

Phenology trend	**1990-2012**	later by 0.5 weeks	
Best transect day 2000-12	May 5, 2000	Park Downs	42
Transects abundance	**1990-2012** loss 35%	**2000-2012** loss 37%	
UK transects abundance	**1976-2012** gain 9%	**10-year trend** loss 30%	
UK 4,361 10k squares	**2005-09** 1,232 = 28%	**10-year trend** loss 1%	

Flight weeks ▲High transect counts △Middle ^Low

Apr					May				Jun				Jul					Aug				Sep			
1	8	15	22	29	6	13	20	27	3	10	17	24	1	8	15	22	29	5	12	19	26	2	9	16	23
△	△	▲	▲	▲	▲	▲	▲	▲	△	△	△	^	^	△	△	△	△	△	△	△	^	^	^	^	^

Brimstone *continued*

Harry E. Clarke

Brimstone female on knapweed. **FK**

THE Brimstone is a remarkable butterfly as it is one of the first species to appear in spring, and the longest-lived as an adult. Brimstones hibernate in holly, ivy and bramble in woodlands, where the wing shape and colour make excellent camouflage.

Males are first to awake from hibernation in March, some 21 days before females, although they can make a brief appearance on any warm day during the winter months. While males are sexually mature on emergence, females do not obtain full sexual maturity until after hibernation, probably to coincide with the emerging buds of the larval foodplants.

Males search for females, as do other members of the family (see Large White), which is why they are seen more often than the females. Unreceptive females adopt the refusal posture of a raised abdomen. Mating typically lasts 1-3 hours, but can be up to 28 hours. Females can mate again up to two times.

Females have an uncanny ability to find isolated foodplants, often travelling several kilometres. They prefer isolated young trees in sunny, relatively exposed positions. Young trees probably have lower toxin levels. Adults spend the late summer and autumn feeding up in order to survive the winter. They have an exceptionally long proboscis, enabling them to feed on flowers with deep nectaries, such as teasel and buddleia.

The strategy of being univoltine and long-lived has proved successful, even though the Brimstone is near its northern range, and limited by the availability of its foodplant. It seems to be doing better on the Chalk, where buckthorn flourishes, than on the damp and acid soils where the more abundant alder buckthorn grows.

Brimstone

weekly transect counts

Hutchinson's Bank, New Addington TQ380617

Martin Wills

	WEEK	2000	2001	2002	2003	2004	2005	2006	2007	2008	2009	2010	2011	2012
1 April	1	16	10	2	11	10	5	3	**12**	1	2	5	-	1
8	2	8	-	1	6	18	5	5	5	1	-	7	19	-
15	3	7	7	11	20	10	**20**	16	**12**	5	22	2	16	-
22	4	16	2	11	**22**	**27**	3	**18**	3	8	23	-	17	9
29	5	4	**19**	1	14	21	6	**18**	1	5	**31**	7	13	7
6 May	6	10	9	2	4	16	4	17	4	4	19	8	20	4
13	7	7	6	5	5	14	5	2	6	8	10	2	3	-
20	8	6	7	4	6	10	9	1	3	4	9	2	**23**	7
27	9	15	3	3	4	9	11	5	5	2	18	**11**	18	9
3 June	10	8	5	-	4	11	12	10	3	5	5	9	17	2
10	11	3	2	6	7	7	-	7	4	3	2	9	8	4
17	12	3	2	3	3	1	2	7	4	**9**	3	9	4	4
24	13	-	1	1	1	3		5	-	5	2	3	4	1
1 July	14	1	3		-	-	3	-	10	-	2	5	8	2
8	15	1	1	-	-	7	6	4	6	2	-	7	5	2
15	16	1	3	5	11	7	5	3	1	6	-	7	6	-
22	17	12	6	-	4	19	7	2	4	2	9	7	12	1
29	18	**25**	3	16	1	10		-	10	6	9	5	20	-
5 August	19	19	2	**23**	-	2		-	1	-	13		-	**17**
12	20	2	3	17	-	-					1	-	1	-
19	21	5	3	3	-	-					1	-	5	9
26	22	-	-	8	-	-				6	-		4	3
2 September	23	-	-	-	-	4				-	-	-	6	-
9	24	1	-	-	-	-				-	-	-	-	1
16	25	-	-	-	-	-				-	-	-	-	-
23	26	-	1	-	-	-					-		-	1
Abundance index		167	97	126	123	160	135	120	95	84	188	110	231	82
Weeks recorded		**21**	**21**	**18**	**16**	**19**				**18**	**18**	**17**	**21**	**18**

Brimstone larva on partly eaten buckthorn leaf. **FK**

Large White *Pieris brassicae* — Harry E. Clarke

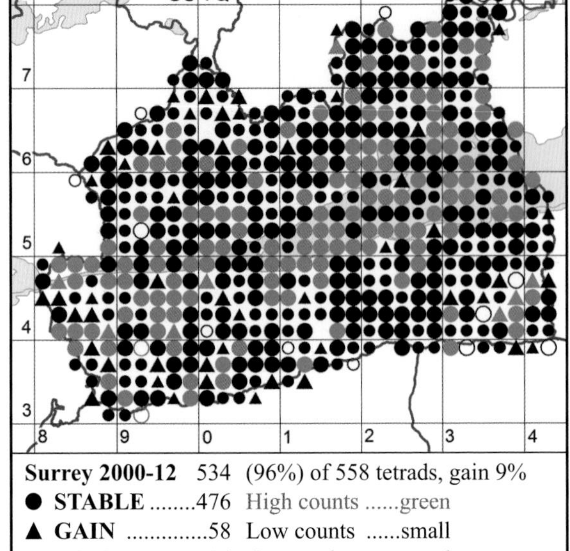

Surrey status: common and widespread; often bracketed with Small White as "Cabbage White".

Flies: late April to June; second brood July to September, reinforced by migrants.

Trends: declining in numbers.

Wingspan: male 58mm, female 63mm.

Identification: can only be reliably identified while at rest. Flight strong and erratic. Wings white; forewing upperside has strong black tips extending along outer margin, female having two black spots and club-shaped mark on inner margin. Hindwing underside yellow. Summer brood more strongly marked than spring brood.

Confusion species: Small White, Green-veined White, female Orange-tip, female Brimstone. Hindwing underside is yellow in both Large and Small White. Green-veined and Small White are similar in size to the male Large White.

Upper forewing	*black tips*	*black spots: female has two; male*
Large White	more extensive on outer margin, strong	none
Small White	more extensive on front margin	one
Green-veined	more extensive on outer margin, broken	one

Habitat: Acid grassland, downland, gardens, orchards, parks, waste-ground (generally dry and sunny sites).

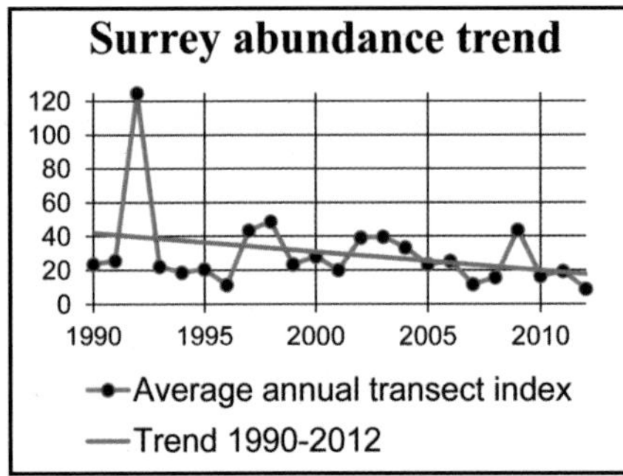

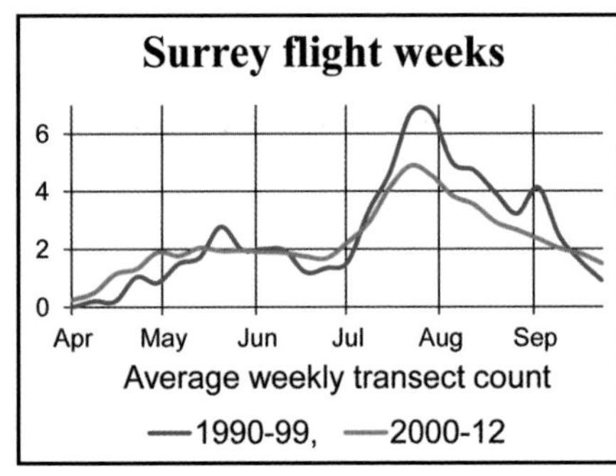

Large White male in spring on bluebell. **FK**

Top transects: Sheepleas, Juniper Hill, Brentmoor Heath, Chobham Common, Pewley Down, Mitcham Common.

Life cycle: usually bivoltine; winters as pupa; adults emerge late April to end of June; second brood July to September. Eggs laid in clusters of up to 50 on leaf underside. The gregarious larvae prefer the outer leaves and are encouraged to eat by the mustard-oil fumes. Their black and yellow markings alert birds to the mustard-oil poison accumulated in their bodies. Pupates away from foodplant.

Larval foodplants, in order of Surrey abundance: oilseed rape, wild mignonette, nasturtium, cabbages. Females are attracted by the smell of mustard oils and prefer larger plants in sunny positions.

Phenology trend	**1990-2012**	earlier by one week	
Best transect day 2000-12	Jul 24, 2003	Sheepleas	147
Transects abundance	**1990-2012** loss 58%	**2000-2012** loss 49%	
UK transects abundance	**1976-2012** loss 36%	**10-year trend** loss 40%	
UK 4,361 10k squares	**2005-09** 2,126 = 49%	**10-year trend** loss 8%	

Flight weeks ▲High transect counts △Middle ^Low

Apr					May				Jun				Jul					Aug				Sep			
1	8	15	22	29	6	13	20	27	3	10	17	24	1	8	15	22	29	5	12	19	26	2	9	16	23
^	^	^	^	△	△	△	△	△	△	△	^	^	△	▲	▲	▲	▲	▲	▲	▲	△	△	△	△	^

Large White *continued*

Harry E. Clarke

THE Large White is a specialist of cultivated brassicas and superbly adapted to take full advantage of suitable foodplants. The female will typically lay 600 eggs during her three-week life span, producing many adults from relatively few plants.

Surrey has a resident population, which provides a small first brood, reinforced by continental migrants. The second brood is significantly larger and can quickly colonise new areas, but the Large White faces a constant battle: cultivated brassicas are sprayed to kill the larvae; and the parasitoid wasps *Trichogramma brassicae*, *Cotesia glomerata* and *Pteromalus puparum* target eggs, larvae and pupae respectively.

An exceptional year for this butterfly was 1992, with 555 adults counted at Sheepleas between the third week in April and the end of August, with a lull of three weeks at the end of June. Other good years were 1998, 2002, 2003 and 2004. The years 2009-11 were stable in Surrey, with over 500 adults recorded on transects, but 2012, as for most species, was poor.

Parasitised larva. **MB**

Our four pierines (Large, Small and Green-veined Whites, Orange-tip) have a similar mating strategy. A patrolling male approaches anything white and is able to distinguish a female by UV reflections from the underside of her wings. He will attempt courtship but quickly gives up if her scent tells him she has recently mated.

The male releases a pheromone from his wings when in flight, which the female is able to detect at short distances. The female spreads her wings and raises her abdomen in the mating refusal posture, but will close her wings to allow the male to land beside her if she accepts his advances. The male bends his abdomen sideways to allow the genitals to unite, and the pair often take off in a short post-nuptial flight.

In addition to sperm, the male passes protein-rich material of up to 15% of his body weight, which provides nutrients for the female and developing eggs (see pages 16-17). This additional material has been termed a "nuptial gift". The male also passes an anti-aphrodisiac, which other males can detect for up to five days. Females can mate again up to three times (average 1.22), which enables them to live longer and produce larger eggs.

Large Whites seek out white flowers for roosting, where they are well camouflaged. White dead-nettles and broad beans have been noted as favourites. Pupal diapause is triggered by lower temperatures and shorter daylight, although larvae have been observed overwintering as far north as Nottingham, pupating in late March. Once diapause has been triggered, the pupa requires a prolonged exposure to the cold before emergence can occur.

Large White female in summer on Michaelmas-daisy. **GE**

Large White

weekly transect counts

Mitcham Common A TQ285680 — **Paul Moorhouse, Neil Vigar *et al.***

	WEEK	2000	2001	2002	2003	2004	2005	2006	2007	2008	2009	2010	2011	2012
15 April	3	-	-		-	-	-	-	**4**		-		-	1
22	4	-	-			-	1		3		1	-	-	
29	5	1	-			-	-	-	-		2		-	
6 May	6	1	-		-	1	-	**4**	1	-	-		-	
13	7	2	-			-	1	3	3		-	-	-	
20	8	-	1			-	-		-	-		-	-	**2**
27	9		-		-	-	-		-	-	1		-	
3 June	10	-	-		-	-	-	2	-	-	1	1	-	-
10	11	-	-		-	2	-	-	1		-	1	-	
17	12	1	-		-	-	1	-	-	1	1	-	-	-
24	13	1	-		-	2	-	-	3	**5**	4	1	-	-
1 July	14	1	-		1	-	-	-	-	-	4	1		
8	15	-	**3**		-	2	3	3	-	1	1	1	3	1
15	16	**3**	-		7	**6**	**5**		-	-	**7**		**5**	
22	17	-	1		**9**	-	4	-	-	2	2	3	**5**	
29	18	**3**	1		**9**	-	-	1	-	1	3		3	1
5 August	19	1	-		1	-	-	-	-	-			-	1
12	20	-	-		1	-	-	-	-	2	1	-		-
19	21	-	-		3	-	1		-		-		1	
26	22	-	-			-	2	-	-	-	1	**3**		
2 September	23	-	-		-	-	-	-	-	1	-	-	-	-
9	24	-	-		-	-	-	-	-	1		-	-	
16	25	-	-		2	-	-	-	-	3	-	-	-	-
Abundance index		17	10		35	13	18	NI	15	21	34	NI	20	9
Weeks recorded		**9**	**4**		**8**	**5**	**8**	**5**	**6**	**9**	**13**	**7**	**7**	**5**

Small White *Pieris rapae*

Harry E. Clarke

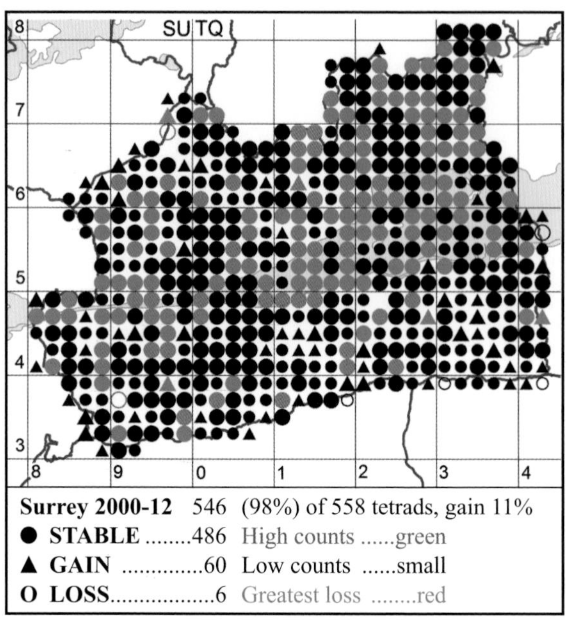

Surrey status: common and widespread; often bracketed with Large White as "Cabbage White".

Flies: overlapping broods from late April (or earlier) to September and even October.

Trends: stable.

Wingspan: 38-57mm.

Identification: can only be reliably identified while at rest. Flight strong and erratic. Wings white; hindwing underside yellow; black tip to upper forewing is more extensive on front margin; male has one black spot, female two. Summer brood more darkly marked than spring brood.

Confusion species: male Large White (see table on page 56), Green-veined White, female Orange-tip. Hindwing underside is yellow in both Large and Small White. Male Large White has no black spots on upper forewing, Small White has one; female Large White is clearly larger.

Habitat: any, including gardens.

Top transects: Juniper Hill, Mitcham Common A & B, Sheepleas, South Norwood CP.

Life cycle: usually multivoltine; winters as a pupa, with adults emerging end April. Eggs are laid singly, usually on the leaf underside. The larvae, camouflaged green, pupate away from the foodplant on trees, walls, etc.

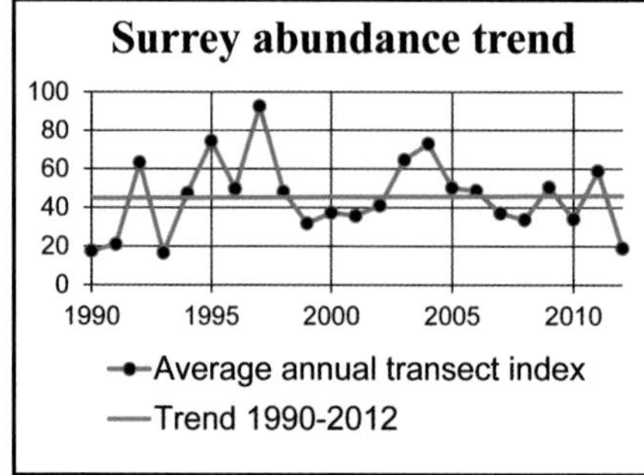

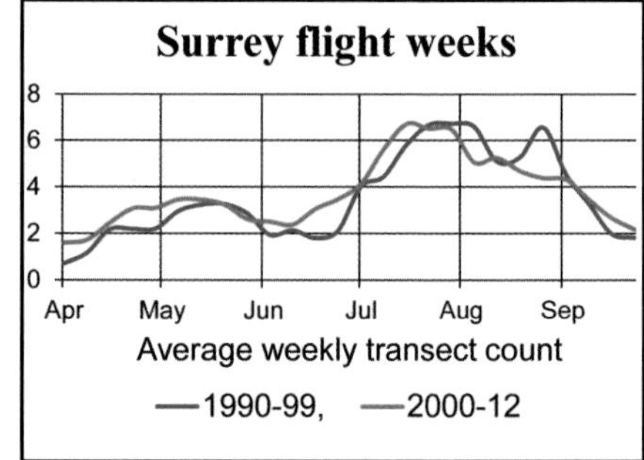

Small White pair, male above, on oxeye daisy. **FK**

Larval foodplants: cultivated brassicas, especially cabbage, and nasturtium. Surrey abundance order: garlic mustard, hedge mustard, charlock, wild mignonette, oilseed rape, hoary cress, nasturtium, cabbage. Females are attracted by the smell of mustard oils and prefer small plants in sheltered positions.

THE Small White is a habitat generalist and therefore less often affected by habitat change than other species. It is the most successful of our pierids, being three times more numerous than Green-veined White and Large White. Surrey's resident population is reinforced by continental migrants in both the first and subsequent broods. Most years the third brood overlaps the second brood.

Numbers fluctuate from year to year. Good years were 1992, 1995, 1997, 2003, 2004, and 2011. A good count was in 2004 on Mitcham Common B transect (transect A was also good). Second-brood numbers started to build from the start of July, peaking at 82 in mid-July. Numbers dropped from the start of August but counts in the teens continued for the first three weeks of September.

See Large White for mating strategy (page 58). Females frequently mate again up to five times (average 2.4), which enables them to live longer, and produce larger eggs.

Small Whites prefer white flowers for both nectaring and roosting, where they become well camouflaged. Pupal diapause is triggered by lower temperatures and shorter daylight length in the larval stage. Once diapause has been triggered, the pupa requires a prolonged exposure to the cold before emergence can occur.

Flight weeks ▲High transect counts △Middle ^Low

Apr					May				Jun				Jul					Aug				Sep			
1	8	15	22	29	6	13	20	27	3	10	17	24	1	8	15	22	29	5	12	19	26	2	9	16	23
^	^	^	△	△	△	△	△	^	^	^	△	△	△	▲	▲	▲	▲	▲	▲	▲	△	△	△	△	^

Small White *continued*

Small White — weekly transect counts

Mitcham Common A TQ285680 — **Paul Moorhouse, Neil Vigar *et al.***

	WEEK	2000	2001	2002	2003	2004	2005	2006	2007	2008	2009	2010	2011	2012
1 April	1	-	-			-	-		3		-	1		4
8	2	-	-			1		-	2			1	10	
15	3	-	-		5	1	11	-	12		16		19	2
22	4	-	-			2	18		**33**		30	8	13	
29	5	4	-			-	8	13	28		26		17	
6 May	6	6	6		11	4	17	18	9	9	11		4	
13	7	6	2			6	17	2	13		14	7	5	
20	8	3	**12**			3	2		11	1		10	5	9
27	9		1		-	6	3		3	-	5		3	
3 June	10	6	-		2	1	1	4	1	1	1	4	2	-
10	11	5	1		-	-	1	2	7		3	4	17	
17	12	-	-		-	-	-	1	16	3	2	2	17	1
24	13	1	-		**20**	-	4	1	15	7	11	1	25	3
1 July	14	4	-		17	8	2	3	18	14	34	10		
8	15	-	4		12	32	**30**	24	24	**25**	37	14	27	9
15	16	10	9		10	51	17		30	20	**46**		**47**	
22	17	11	9		7	61	17	**27**	13	15	7	**30**	26	
29	18	9	8		12	**64**	15	9	14	21	7		19	**22**
5 August	19	**13**	3		13	28	17	12	7	6			12	13
12	20	5	4		9	9	5	16	3	9	13	15		16
19	21	9	4		5	11	9		1		12		15	
26	22	3	-			11	7	14	-	6	26	1		
2 September	23	3	4		18	11	10	9	5	7	3	3	22	8
9	24	1	-		5	10	1	-	4	9		2	10	
16	25	-	-		4	3	2	3	4	8	2	2	14	2
23	26	-	-		4		-	3	-	-	-	4	3	
Abundance index		110	70		194	299	217	211	279	201	323	NI	414	167
Weeks recorded		**17**	**13**		**16**	**20**	**22**	**17**	**24**	**16**	**20**	**18**	**22**	**11**

Phenology trend	**1990-2012**	earlier by 1.5 weeks	
Best transect day 2000-12	Jul 15, 2004	Mitcham Common B	82
Transects abundance	**1990-2012** gain 3%	**2000-2012** loss 21%	
UK transects abundance	**1976-2012** loss 29%	**10-year trend** loss 55%	
UK 4,361 10k squares	**2005-09** 2,060 = 47%	**10-year trend** loss 4%	

Green-veined White *Pieris napi*

Harry E. Clarke

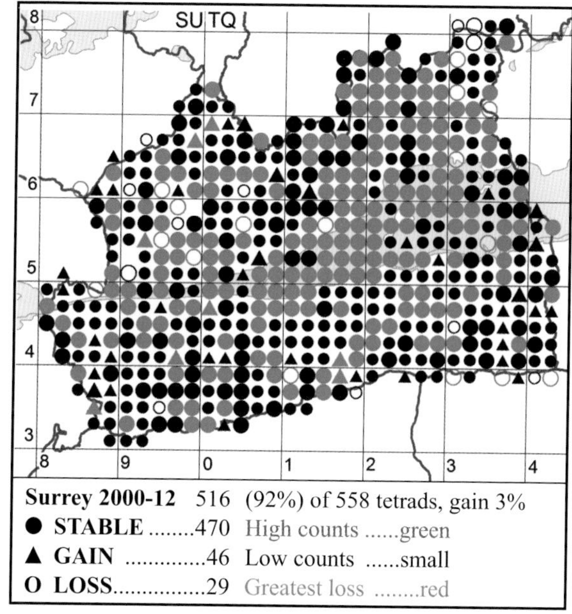

Surrey status: common and widespread.
Flies: mid-April to early June; late June to September.
Trends: declining due to habitat loss.
Wingspan: 40-52mm.
Identification: can only be reliably identified while at rest. Flight strong and erratic. Wings white; hindwing underside yellow with prominent green-veining (actually black scales over yellow ones); female has two black spots on forewing upperside; male has only one, which is faint or absent in spring. Black wing-tips extend along front margin. Second-brood butterflies are larger, with stronger upperside markings but reduced veining, especially females.
Confusion species: male Large White (see table on page 56), Small White, female Orange-tip. Green-veined White is the only butterfly with underside green-veining.
Habitat: generally damp and shady sites, e.g. woods, woodland margins and hedgerows, pastures, river banks, ditches.
Top transects: South Norwood CP, Sheepleas, Juniper Hill, Hutchinson's Bank.
Life cycle: usually bivoltine, although in 2011 there appears to have been a third brood at the end of August. Winters as pupa. Eggs are laid singly on underside of foodplant. The camouflaged green larvae feed on leaves and can share the same plant with Orange-tips. Pupates usually low down, away from foodplant.

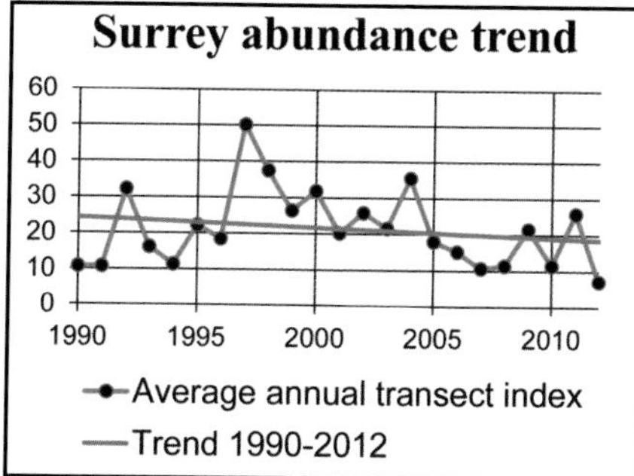

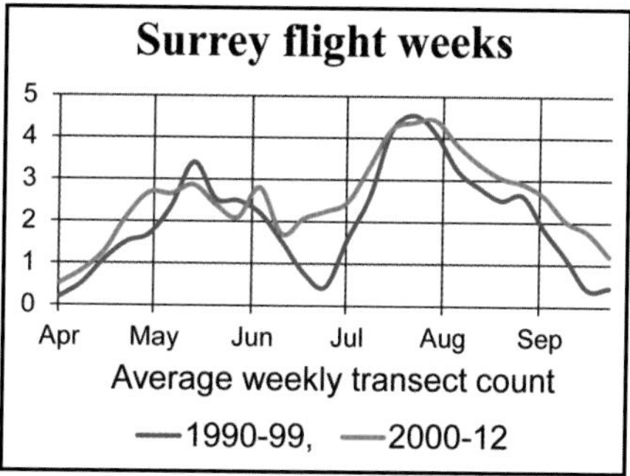

Green-veined White *continued* **Harry E. Clarke**

THE Green-veined White, with its ability to exploit damp and shady habitats, and extensive northerly range, is Britain's most widespread butterfly.

It is often confused with the Large and Small White, but Green-veined White larvae prefer similar foodplants to the Orange-tip. Whereas Orange-tip larvae feed on the flowers and seed pods, Green-veined White larvae eat the leaves. Consequently the Green-veined White can be found in far larger numbers than is possible for the Orange-tip.

Foodplant selection is triggered by the presence of mustard oils and their derivative glucosinolates, which the pierines detect through chemosensory hairs on their forelegs. Reproductive rate appears to be limited by difficulties in finding suitable larval foodplants.

Green-veined White: spring male on withered daffodil. **FK**

South Norwood Country Park is by far Surrey's best transect site, with three times the total of Sheepleas, the next best. However a gradual reduction of wetter areas in parts of South Norwood CP has favoured the Small White, which has increased in numbers, whereas the Green-veined White has shown a corresponding decline.

Good years have been 1992, 1997, 1998, 2002, 2004, 2009, 2011. A five-year moving average shows a downward trend from the mid-1990s, with 2007 being a particularly poor year, although numbers did recover by 2009. The Green-veined White is a vagrant, easily able to exploit new areas, but it is not migratory.

See Large White for mating strategy (page 58). Females frequently mate again, up to five times (average 2.28), which enables them to live longer, and produce larger eggs.

Flight weeks ▲High transect counts △Middle ^Low

Apr					May				Jun				Jul					Aug				Sep			
1	8	15	22	29	6	13	20	27	3	10	17	24	1	8	15	22	29	5	12	19	26	2	9	16	23
^	^	^	△	△	△	△	△	△	△	^	△	△	△	▲	▲	▲	▲	▲	▲	▲	△	△	^	^	^

Green-veined White — weekly transect counts

South Norwood CP TQ352684 — **Malcolm Bridge**

	WEEK	2000	2001	2002	2003	2004	2005	2006	2007	2008	2009	2010	2011	2012
1 April	1	-	-	-	-	-	-	-	-	-	-	-	-	2
8	2	-	-	3	-	1	-	-	-	-	1	-	1	2
15	3	-	-	6	-	-	-	1	-	-	5	-	7	
22	4	1	-	13		-	-	2	4	-	9	-	15	
29	5	14	1	8	5		2	1	**11**	-	17	-	13	6
6 May	6	10	-		**13**	-	-	4	5	1	1	6	11	5
13	7	15	5	20		4	4	3	2	-		4	8	10
20	8	16	2	16	3	13	3	6	4	1	5	8	4	5
27	9	5	4	21	2			4	2	2	6	6		5
3 June	10	2	3	15	1	1	3	4	-	-		6	-	
10	11	-	4	10			1	1	-	-	-	2	-	2
17	12	4		7	-	-	2	1	-	-	-	1	1	1
24	13	3	2	9	-	-	-	4		2			12	
1 July	14	1	1	1	2	7	-	7	1	2	1	10	10	
8	15	13		11	7		10	6	9	15	15	-	3	1
15	16	22	6	21	9	14	**20**	10	9	**17**	**40**	1	**32**	1
22	17	29	29	**36**	12	**32**	3	4	8	16	25	**12**	9	8
29	18	**41**	**39**	25	6	29	10	8	2	13	17	7	10	**11**
5 August	19	20	18	18	9		4	-	1	10	26		4	
12	20	40	7	12	10	4	-	**14**	1	4	8	6	2	
19	21	18	14	10	7	4	1	7	-	2	20	-	10	
26	22	9	12	2	1	12	1	6		2	11	5	12	
2 September	23	8	6	4	1		11	2	1	-	5	5	8	
9	24	1		4	4	13	2	2	1	-	2	3	3	
16	25	1	1	-	6	3	2	1	-	2	3	2	4	
23	26	2	1	-	1	-	-	2	-	1	-		2	
Abundance index		275	165	286	108	192	82	95	59	86	217	97	186	NI
Weeks recorded		**22**	**18**	**22**	**18**	**13**	**16**	**23**	**15**	**15**	**19**	**16**	**22**	**13**

Larval foodplants, in order of Surrey abundance: garlic mustard, hedge mustard, cuckooflower, hairy bitter-cress, charlock, wild radish, water-cress, large bitter-cress, nasturtium, wild cabbage.

Phenology trend	**1990-2012**	earlier by 2 weeks	
Best transect day 2000-12	Jul 29, 2000	South Norwood CP	41
Transects abundance	**1990-2012** loss 24%	**2000-2012** loss 56%	
UK transects abundance	**1976-2012** loss 13%	**10-year trend** loss 16%	
UK 4,361 10k squares	**2005-09** 2,594 = 59%	**10-year trend** loss 3%	

Orange-tip *Anthocharis cardamines* **Harry E. Clarke**

Surrey status: common and widespread, less so on western heaths and in London's suburbs.

Flies April to early June.

Trends: stable.

Wingspan: 40-52mm.

Identification: only the male has unmistakable orange patches; forewing upperside has black tips extending along front margin, and one black spot; hindwing underside mottled green.

Confusion species: female in flight and when resting with wings open resembles Small and Green-veined White, and male Large White. Mottled green underside is distinctive, and only in rare second broods could it be confused with the Bath White, a very rare migrant.

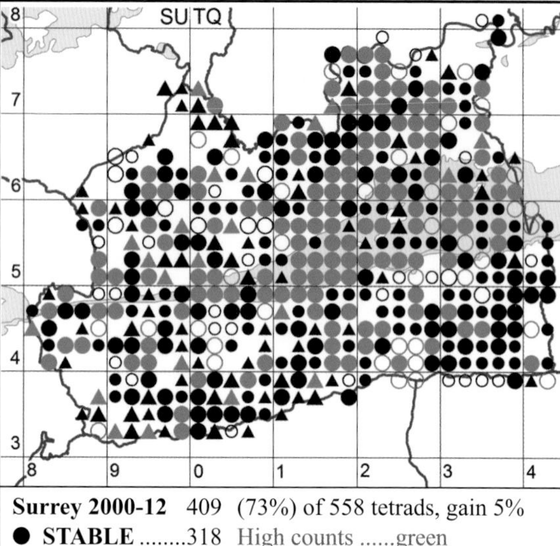

Habitat: generally damp and shady sites - woodland margins and hedgerows, damp pastures, gardens, orchards, parks.

Top transects: Ashtead Common, Coulsdon Common, Farthing Down New Hill, Headley Warren, South Norwood CP, Bealeswood.

Life cycle: usually univoltine; winters as pupa.The pale-green eggs, laid singly on the flower stalk, turn orange within a few days. The larvae hatch after a week or two to feed on the flowers, developing seedpods and sometimes leaves. There is rarely enough food

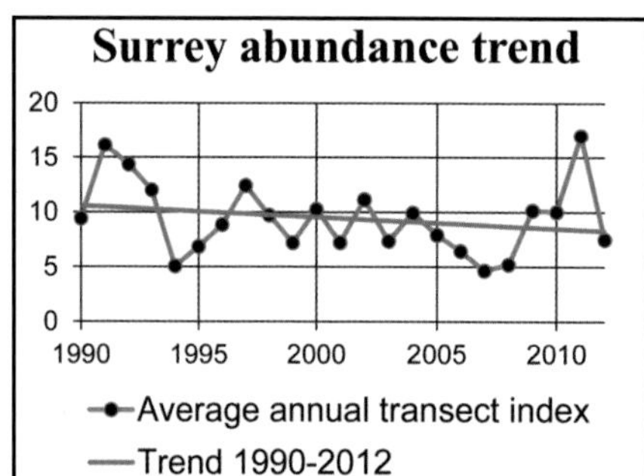

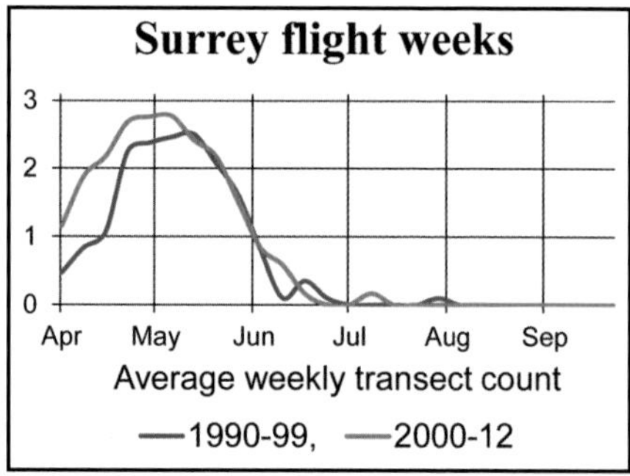

Orange-tip male on a wild cherry. **GE**

for more than one larva, and any competitor is eaten. The larva is well camouflaged, lying along the seedpod. Pupation occurs in July on an upright stem, away from the foodplant. Pupae may be either green or brown. Adults usually emerge in the following spring, or in unfavourable conditions may be delayed for another year. Very rarely adults emerge in late July or early August, but any eggs laid would be unsuccessful due to lack of foodplants.

Larval foodplants: cuckooflower is preferred on heavy soils, garlic mustard on dry sites. Surrey abundance order: garlic mustard, hedge mustard, cuckooflower, charlock, honesty, winter-cress, dame's-violet, turnip, large bitter-cress, hairy rock-cress.

Phenology trend	**1990-2012**	earlier by one week	
Best transect day 2000-12	May 20, 2012	Bealeswood	17
Transects abundance	**1990-2012** loss 22%	**2000-2012** gain 19%	
UK transects abundance	**1976-2012** gain 20%	**10-year trend** gain 59%	
UK 4,361 10k squares	**2005-09** 2,192 = 50%	**10-year trend** no change	

Flight weeks ▲High transect counts △Middle ^Low

Apr					May				Jun				Jul					Aug				Sep			
1	8	15	22	29	6	13	20	27	3	10	17	24	1	8	15	22	29	5	12	19	26	2	9	16	23
△	△	△	▲	▲	▲	△	△	△	△	^	^			^											

Orange-tip *continued* — **Harry E. Clarke**

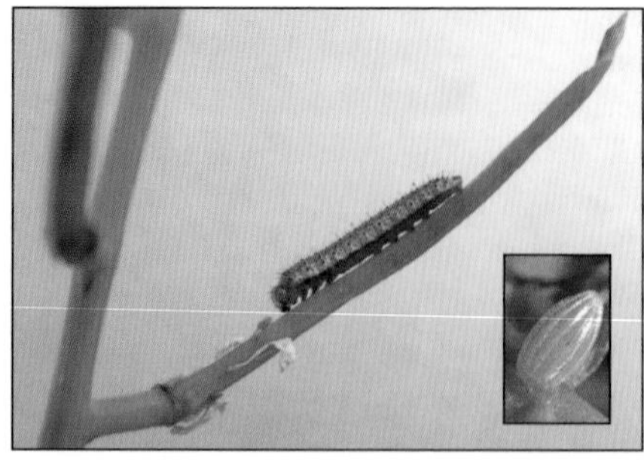

Orange-tip larva. **MB** *egg.* **BH**

THE male Orange-tip on a sunny day, signifying the arrival of spring, is my favourite butterfly. The orange tips to his white wings advertise to birds that he is poisonous as he searches for females along hedgerows and in gardens.

See Large White for mating strategy (page 58). Females rarely mate a second time (average 1.17). Some strange behaviour has been recorded: e.g. a female was netted mating with a male Little Emerald moth (*Jodis lactearia*) at Staffhurst Wood in June 1971.

Favoured foodplants, normally flowering from April to July, have seedpods that are more than three times longer than wide. Selection is triggered by the presence of mustard oils and their derivative glucosinolates, which are detected by chemosensory hairs on the forelegs. Orange-tips prefer prominent, isolated, unshaded brassicas with large flowers, growing within a metre of hedge, bank or wood edge.

The Orange-tip seeks out cow parsley and garlic mustard for roosting. With its wings tightly closed, the speckled white and green resembles the small white flowers of its host.

Diapause in the Orange-tip is poorly understood. Pupae have been known to stay in hibernation for up to two years. Rare second broods in Surrey include:
Aug 21, 1952 – Tulse Hill; **Sep 20, 1970** – Staffhurst Wood (male); **Aug 1, 1990** – Denbies Hillside; **Jun 26, 1995** – Brentmoor Heath; **Jul 9, 2001** – Wingate Hill (2 adults).

Orange-tip — weekly transect counts
Coulsdon Common TQ320570 — **Andrew Scott, Mike Enfield**

WEEK		2000	2001	2002	2003	2004	2005	2006	2007	2008	2009	2010	2011	2012
1 April	1	-	-	-	-		-		-		-		-	1
8	2				-	1		-	**2**	-		-	7	1
15	3	-		**6**	-		-	-	**2**		2		**11**	
22	4		-	**6**	**8**	2	7	1	**2**	-	**3**	2	8	
29	5	2	-	3	-	**5**	**8**	**4**	-	**3**	1		1	
6 May	6	**6**	**6**	4	-	1		**4**	-	1	**3**	**4**	5	**4**
13	7	5	**6**	1	1	1	2		-	2	1	1	-	2
20	8	-	3		-	1	-	2	-	1	-	2	-	3
27	9	1	1	-	-	-	-		-	1	-	-	-	1
3 June	10	-	1		-	-	-	1	-	-	-	-	-	-
Abundance index		15	17	23	9	11	22	17	6	8	12	13	36	NI
Weeks recorded		**4**	**5**	**5**	**2**	**6**	**3**	**5**	**3**	**5**	**5**	**4**	**5**	**6**

Green Hairstreak *Callophrys rubi*

Harry E. Clarke

Surrey status: commonest on the Chalk; difficult to locate on the heaths; also in Chiddingfold Forest.
Flies: mid-April into June.
Trends: stable.
Wingspan: 27-34mm.
Identification: underside metallic green with white streak or spots on hindwing; brown upperside evident in flight; small tail on hindwings. Male has grey androconial scales near front margin of forewing.
Confusion species: other Lycaenidae in flight; at rest, the green underside is unique.
Habitat: woodland, heathland, acid grassland, dry pasture, downland, scrub.
Top transects:
Denbies Landbarn B,
Headley Heath,
Oxted Downs,
Pewley Down,
Hutchinson's Bank,
Witley Common.
Life cycle: univoltine; winters as pupa, emerging mid-April. Lays singly on young shoots. Larva well camouflaged and cannibalistic. Pupates towards end of July at ground level.
Larval foodplants: broom, dyer's greenweed, common rock-rose, common bird's-foot-trefoil, gorse, bilberry, plus many secondary plants.

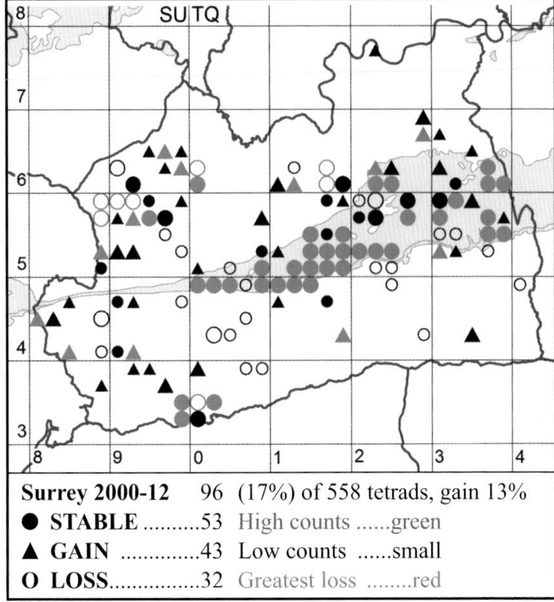

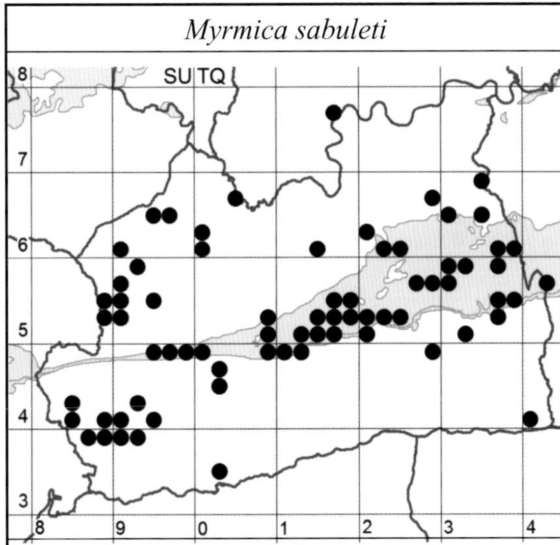

Map shows how distribution of the red ant *Myrmica sabuleti* mirrors that of the Green Hairstreak. Data from SWT's *Ants of Surrey* (Pontin, 2005).

Green Hairstreak *continued*

Harry E. Clarke

THE Green Hairstreak has the widest range of any of the Hairstreaks but is found in only small numbers in Surrey. The complexities of its life cycle and habitat requirements are poorly understood. As with other members of the Lycaenidae, there seems to be an association with ants, but only in the pupal stage.

The Green Hairstreak is the first Hairstreak to appear, from mid-April. The territorial male perches on a prominent branch or twig, often of hawthorn, and usually on the edge of grassland. He will investigate any passing butterfly, or other insect, to see whether it is a female. In doing so, he can lose his perch to a rival. The same perch can be used from year to year.

Courtship probably involves the male emitting a pheromone from the scent scales on his forewing to attract females, which spend most of their time searching for nectar or foodplants. They lay a single egg near to a bud and different females can lay on the same plant.

The larvae eat young leaves and flower buds of the host plant. They are able to deal with the poisons of greenweed, one of their favourite foodplants, by excreting the poisons in their frass. The larvae are cannibalistic and have been reported as being parasitised by the tachinid fly *Aplomyia confinis* and the parasitoid wasp *Distatrix sancus* (non-British).

Pupae have been found in nests of the red ant *Myrmica sabuleti*, which prefers dry, sunny sites on downland and sandy heaths. There seems to be a strong correlation between the Surrey distribution of the ant and the Green Hairstreak. The ant makes a chirping sound when under stress. The pupae also emit a sound when disturbed, which possibly encourages ants to come to their aid. Pupae also exude a substance that is attractive to ants.

Phenology trend	**1990-2012**	earlier by 1.5 weeks	
Best transect day 2000-12	May 1, 2001	Nore Hill	16
Transects abundance	**1990-2012** loss 4%	**2000-2012** gain 3%	
UK transects abundance	**1976-2012** loss 43%	**10-year trend** loss 26%	
UK 4,361 10k squares	**2005-09** 1,002 = 23%	**10-year trend** gain 6%	

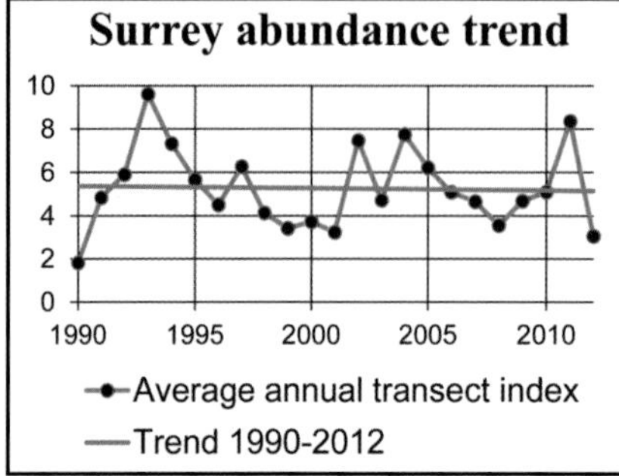

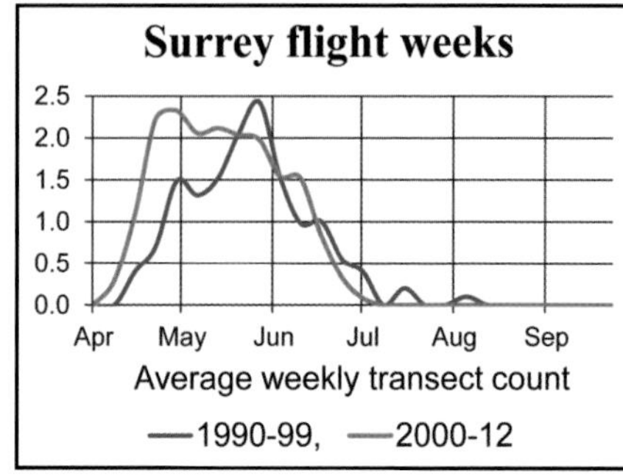

Green Hairstreak on green alkanet. **GE**

Green Hairstreak Denbies Landbarn B TQ135499													weekly transect counts **Gail Jeffcoate, Robert Cramp**
WEEK		2000	2001	2002	2003	2004	2005	2006	2007	2008	2009	2010	2011	2012
8 April	2				1	-	-		-		1	-	2	-
15	3			-	1		1	-	**10**	-	**4**	-	1	
22	4			**9**	2	-	**7**	4	7	-	3	2	**9**	
29	5			5		-	5	**5**	-	-	**4**		3	**2**
6 May	6				2	**4**	3	3	-	-	2	-	3	-
13	7			2	1	3	6	3	-	-		**3**	3	
20	8			1	1	3	2		-	1	2	2	-	**2**
27	9			2	**4**	2	1	3	-	-	2	**3**	-	1
3 June	10				-	-	3	-	-	-	2	1	-	-
10	11			-	1	-	-	1		-	-	-	-	-
Abundance index				27	14	12	28	24	17	1	20	12	23	NI
Weeks recorded				**5**	**8**	**4**	**8**	**6**	**2**	**1**	**8**	**5**	**6**	**3**

Flight weeks ▲High transect counts △Middle ^Low

Apr					May				Jun				Jul					Aug				Sep			
1	*8*	*15*	*22*	*29*	*6*	*13*	*20*	*27*	*3*	*10*	*17*	*24*	*1*	*8*	*15*	*22*	*29*	*5*	*12*	*19*	*26*	*2*	*9*	*16*	*23*
	^	△	▲	▲	△	▲	△	△	△	△	△	^	^												

Brown Hairstreak *Thecla betulae*

Ken Willmott

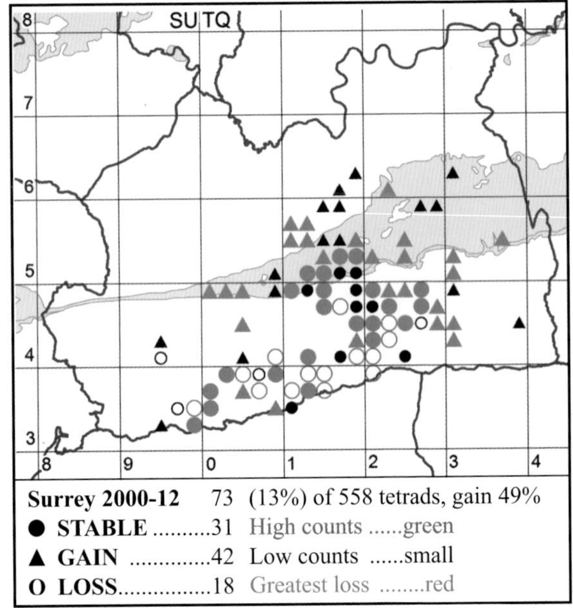

Surrey status: often the last species to emerge; elusive and restricted, but extending onto the Chalk from its stronghold in the Weald; even found in gardens where pioneering females locate exotic species of *Prunus*.

Flies: late July to late September.

Conservation: protected from sale; UK Biodiversity Action Plan priority species; BC 2010 Red List: vulnerable.

National distribution: local in south of England, but organised winter searches for eggs regularly find new breeding areas. Very local in central and eastern England; common in parts of Devon, south-west Wales and the Burren area of Ireland.

Trends: expanding north and west in Surrey. Monitoring has increased in popularity in recent years due to the ease of locating eggs on blackthorn twigs, either in September or in winter, producing records without the need to observe the elusive adults.

Wingspan: male 36-41mm, female 39-45mm.

Identification: sexually dimorphic; male upperside brown, with pale sex brand on forewings and orange-red tails on hindwings, which are shorter than those on the female; female has orange-red patch on forewing, visible in flight. Underside is golden orange and red, more intense in the female, with two black-edged white hairstreaks, one incomplete.

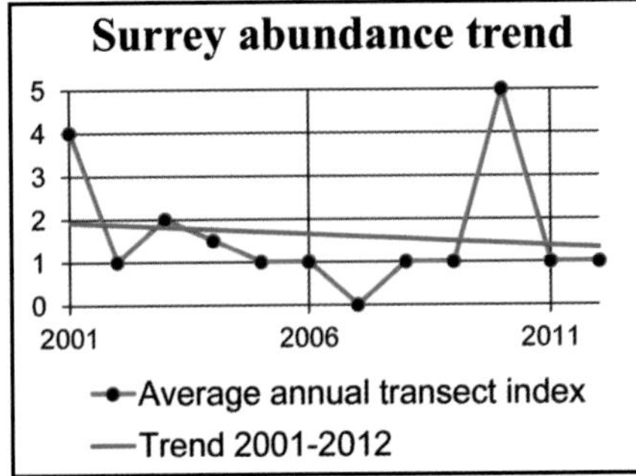

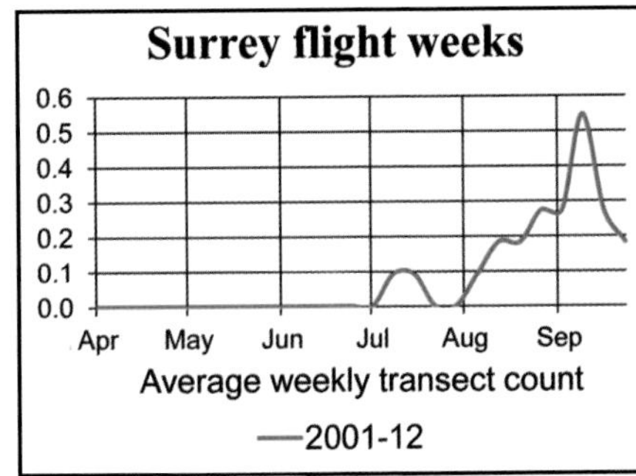

Brown Hairstreak female resting on hawthorn. **KW**

Confusion species: orange-coloured female Gatekeepers can still be flying when Brown Hairstreaks emerge; they lack the underside hairstreak marking and the upper forewings are paler and less red. Be aware of this, because the Gatekeeper flies along hedgerows and may alight on blackthorn.

Habitat: farmland where hedgerows with blackthorn are not too severely cut on an annual basis; downland where blackthorn is a constituent of the scrub, as on Surrey's North Downs. Here the blackthorn is at the top and bottom of slopes, sometimes forming large banks, which are particularly useful when supported by taller trees such as ash and beech from which Brown Hairstreaks may descend. In recent years Brown Hairstreaks are increasingly appearing in rural gardens, including my own in Leatherhead. So far, Surrey garden sightings appear to be dispersing females seeking egg-laying sites.

Key sites: Holmwood Common, Bookham Common, Chiddingfold Forest and surrounding farmland. The species is not suited to transect recording.

Life cycle: univoltine; August/September eggs sit exposed on bare blackthorn twigs for eight months and hatch the following April/May according to temperature. In late June the larva turns from bright green, well camouflaged on the underside of a blackthorn leaf, to a muddy-brown colour for its journey to the ground below the bush, where it pupates. Many fall victim to rodents but successful ones emerge within 3-4 weeks.

Larval foodplants: blackthorn (sloe); also bullace, cherry plum, garden species of *Prunus*.

Brown Hairstreak *continued* — **Ken Willmott**

FINDING an adult Brown Hairstreak is one of the most difficult tasks for a butterfly enthusiast. Populations may cover a wide area, usually at low density. On emergence, males fly into the canopy to establish territories, most frequently using ash trees, but also oak. They occasionally descend to nectar on flowers early in their season.

The best way to observe adult behaviour is to find a "master" tree, where males feed on aphid honeydew. They also crawl along twigs until they locate small breathing pores or lenticels, into which they seem able to insert their proboscis to extract sugary nutrients. Clashing territorial males do not produce as dramatic a spectacle as the sunny-evening disputes of the more-numerous Purple Hairstreak. Binoculars are essential for such observations.

Brown Hairstreak female on hemp-agrimony. **BH**

On emergence, the female tracks down a master ash to mate with a male, many of which can be resident on a particularly suitable tree. After mating, females will also return to the trees to obtain nutrition for egg-production from both aphid secretions and the lenticels.

Ash dieback, *Chalara fraxinea*, is a recent concern for the Brown Hairstreak. It may also threaten the Purple Hairstreak, which uses ash as a secondary territorial platform. Ash dieback does not affect larval foodplants and it is hoped that the problem will not be as drastic as Dutch elm disease, which decimated the larval foodplant of the White-letter Hairstreak.

Phenology trend	**2001-2012**	earlier by 0.5 weeks	
Best transect day 2000-12	Sep 12, 2010	Howell Hill	2
Transects abundance	**2001-2012** loss 31%		
UK transects abundance	**1983-2012** loss 11%	**10-year trend** loss 75%	
UK 4,361 10k squares	**2005-09** 136 = 3%	**10-year trend** gain 1%	

Flight weeks (all records) ▲High counts △Middle ^Low

Apr					May				Jun				Jul					Aug				Sep			
1	8	15	22	29	6	13	20	27	3	10	17	24	1	8	15	22	29	5	12	19	26	2	9	16	23
														^	^	^	△	△	▲	▲	▲	▲	▲	△	△

My first observations of master ashes indicated it was younger trees that were particularly attractive to Brown Hairstreak congregations. However, in August 2012 on Bookham Common, a female was seen feeding avidly on twig lenticels in an old, gnarled ash. A week later a male was located feeding on the lenticels of a young ash growing below the old one. Most of the activity around these ashes occurs in the afternoon and goes on into the evening on fine days.

Brown Hairstreak eggs. **BH**

A Brown Hairstreak on blackthorn will invariably be a female. She crawls down a stem of fresh growth until reaching the older wood, where she carefully deposits a single egg on a fork or spike, the majority at 1-2m height. In suitable weather this is usually between noon and 2pm, but later should conditions be unfavourable during that period.

It is unusual to find two eggs side by side and I initially thought this was the work of separate females choosing the same site. Eventually I observed a female depositing two eggs in quick succession. To find larvae, gently bend a likely twig and inspect the underside of the leaves. It is rewarding to see a fully-grown, bright-green larva in its natural resting position!

Conservation of the Brown Hairstreak involves encouraging farm managers to make any hedgerow cuts in early to mid-July when the larvae are pupating on the ground among leaf litter. If the hedgerow is cut in early August (perhaps after a crop has been harvested and cutting machinery has access to the hedgerows) females will continue to deposit eggs on the remaining blackthorn. However, if the cut is made in late August many eggs that have already been deposited will perish. A rotational cut would guarantee a safe haven for a percentage of overwintering eggs.

Brown Hairstreak										weeks with GB transect record				
	WEEK	2000	2001	2002	2003	2004	2005	2006	2007	2008	2009	2010	2011	2012
08-Jul	15									✓			✓	
15	16						✓		✓			✓		
22	17				✓			✓	✓	✓	✓		✓	
29	18					✓	✓	✓			✓	✓	✓	
5 August	19	✓	✓	✓	✓	✓	✓	✓	✓	✓	✓	✓	✓	✓
12	20	✓	✓	✓	✓	✓	✓	✓	✓	✓	✓	✓	✓	✓
19	21	✓	✓		✓	✓	✓	✓	✓	✓	✓	✓	✓	✓
26	22	✓	✓	✓	✓	✓	✓	✓	✓	✓	✓	✓	✓	✓
2 September	23	✓	✓	✓	✓	✓	✓	✓	✓	✓	✓	✓	✓	✓
9	24	✓	✓	✓	✓	✓	✓	✓	✓	✓	✓	✓	✓	✓
16	25	✓		✓	✓	✓	✓	✓	✓	✓	✓	✓		✓
23	26		✓	✓	✓	✓	✓	✓		✓	✓			✓
Weeks recorded		**7**	**7**	**7**	**9**	**9**	**10**	**10**	**9**	**10**	**10**	**9**	**9**	**8**

Purple Hairstreak *Favonius* (formerly *Neozephyrus*) *quercus* **Alan Hunt**

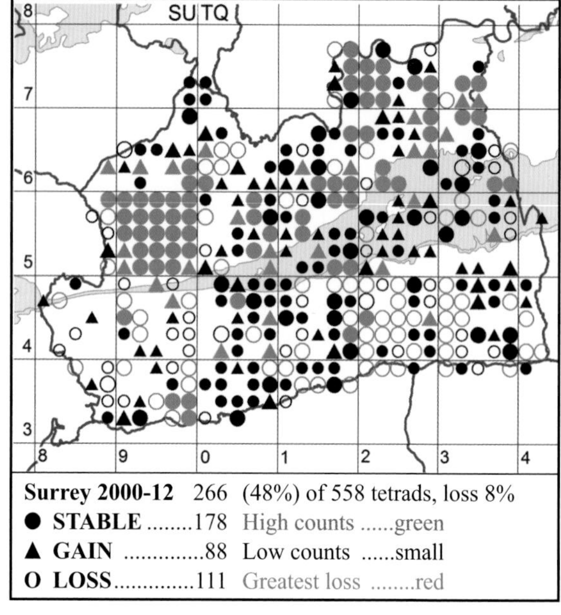

Surrey status: common, although often overlooked because it spends most of its time in the oak canopy.

Flies: late June to mid-August, peaking mid-July. Not suited to transect monitoring, so a table of flight weeks from all GB transects is also shown.

Trends: stable; many apparent losses are likely to be due to under-recording.

Wingspan: male 33-40mm, female 31-38mm, a rare example of the male being larger.

Identification: upperside almost black, with male having purple/indigo sheen over all four wings, reduced in female to streaks in middle of forewing. Underwings silvery-grey with orange eyespot near hindwing tail; prominent white hairstreak near outer margin of both wings. Frequently rests with wings open, unlike White-letter or Black Hairstreak.

Confusion species: White-letter Hairstreak is an elm specialist, appears smaller and darker, and never exhibits the Purple Hairstreak's silvery appearance in flight. It also tends to hug the canopy to a greater extent. Some Browns fly high in the canopy in the evening and can be difficult to distinguish when sun is low.

Habitat: any woodland with oaks, oak coppices, small oak patches in conifer plantations, tree lines, and even isolated oaks in hedgerows/fields when there is a population explosion.

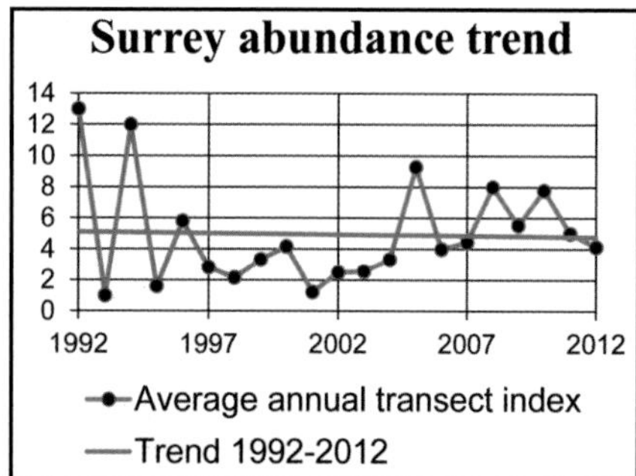

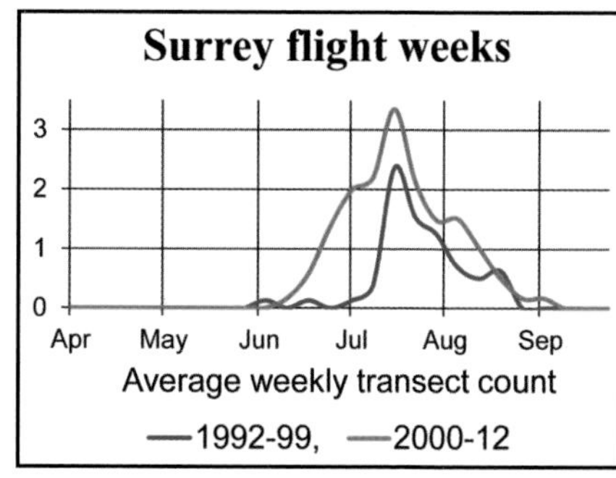

Top transects: Richmond Park, Ashtead Common, Mitcham Common, Wimbledon Common.

Other key sites: Bookham Common, Chiddingfold Forest, Broadstreet Commons (Guildford).

Life cycle: univoltine; winters as egg, which is laid in July or early August on oak at the tip of a twig or at the base of a bud, with a preference for sheltered, sunny boughs. The larva is fully developed at three weeks but remains in the egg. It emerges in April and enters a flower bud where it feeds totally concealed. Later instars weave a silk nest where they remain hidden, emerging at night to feed. Pupation takes place on the ground under leaf litter. An association with ants has been recognised.

Larval foodplants: mainly pedunculate oak, but will readily use sessile and Turkey oaks. Cut-leaved oaks appear not to be used.

Purple Hairstreak resting on wood sage. **GW**

Phenology trend	**1992-2012**	earlier by 2 weeks	
Best transect day 2000-12	Jul 21, 2008	Mitcham Common	18
Transects abundance	**1992-2012** loss 6%	**2000-2012** gain 117%	
UK transects abundance	**1976-2012** loss 8%	**10-year trend** loss 8%	
UK 4,361 10k squares	**2005-09** 847 = 19%	**10-year trend** loss 16%	

Flight weeks ▲High transect counts △Middle ^Low

Apr					May				Jun				Jul					Aug				Sep			
1	8	15	22	29	6	13	20	27	3	10	17	24	1	8	15	22	29	5	12	19	26	2	9	16	23
										^	△	△	△	▲	▲	▲	△	△	△	△	^	^			

Purple Hairstreak *continued* **Alan Hunt**

IF ever there was a butterfly to which the maxim "seek and ye shall find" applies, it is the Purple Hairstreak. A comprehensive survey of hectad SU95 (north of Guildford, west of Woking) showed a presence in every monad containing oaks. The largest populations tend to be on clay but scattered colonies can be found across the heaths of West Surrey and in urban settings.

Purple Hairstreak female. **BH**

The best time to observe the adults is 6.30-8.30pm when the butterfly puts on a wonderful display with sudden hops from one perch to another, conga lines of three or four weaving around the canopy, and aerial battles between two or three males tumbling like silver coins against the sky. Adults can also be seen when they descend to nectar on bramble or thistle near the parent oak. More commonly they feed on aphid honeydew on oak or ash.

This butterfly is noted for regular population explosions, and in those years it is easy to record three-figure counts in an hour on good sites. In poor years it retreats to its core colonies, abandoning many smaller sites. One feature that has been noted is a predilection to inhabit certain oaks year after year, while ignoring others, possibly due to higher tannin levels.

Transects do not monitor this butterfly well as it tends to be fairly quiescent during the day. A better method is to scan a tree line or a woodland ride, spending a set time at each tree during the evening. Warm and sunny evenings are best but the butterfly can often be seen in cloudy conditions. Wind causes them to stay closer to the canopy where they can be difficult to observe. Their presence can also be confirmed by finding eggs on the tips of the lower branches of oaks during the winter.

The larvae are difficult to find as they feed at night, remaining hidden during the day. Likewise the pupa is rarely seen, being buried under leaf mould on the ground. The finding of pupae in ant nests suggests that ants play a part in the lifecycle of the Purple Hairstreak, a feature that is well documented in other lycaenids.

Peter and Ben Kirby from Kent are Purple Hairstreak enthusiasts, and I recommend their website *www.quercus2.co.uk.*

Purple Hairstreak

Richmond Park TQ190730

weekly transect counts

Raymond Garrett, Piers Eley

	WEEK	2000	2001	2002	2003	2004	2005	2006	2007	2008	2009	2010	2011	2012
10 June	11				-	-	-	-	1	-		-	-	-
17	12					-	**2**	-	-	-	2	-	-	-
24	13				**2**	-	-		**7**	-	**5**	2	-	-
1 July	14				**2**	6		**5**	-	-	-	-	1	-
8	15				**2**	-	-		-	-	-	-	-	-
15	16				1	**11**		-	-	**4**	-	**10**	**8**	-
22	17					1	-	3	-	2	-	2	-	-
29	18					1	-		-		1	1	3	-
5 August	19					3	-	-	-	-	-	-	1	-
Abundance index					8	15	3	NI	8	7	11	17	12	
Weeks recorded					**4**	**5**	**1**	**2**	**2**	**2**	**3**	**4**	**4**	**0**

Purple Hairstreak

weeks with GB transect record

	WEEK	2000	2001	2002	2003	2004	2005	2006	2007	2008	2009	2010	2011	2012
27 May	9								✓					
3 June	10					✓							✓	
10	11							✓	✓	✓	✓	✓	✓	
17	12		✓		✓	✓	✓	✓	✓	✓	✓	✓	✓	
24	13	✓		✓	✓	✓	✓	✓	✓	✓	✓	✓	✓	
1 July	14	✓	✓	✓	✓	✓	✓	✓	✓	✓	✓	✓	✓	✓
8	15	✓	✓	✓	✓	✓	✓	✓	✓	✓	✓	✓	✓	✓
15	16	✓	✓	✓	✓	✓	✓	✓	✓	✓	✓	✓	✓	✓
22	17	✓	✓	✓	✓	✓	✓	✓	✓	✓	✓	✓	✓	✓
29	18	✓	✓	✓	✓	✓	✓	✓	✓	✓	✓	✓	✓	✓
5 August	19	✓	✓	✓	✓	✓	✓	✓	✓	✓	✓	✓	✓	✓
12	20	✓	✓	✓	✓	✓	✓	✓	✓	✓	✓	✓	✓	✓
19	21	✓	✓	✓	✓	✓	✓	✓	✓	✓	✓	✓	✓	✓
26	22	✓	✓	✓	✓	✓	✓	✓	✓	✓	✓	✓	✓	✓
2 September	23	✓	✓	✓	✓	✓	✓	✓	✓	✓	✓	✓	✓	✓
9	24	✓	✓	✓	✓	✓	✓	✓	✓	✓				✓
16	25								✓					
Weeks recorded		**12**	**12**	**12**	**13**	**14**	**13**	**14**	**16**	**14**	**13**	**13**	**14**	**11**

White-letter Hairstreak *Satyrium w-album* — Malcolm Bridge

Surrey status: widely but thinly distributed.
Flies: late June (earlier in south London in good years) to August. Not suited to transect monitoring, so a table of flight weeks from all English transects is shown.
Conservation: protected from sale; UK Biodiversity Action Plan priority species; BC 2010 Red List: endangered.
Trends: declined massively following the onset of Dutch elm disease (DED) in the 1970s. The elusive nature of this species makes it difficult to judge whether that decline has halted. Eggs, effective for recording Brown and Purple Hairstreaks, are harder to find.

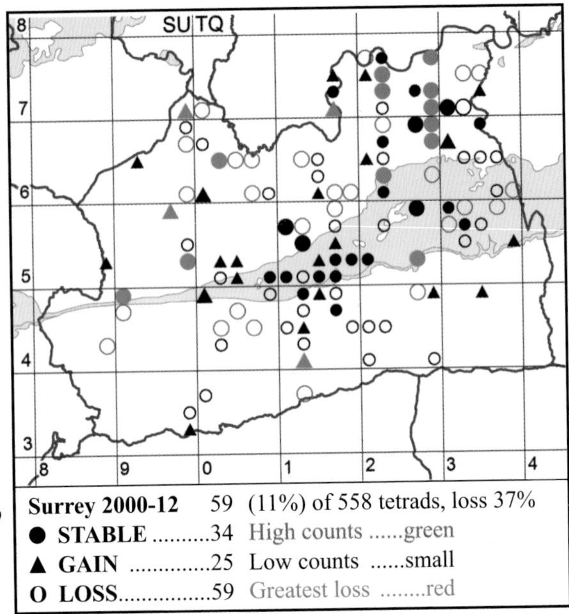

Wingspan: male 25-35mm, female 26-36mm.
Identification: our darkest Hairstreak never rests with open wings so the underside is the only view to enjoy. The white hairstreak line on the lower hindwing forms the W mark that gives the species its vernacular and scientific names.
Confusion species: Purple Hairstreak favours oaks.
Habitat: sunny edge of woodland, copse or hedge. Colonies can survive on a single mature elm.
Key sites: Putney Heath, Streatham and Mitcham Commons, Battersea Park. In the wider countryside the species can be found almost anywhere but chances of a sighting seem to be greatly improved at suburban sites.

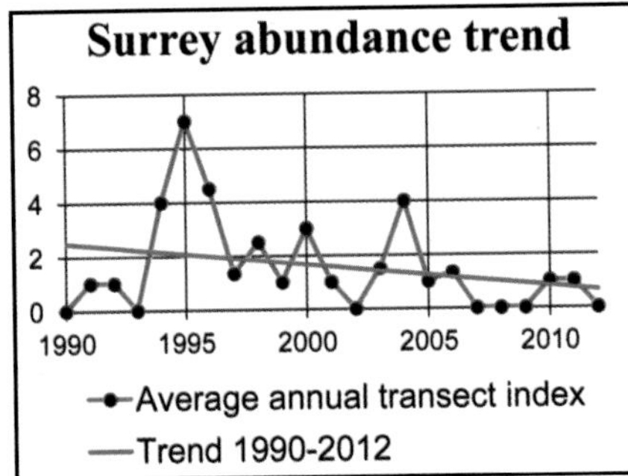

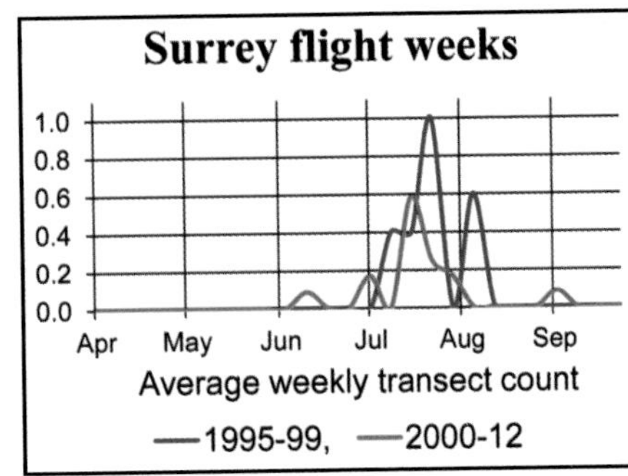

White-letter Hairstreak female on creeping thistle. **GE**

Life cycle: univoltine; winters as egg, with the larva fully formed within.

The larva emerges when elm is coming into flower in late March, and feeds on the sepals and then the soft tissue within the flowers. Its colour and markings, as with other Hairstreak species, are remarkably similar to the swelling buds. Older larvae feed on leaf buds and young leaves after the flowers have set seed.

As it nears full growth the larva feeds on opened leaves when not resting on a silk pad below the leaf. This is also the location where the pupa is formed, from which the adult will emerge some three weeks later.

Males spend most of their days in and above the tree canopy, sunning themselves, feeding on honeydew and awaiting females. In years when aphids are few and their honeydew is lacking, White-letter Hairstreaks will descend from the canopy in search of nectar. Otherwise, sightings at ground level are usually those of egg-laying females, which will lay on the sunny side of an elm from upwards of 2m.

Eggs are laid singly on elm twigs, often at the junction of current and previous year's growth, the girdle scar. The flying-saucer-shaped egg becomes dull brown within a few days, and the earliest eggs seem to suffer more from parasitoid wasps than later ones.

Larval foodplants: elms, including two DED-resistant strains marketed as Triumph and Sapporo Gold.

Phenology trend	**1995-2012**	insufficient data	
Best transect day 2000-12	Jul 17, 2000	Wingate Hill	3
Transects abundance	**1990-2012** loss 74%	**2000-2012** loss 92%	
UK transects abundance	**1976-2012** loss 86%	**10-year trend** loss 69%	
UK 4,361 10k squares	**2005-09** 756 = 17%	**10-year trend** gain 32%	

THE White-letter Hairstreak is probably the most under-recorded species in our county, which makes precise statements about distribution and numbers very difficult. Several summers slip by without my seeing even one, and successful sightings usually require a targeted visit to a site with good elm growth in optimum position.

Early April is the best time to locate mature elms. The ground or pavement will be strewn with large, distinctive seed discs, giving a timely reminder that, despite the ravages of DED, a significant number of trees have survived, often in the most unlikely places, e.g. just within the boundary of Crystal Palace Park, by Crystal Palace Park Road (A234 to Penge and Beckenham).

Make note of elms to visit the following autumn/winter, when eggs are best searched

White-letter Hairstreak *continued* **Malcolm Bridge**

for after leaf fall but before bud burst. The sunniest and most sheltered trees are the most productive. Look for sturdy twigs with rounded flower buds, especially on the higher branches that remain within the reach of an outstretched arm wielding a stick or umbrella handle. The old word "wych" implies flexibility, so a branch carefully dragged down to eye-level should withstand the assault. Concentrate on the girdle scars or forks rather than the numerous flower buds. The dark egg's lighter rim betrays its presence.

A July visit in sunshine with cloud seems to improve the chances of a sighting because each burst of sunshine seems to provoke a flurry of activity. From about 10am to noon is the optimum time. For the rest of the day activity is fitful, but resumes on a warm evening from about 6.30pm (as it does with the Purple Hairstreak, with which it is easily confused in flight).

Thomas studied a colony from a tree that offered a good view of life above the canopy and counted at least 70 individuals in far less time than it took to see 20 from the ground.

Liz Goodyear (BC Herts & Middlesex Branch) notes that almost any elm in Herts/Middx holds a colony, including apparently unpromising single trees beside busy main roads in industrial areas. My own observations, supported by Surrey colleagues Alan Wingrove and Richard Donovan, would confirm that is probably the case throughout Surrey and south London. Research by Martin Greenland (Yorkshire) and Andrew Wood (Herts/Middx) has also helped with this account.

White-letter Hairstreak — weeks with GB transect record

	WEEK	2000	2001	2002	2003	2004	2005	2006	2007	2008	2009	2010	2011	2012
3 June	10					✓		✓					✓	
10	11								✓				✓	
17	12				✓	✓	✓	✓	✓		✓		✓	
24	13		✓	✓	✓	✓	✓	✓	✓	✓	✓	✓	✓	
1 July	14	✓	✓	✓	✓	✓	✓	✓	✓	✓	✓	✓	✓	✓
8	15	✓	✓	✓	✓	✓	✓	✓	✓	✓	✓	✓	✓	✓
15	16	✓	✓	✓	✓	✓	✓	✓	✓	✓	✓	✓	✓	✓
22	17	✓	✓	✓	✓	✓	✓	✓	✓	✓	✓	✓	✓	✓
29	18	✓	✓	✓	✓	✓	✓	✓	✓	✓	✓	✓	✓	✓
5 August	19	✓	✓	✓	✓	✓	✓	✓	✓	✓	✓	✓	✓	✓
12	20	✓		✓		✓	✓	✓	✓	✓		✓		✓
19	21			✓			✓		✓		✓			✓
26	22			✓					✓					
Weeks recorded		7	7	10	8	10	10	10	12	8	9	8	10	8

Flight weeks (all records) ▲High counts △Middle ^Low

Apr					May				Jun				Jul					Aug				Sep			
1	8	15	22	29	6	13	20	27	3	10	17	24	1	8	15	22	29	5	12	19	26	2	9	16	23
										^	△	△	▲	▲	▲	▲	▲	▲	△	^	^				

Small Copper *Lycaena phlaeas*

Geoff Eaton

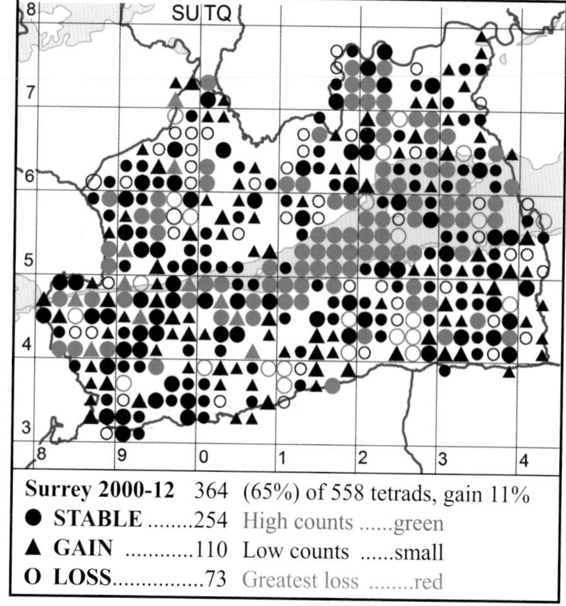

Surrey status: widespread but rarely numerous.
Flies: late April to October; most abundant in July and September.
Trends: although still considered common, appears to have declined in the 20th century, probably due to the loss of unimproved grassland through intensive farming as in East Anglia. Numbers on Surrey transects have been encouraging.
Wingspan: male 26-36mm, female 30-40mm.
Identification: distinctive. Upper forewing shining copper (orange-brown) with black spots and black outer margin; hindwing black with copper band. Under forewing pale orange with black spots; hindwing grey-brown with smaller black spots and orange band. Larger female's forewing has more rounded inner margin.
Variations/aberrations: distinctive form *caeruleopunctata* has row of blue spots on hindwing upperside.
Confusion species: none.
Habitat: unimproved grassland, hedgerows, heathland, woodland rides and clearings; waste ground and marginal land where sorrels flourish are especially favoured. Occasionally visits gardens.

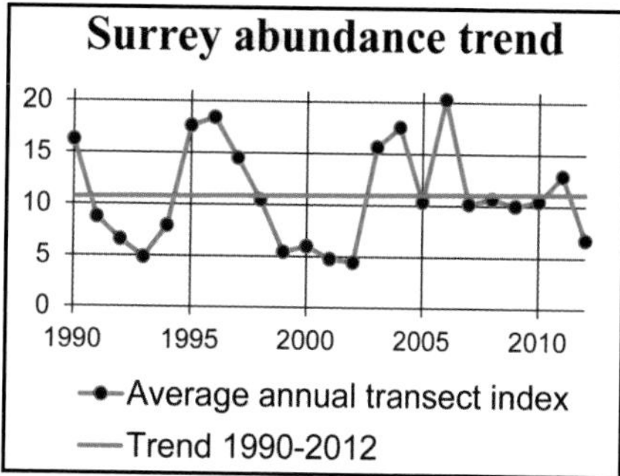

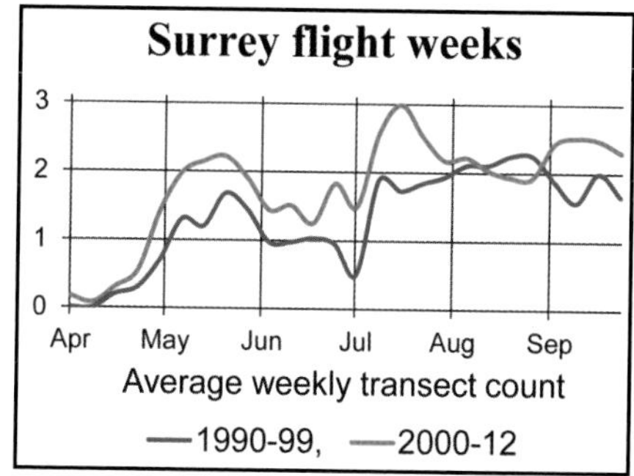

Small Copper *continued* — Geoff Eaton

Small Copper pair: female (right) has more rounded inner margin of forewing. **GE**

Top transects: Park Downs, Fairmile Common, Farthing Downs, Headley Heath, Mitcham Common, Nore Hill, Richmond Park.

Life cycle: usually bivoltine (spring and summer), but sometimes there is a third brood plus a possible fourth partial brood, even into November. Winters as larva.

Eggs are usually laid singly, but with several on the same leaf; they hatch in a week or two. The larvae feed from the underside of the sorrel leaf, but do not penetrate the upper surface. The resulting transparent window effect is distinctive.

In summer, larvae may pupate in three weeks, but those that have not pupated by the end of October enter hibernation. The pupa may be attended by ants, possibly among leaf-litter, and it hatches after about four weeks. Adult lifespan is 2-3 weeks.

Larval foodplants: common sorrel, sheep's sorrel; occasionally dock.

THE male Small Copper is a particularly energetic butterfly with a rapid flight that is difficult to follow. Having established his territory, he sits at a strategic point, with wings half-cocked, ready to challenge any intruder. After investigation the male will usually return to his chosen perch, which may be a flower or grass head, or even a warm spot on the ground.

The same pair, female on right, showing undersides. **GE**

If he encounters a female, he will pursue her vigorously. Courtship is reportedly brief and direct, with the two butterflies flying close together at high speed. I have seen this once, with the pursuit flight interrupted by the pair settling briefly, close together on low vegetation, before continuing the chase. On one occasion on Horsell Common I observed a courtship pursuit on the ground. After landing, the female moved rapidly across a sandy path, opening and closing her wings as she went. With the male always close behind, the female then climbed over and through the adjacent short vegetation, but eventually she flew away.

This butterfly is usually found in small, discrete colonies and numbers vary from year to year. Spring numbers are typically low, while good summers produce higher numbers in the second brood with the possibility of one or even two later broods. However, this species is greatly affected by spells of extreme weather. Although warm, dry, sunny conditions are favoured, drought may affect the larval foodplants, while wet summers can be equally disastrous. Depleted populations may take several years to recover.

The Small Copper can be anticipated in a wide range of habitats, but because it usually occurs in low numbers, you can rarely be sure of finding it. When you do, whether it is perched on stitchwort in the spring or mating in the October sunshine, this delightful little jewel of a butterfly is guaranteed to lift the heart.

Small Copper *continued*

Small Copper	Park Downs, Banstead TQ265585												Jill Hall
	WEEK	2000	2001	2002	2003	2004	2005	2006	2007	2008	2009	2010	2011	2012
22 April	4		-	-	-	-	-	-	-	-	-	-	1	-
29	5	-		-	-		-	-	**4**	-	-	-	4	-
6 May	6	-	-	-	-	1	-	-	1	-	-	-	4	1
13	7	**2**	-	-	1	4	1	1	1	-	3	-	2	2
20	8	1	-	-	-		1	1	1	-	-	-	3	1
27	9	-	-	1	1	2	1	-	-	-	2	-	-	2
3 June	10	-	-	-	-	7	2	3	1	2	-	-	-	-
10	11	-	-	-	-	-	1	-	-	-	-	1	-	-
17	12	-	-	-	-	2	1	-	-	-	-	-	1	-
24	13	-	-	-	1	-	-	-	-	-	-	-	-	-
1 July	14	-	-	-	2	-	-	-	1	-	-	-	2	-
8	15	-	-	-	2	-	-	-	-	-	-	4	4	-
15	16	-	-	-	3	-	-	-	1	-	3	1	5	-
22	17	-	-	-	1	-	-	**7**	-	1	-	**11**	5	-
29	18	-	2	-	2	1	1	**7**	1	3	**6**	3	4	-
5 August	19	-	-	**2**	1	9	1	6	1	**5**	2	5	**10**	**3**
12	20	1	**3**	**2**	4	7	3	6	1	1	2	9	1	2
19	21	**2**	-	1	6	5	4	1	-	-	1	2	1	1
26	22	1	-	-	3	**13**	2	2	1	-	1	-	-	2
2 September	23	-	-		12	8	3	3	-	-	1	4	2	2
9	24	-	-	-	6	1	2	3	-	1	2	1	-	-
16	25	-	1	1	13	1	**6**	2	-	-	3	5	2	1
23	26	1	2	-	**19**	1	5	3		-	1	3	6	-
Abundance index		8	6	7	58	39	34	44	15	13	28	50	60	17
Weeks recorded		6	4	5	16	14	15	13	11	6	12	12	17	10

Phenology trend	**1990-2012**	earlier by 1.5 weeks	
Best transect day 2000-12	Jul 12, 2006	Fairmile Common	61
Transects abundance	**1990-2012** gain 4%	**2000-2012** gain 27%	
UK transects abundance	**1976-2012** loss 23%	**10-year trend** loss 16%	
UK 4,361 10k squares	**2005-09** 1,927 = 44%	**10-year trend** loss 6%	

Flight weeks Small Copper																									▲High transect counts △Middle ^Low
Apr					May				Jun				Jul					Aug				Sep			
1	8	15	22	29	6	13	20	27	3	10	17	24	1	8	15	22	29	5	12	19	26	2	9	16	23
^	^	^	^	^	△	△	△	△	^	△	^	△	△	▲	▲	▲	△	△	△	△	△	▲	▲	▲	▲

Small Blue *Cupido minimus* — **Malcolm Bridge**

Surrey status: confined to sheltered spots on the Chalk.

Flies: second half of May, or earlier after a warm spring, and June, peaking usually in the first two weeks; partial second brood in late July and August.

Conservation: protected from sale; UK Biodiversity Action Plan priority species; BC 2010 Red List: near-threatened. Surrey BAP species.

Trends: steady decline of numbers and colonies throughout its national range over recent decades, but well-orchestrated conservation efforts in Surrey have reversed the downward trend.

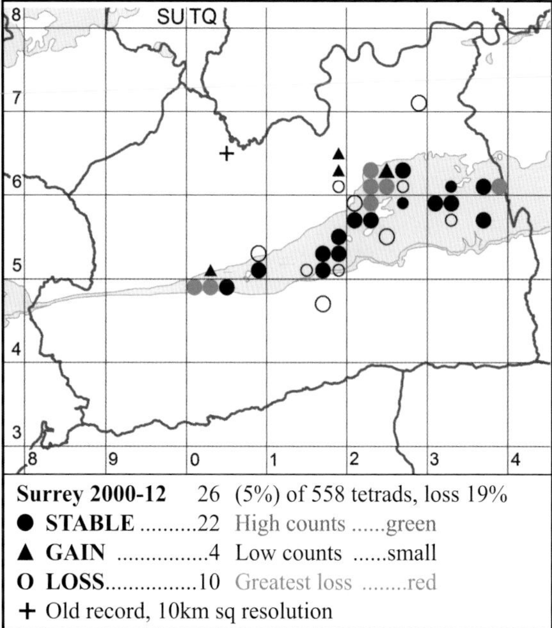

■ *SMALL BLUE female on kidney vetch: page 209*

Wingspan: 18-25mm.

Identification: our smallest butterfly; male upperside is grey-black with a dusting of blue scales; female is dark brown with no hint of blue. Underside pale blue with a scatter of small black dots. In flight it is less silvery than the similar-sized Brown Argus.

Confusion species: Holly Blue, which is larger and common, has similar underside but with a scatter of small black flecks rather than dots. The willingness of the Small Blue to pose open-winged makes such confusion unlikely, except on the signage of nature reserves where it is often portrayed with closed wings.

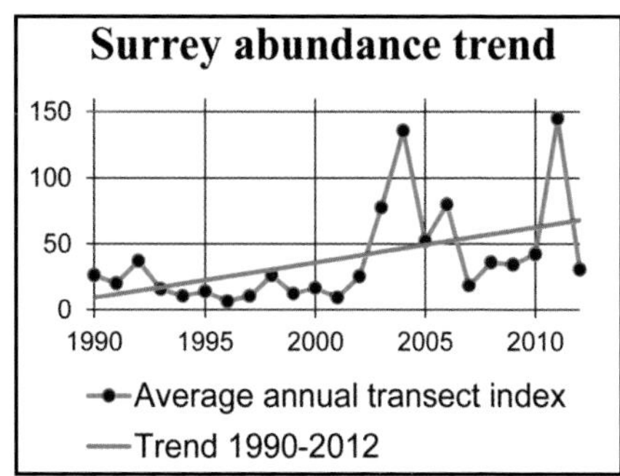

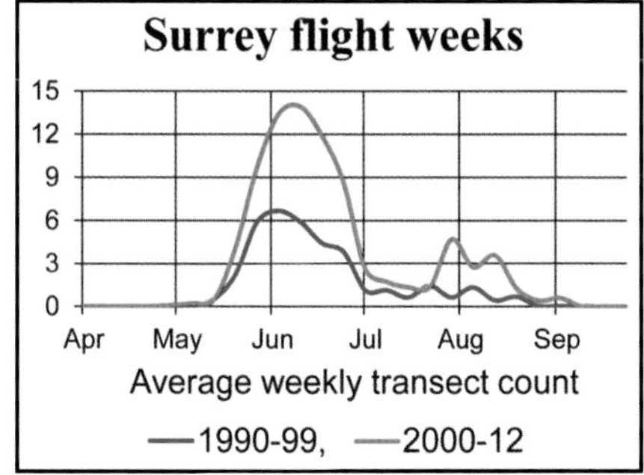

Small Blue *continued* **Malcolm Bridge**

Habitat: old chalk quarries or workings (e.g. Howell Hill) and steep, chalky embankments (the Cutting at Hutchinson's Bank). Avoids open downland except for the most sheltered spots. Elsewhere, abandoned railway lines or newly created or disturbed road verges (A27 between Hove and Shoreham, Sussex) are used if kidney vetch is present and the site is sheltered. Thomas has described the best sites as: "Sun-baked, sheltered terrain with rough or broken ground."

Top transects: Howell Hill, Banstead Downs, Box Hill, Hutchinson's Bank, Pewley Down. Howell Hill and Hutchinson's Bank are relatively small sites and provide the best chance of sightings; larger sites such as Box Hill and Banstead Downs demand a degree of local knowledge.

Other key sites: Merrow Down and golf course; Warren Farm, Ewell.

Life cycle: usually univoltine but in the south of England regularly produces a small second brood in August, particularly at its best sites; winters as fully-grown larva.

Small Blue female on bird's-foot-trefoil. **FK**

Males perch on taller vegetation at the bottom of sheltered slopes, wings half open; females visit and mating follows the briefest courtship. Thereafter the female will avoid the area and seek out kidney vetch in a warm and sheltered spot.

The majority of her eggs are laid singly within 50m of her pupation site. Even though the young larvae are prone to cannibalism, in good habitat different females frequently lay on the same flower head. The pale-blue eggs are fairly easy to find, despite being tucked away in the silky down at the base of the flower, but care must be taken because the flowers are brittle and break apart easily.

Eggs hatch in 2-3 weeks and the young larva burrows into the flower head to feed on anthers and seed. The older, grey-pink larva lives on flower clusters and in July can be found feeding head-down. Unusually for a Blue, it is rarely attended by ants. In late July a few new butterflies emerge, but most final instars hide in a shallow crevice, often under moss, and hibernate for the next nine months. Emerging in a typical year in late April, the larva pupates under low vegetation without further feeding.

Larval foodplants: exclusively kidney vetch.

Small Blue pair at Warren Farm, male on left. **JFK**

A GREAT conservation effort, guided in many cases by Gail Jeffcoate, has been made in Surrey over the last decade to reverse the decline of the Small Blue, which is scattered in isolated colonies along the North Downs. The creation of scrapes of bare chalk underpins much of this management effort. On some sites the bare ground has been sown with locally harvested kidney vetch seed; on others (e.g. Hutchinson's Bank) kidney vetch plugs have been planted into new scrapes with some success.

Kidney vetch, a speedy coloniser of bare limestone, is a poor competitor and disappears as soon as other plant species become established. It is a short-lived perennial and a high percentage of plants fail to survive the next winter after first flowering.

A small colony can survive on relatively few flowering plants, with Thomas suggesting as few as two dozen. Mike Slater, who coordinates excellent Small Blue work in Warwickshire, considers about 50 plants in flower as a minimum.

The colonies at Box Hill and to the east have been the focus of significant conservation effort, with Butterfly Conservation working well with partners such as the Lower Mole Project, the Downlands Countryside Management Project, and the Surrey and London Wildlife Trusts.

The boroughs of Reigate & Banstead and Croydon have recognised that they host key colonies and both have adopted the butterfly as a flagship species for their Biodiversity Action Plans. Great work continues and it is planned to establish good habitat within reach of existing colonies to reduce their isolation. A similar approach is planned for the western colonies between Guildford (Pewley Down) and Dorking, where potentially suitable habitat exists, to create a metapopulation rather than two or three small, isolated colonies. The Small Blue illustrates what can be achieved when conservation groups and concerned local authorities coordinate their efforts.

Outside Surrey the Small Blue occurs mainly in the south of England; there are scattered colonies in south Wales, Scotland as far north as John O'Groats, and Ireland. It tends to be rare wherever it occurs with exceptions in the Cotswolds, Salisbury Plain and south Dorset. It remains much rarer than its larval foodplant.

Small Blue *continued*

Small Blue — weekly transect counts
Howell Hill, Ewell TQ239619 — **Richard Donovan**

	WEEK	2000	2001	2002	2003	2004	2005	2006	2007	2008	2009	2010	2011	2012
6 May	6			-			-	-	1	-	-		1	-
13	7			-		1	-	-	-	-		-		-
20	8				1	11	-		-		9	2	36	1
27	9				26	39	6	24	12	**23**	19	7	40	11
3 June	10			10	**86**	**129**	26	21	14	17	18	18	**54**	5
10	11			**23**	83	56	39	**97**	**16**	11	**27**	**32**	24	
17	12				40	31	**55**	57	7	11	8	18	4	**20**
24	13			21	21	18	51	41		8	2	3	8	5
1 July	14			7	3			10	-	5	1	3	2	
8	15			3	1	3	4	1	1	-		-	-	2
15	16			1	-	1	1	1		-	-	-	2	-
22	17				2	-	4	1	-	-	-	7	3	1
29	18			-	15	4	38	3	-		9	20	5	-
5 August	19			1	5	2	14	6	1	1	3	2	5	5
12	20			-	-	-	5	2		3	2	2	5	5
19	21			-	-	-	4	1	-	-			2	
26	22			-	1	-	-	-	-		-	1	-	
2 September	23				-	-	1	-			-	-		-
Abundance index				98	284	305	248	267	48	81	99	111	195	74
Weeks recorded				**7**	**12**	**11**	**13**	**13**	**7**	**8**	**10**	**12**	**14**	**9**

Phenology trend	**1990-2012**	no change	
Best transect day 2000-12	Jun 6, 2004	Howell Hill	129
Transects abundance	**1990-2012** gain 679%	**2000-2012** gain 85%	
UK transects abundance	**1978-2012** gain 21%	**10-year trend** no change	
UK 4,361 10k squares	**2005-09** 238 = 5%	**10-year trend** loss 4%	

Flight weeks ▲High transect counts △Middle ^Low

Apr					May				Jun				Jul					Aug				Sep			
1	8	15	22	29	6	13	20	27	3	10	17	24	1	8	15	22	29	5	12	19	26	2	9	16	23
				^	^	^	△	▲	▲	▲	▲	▲	△	△	△	△	△	△	△	△	^	^			

■ GAIL JEFFCOATE's Species Action Plan for the Small Blue, prepared for the Surrey Biodiversity partnership, is at:
www.surreybiodiversitypartnership.org/xwiki/bin/view/Species/SmallBlue

Silver-studded Blue *Plebejus argus* **Howard Street**

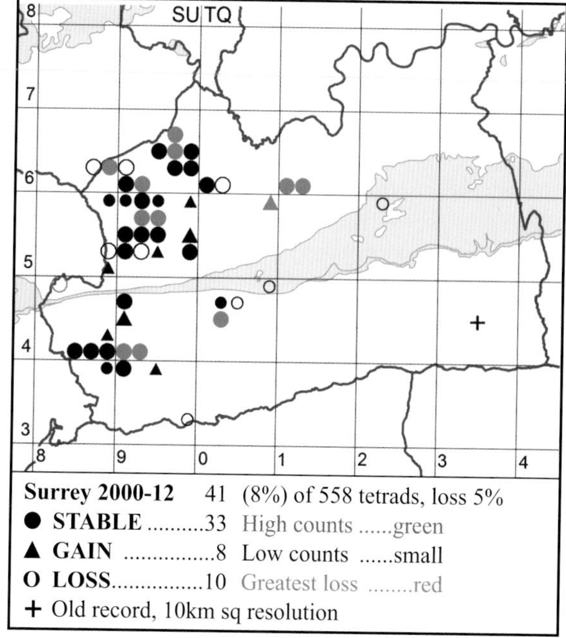

Surrey status: locally abundant on heathland, including the Thames Basin heaths shared with south-east Berkshire and north-east Hampshire.

Flies: early/mid-June to late July, occasionally into August.

Conservation: protected from sale; UK Biodiversity Action Plan priority species; BC 2010 Red List: vulnerable.

The Surrey Heathland Project (SHP) regards the species as an indicator of improving heathland habitat.

Trends: long-term decline has stabilised in recent years as a result of a huge programme of heathland restoration. During 2002-2008 SHP restored and recreated 1,500ha of heathland over 26 sites. My monitoring of 13 smaller heaths around Pirbright, which benefited from the SHP, confirmed stable distribution, and significant increases in numbers at certain sites.

Wingspan: male 26-32mm, female 25-31mm.

Identification: a comparatively small Blue. Male's upperwings are deep blue with a black margin and contrasting white fringe. Female is brown, similar to Brown Argus, occasionally with varying amounts of blue radiating from the body. The patterned underside is distinguished by the hindwing's eponymous silver-blue "studs" on black spots in an orange band.

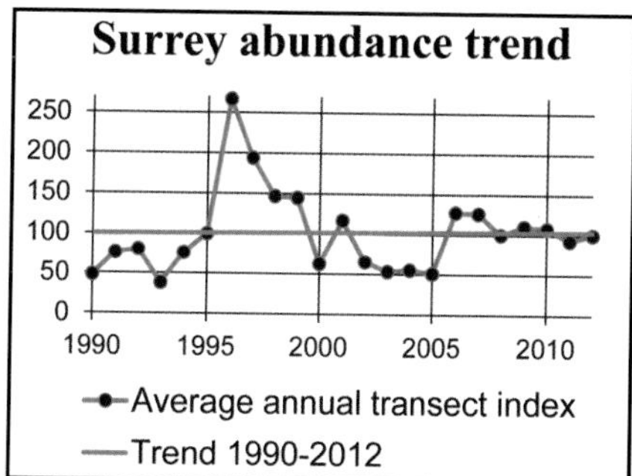

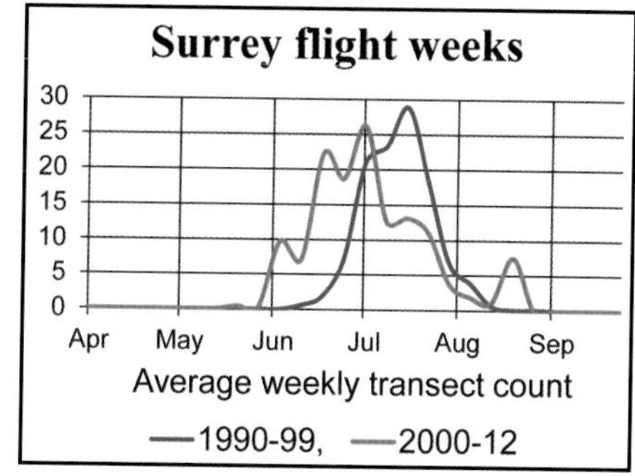

Silver-studded Blue *continued* — Howard Street

Variations/aberrations: there are two surviving British subspecies, *argus* on heathland and *caernensis* on Llandudno's Great Orme headland. Subspecies *cretaceus* once bred on a few downland sites, including some in Surrey, but is now extinct. There is also an unnamed variation on the limestone of Portland.

Confusion species: when seen in colonies, characteristically just above the heather within a small area, there can be no mistaking this butterfly. However, a solitary specimen on a site where it was not previously known to exist (as I found on two occasions when monitoring for SHP), could, without photographic evidence, be dismissed as a Common Blue or, in the case of a lone female, a Brown Argus.

Silver-studded Blue male on bell heather. **GW**

Habitat: in Surrey, confined to heathland, both wet and dry. It needs a succession of sparse young heather which, apart from wild fires, requires habitat management.

Top transects: Fairmile Common, Chobham Common, Frensham Common, Witley Common, Brentmoor Heath.

Other key sites: Dawney Hill (see page 194) has had high densities in recent years. Sheet's Heath, Thursley Common and Whitmoor Common also have good numbers.

Life cycle: univoltine; eggs are laid singly in midsummer and hatch the following spring when the larvae browse on emerging heather shoots. The larva is attended by black ants in a symbiotic relationship: the ants feed off caterpillar secretions and provide protection, in particular to the pupa, which forms underground in the ant nest.

Larval foodplants: gorse, heathers.

Phenology trend	**1990-2012**	earlier by 2.5 weeks	
Best transect day 2000-12	Jul 2, 2010	Fairmile Common	268
Transects abundance	**1990-2012** gain 4%	**2000-2012** gain 58%	
UK transects abundance	**1979-2012** gain 5%	**10-year trend** loss 40%	
UK 4,361 10k squares	**2005-09** 91 = 2%	**10-year trend** loss 3%	

Flight weeks ▲High transect counts △Middle ^Low

Apr					May				Jun				Jul					Aug				Sep			
1	8	15	22	29	6	13	20	27	3	10	17	24	1	8	15	22	29	5	12	19	26	2	9	16	23
							^	^	△	△	▲	▲	▲	△	▲	△	△	^	^	^					

Silver-studded Blue pair, male on left. **GE**

ALTHOUGH the Silver-studded Blue inhabited the North Downs prior to myxomatosis in the 1950s, the acid heathland of West Surrey has always been its stronghold. The loss of heathland to development and neglect has caused a corresponding reduction in populations. However the restoration work of the SHP has stemmed the downward trend and, on some sites, encouraged significant increases in numbers.

Monitoring of Silver-studded Blue on 13 small heaths around Pirbright has served as an indicator of the success of the project and has shown that the butterfly is able to survive in small numbers where conditions are less than favourable. In such cases it will respond rapidly and predictably to habitat management that includes heather rejuvenation. However, because of its sedentary nature – rarely straying far from its patch – this butterfly, once lost from a site, is unlikely to recolonise it by migration

Provided that funding continues for heathland maintenance (which, at present, looks assured) and that the work includes continuous heather rejuvenation, Silver-studded Blue colonies should grow and Surrey, along with Dorset and Hampshire, will continue to be the British stronghold for this exquisite heathland icon.

Silver-studded Blue — weekly transect counts

Fairmile Common, Cobham TQ118617 — **Dave Page**

	WEEK	2000	2001	2002	2003	2004	2005	2006	2007	2008	2009	2010	2011	2012
20 May	8							-	-	-		-	5	-
27	9										4			-
3 June	10							-	2	-	49	-	**186**	
10	11							13	86	5	78			
17	12							119	**207**	23	**116**	152		25
24	13							128		112	64		104	
1 July	14							**133**	29	**116**		**268**		**134**
8	15							8	16	22	26	2	7	
15	16							26	15	42			2	
22	17									4			-	104
29	18							-		-			-	84
Abundance index								450	516	346	407	NI	NI	NI
Weeks recorded								**6**	**6**	**7**	**6**	**3**	**5**	**4**

Brown Argus *Aricia agestis*

Harry E. Clarke

Surrey status: stronghold on the Downs, but expanding distribution.

Flies: May to June and late July to mid-September.

Trends: declining in numbers but expanding in distribution.

Wingspan: 25-31mm.

Identification: upperside brown, with white fringe; black spot on middle of forewing; orange crescents with black spots near outer margin of hindwing; orange spots on forewing, extending in female to front margin. Undersides pale brown, with orange spots near margin and black spots within white circles. Looks silvery in flight.

Surrey 2000-12 132 (24%) of 558 tetrads, gain 16%
● **STABLE** ....62 High counts ......green
▲ **GAIN** ....70 Low counts ......small
O **LOSS**................52 Greatest loss ....red

Variations/aberrations: orange is replaced with yellow (ab. *pallidior)* or white (ab. *graafii*).

Confusion species: female Blues. Brown Argus has no blue near body and, along with Silver-studded Blue, lacks black spot near body on forewing underside. Brown Argus has two black spots on front margin of hindwing in the shape of a colon or figure eight. Black spots on upper hindwing of female Common Blue are fringed with white/blue.

Habitat: downland, heathland, open woodland.

Top transects: Headley Heath, Juniper Hill, Sheepleas, Denbies Landbarn, Headley Warren.

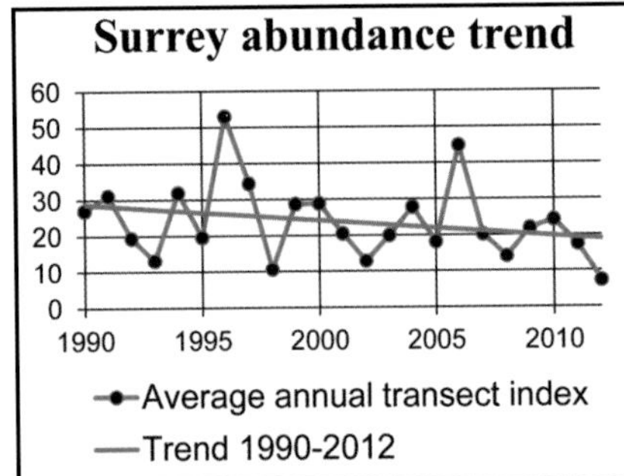

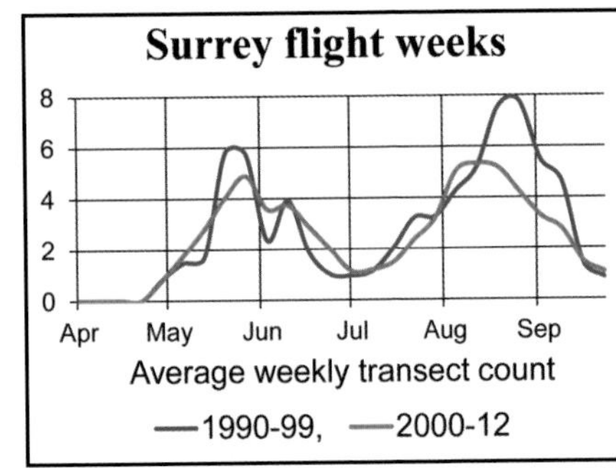

Brown Argus female, abdomen raised in rejection mode; male above. **FK**

Life cycle: bivoltine; winters as larva, pupating in early April and emerging in second week in May. Eggs laid singly on underside of foodplant. Pupates at base of foodplant, attached by a few silk threads, but larvae are often taken into ant nests.

Larval foodplants: primarily common rock-rose on the Chalk; elsewhere:
cut-leaved crane's-bill,
dove's-foot crane's-bill,
common stork's-bill.

■ *Comparison photo: page 100*

The Brown Argus lives in small colonies, its stronghold being the Downs where rock-rose is the larval foodplant. In recent years it has expanded its distribution by switching to cut-leaved crane's-bill and other Geraniaceae. Colonies on the Chalk remain significantly larger than those off it, which include Mitcham Common (max transect count 19), where the butterfly arrived in the early 1990s. The trend towards expansion has continued, with the Brown Argus now recorded widely across the county. Unusually, recent second broods have been not much bigger than the first, which suggests the butterfly is under threat.

Weather in late March determines when the larva will resume feeding, and consequently when in May the first adults will emerge. Males patrol a territory looking for females, and chasing off rivals. Average dispersal between colonies is only 100m, but distances of a few kilometres have been recorded. Adults roost head-down on grass stems, often in the company of other Blues.

Mating and egg-laying require sunshine. As the adults live for only a few days, wet summers can have a dramatic effect on their ability to reproduce. Females search out plants with higher nitrogen content, and require a relatively short turf, with vegetation 1-10cm tall. Eggs, laid singly on the underside of the leaf near to the midrib, hatch after about six days.

The young larva creates a characteristic mine on the leaf underside, circular in shape without any frass as the larva only half enters the mine. The micro-moth *Mompha miscella* produces a similar leaf-mine, but with frass and the larvae entirely within the mine. Later instars consume the whole leaf, feeding by day and resting below the leaf.

The larva is usually attended by ants, including *Lasius alienus* (dry, sunny chalk grassland), *Lasius flavus* (abundant in pastures) and *Myrmica sabuleti* (dry, sunny sites). The ants feed on secretions from Newcomer's gland (or dorsal nectary gland) on the seventh abdominal segment, for which plants with high nitrogen content are required.

Larval diapause is controlled by daylight length and temperature. Despite the association with ants, the Brown Argus is still the victim of various parasitoids.

Brown Argus *continued*

Brown Argus — weekly transect counts

Headley Heath TQ195533 — **Donna Dawson, Gordon Flower**

WEEK		2000	2001	2002	2003	2004	2005	2006	2007	2008	2009	2010	2011	2012
29 April	5	-	-		2	-	-	-	9	-	1	-	6	-
6 May	6	-	-		6	-	-	-		-	**13**	-	**17**	-
13	7	6	-		14	-	-	-	**31**	-		11	14	-
20	8	11	-		5	9	1	8	27	**15**	6	10	8	2
27	9	9	**22**		-	7	**19**	16	29	11	9	**21**	1	**9**
3 June	10	10	10		6	**11**	7	8	2	7	3	14	2	
10	11	13	12		6	2	9	5	-	8	-	-	-	3
17	12	7	10		4	4	9	3	-	3	-	4		1
24	13	-	6		2	2	-	2	-	-	-	-	-	-
1 July	14	1	2		-	1	-	-	-	-	-	-	-	-
8	15				-	-	-	-	-	-	-	-	3	
15	16		-		2	-	1	-	1	-	-	-	1	5
22	17	-	1		2	1	-	8	1	-	-	-	-	-
29	18	1	6		11	5	6	13	1	1	3	-	3	2
5 August	19	2	3		**15**	8	3	23	5	-	-	-	3	1
12	20	18	13		3	7	15	9	2	2	2	3	6	2
19	21	37	20		6	5	11		1	4	4	3	4	2
26	22	**51**	11		4	8	2	**45**	-	5	11	1	3	
2 September	23	24			5	10	3	16	1	-	3	2	3	1
9	24	14			4	3	5		-	-	-	-	2	1
16	25				3	-	-		-	-	-	-	1	-
23	26	-	-		3	-	-	8		-	-	-	-	-
Abundance index		211	117		109	107	91	215	127	57	NI	NI	84	42
Weeks recorded		**14**			**19**	**15**	**13**	**13**	**12**	**9**	**10**	**9**	**16**	**11**

Phenology trend	**1990-2012**	earlier by one week	
Best transect day 2000-12	Aug 14, 2004	Sheepleas	67
Transects abundance	**1990-2012** loss 34%	**2000-2012** loss 31%	
UK transects abundance	**1976-2012** gain 6%	**10-year trend** loss 35%	
UK 4,361 10k squares	**2005-09** 795 = 18%	**10-year trend** gain 10%	

Flight weeks Brown Argus — ▲High transect counts △Middle ^Low

Apr					May				Jun				Jul					Aug				Sep			
1	8	15	22	29	6	13	20	27	3	10	17	24	1	8	15	22	29	5	12	19	26	2	9	16	23
				^	△	△	▲	▲	△	△	△	△	^	^	^	△	△	▲	▲	▲	▲	△	△	^	^

Common Blue *Polyommatus icarus*

Harry E. Clarke

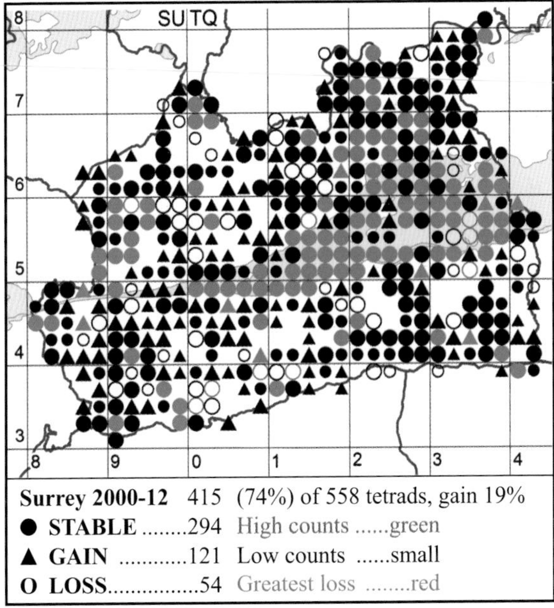

Surrey status: common and widespread.
Flies: May to June and late July to September, usually peaking in August.
Trends: declining.
Wingspan: 29-38mm.
Identification: male blue with unbroken white fringe and narrow black margin; female varies from brown to violet-blue, with orange and black spots on hindwing, orange spots extending to forewing. Underside: female brown, male grey-brown; forewing has two black spots close to the body (often only one visible); orange spots on hindwing, in females extending to front of forewing.
Variations/aberrations: males vary from pale violet to deep blue, or even pale buff or grey. Females range from dusky brown to rich blue; orange spots vary in size and prominence. Underside orange spots vary to pale yellow.
Confusion species: Silver-studded Blue (heathland) has thicker black margin; white fringe is distinctly broken in brighter Adonis and paler Chalkhill. Female Common Blue has a lot of blue on upperside (especially in Surrey), Brown Argus has none. Brown Argus and Silver-studded Blue lack black spot on underside of forewing close to the body. Underside of Holly and Small Blue is distinctly plainer than other Blues.
Habitat: woodland, heathland, downland, dry pasture, waste ground.
Top transects: Box Hill, Denbies Landbarn, Sheepleas, Park Downs, Nore Hill.

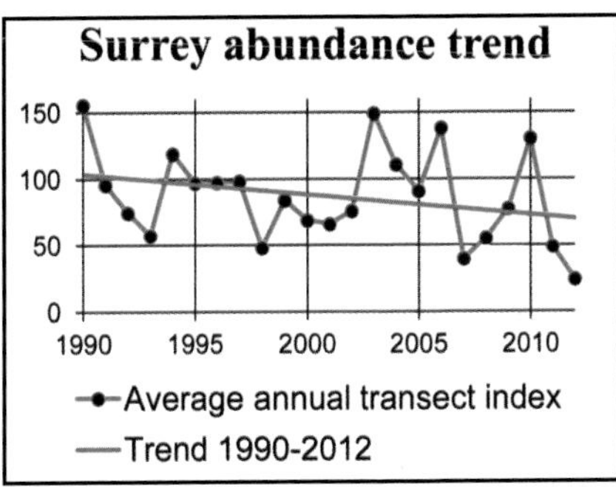

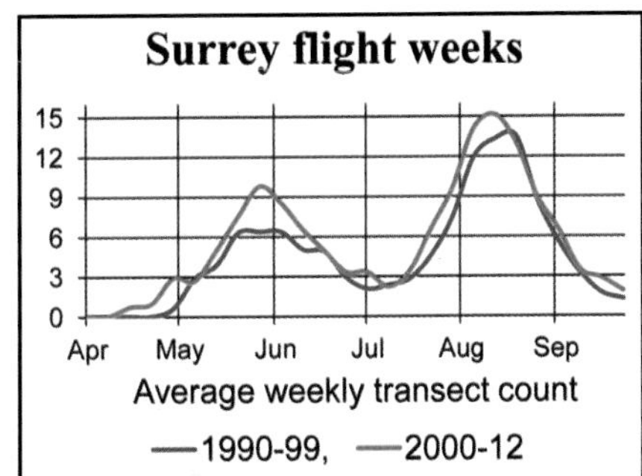

Common Blue *continued* **Harry E. Clarke**

AS its name suggests, the Common Blue is the commonest Blue in Surrey, widely distributed in good numbers but never in the same abundance that the Chalkhill Blue can reach at its best sites. The second brood is usually, but not always, up to 50% larger than the first, from which some butterflies may still be flying when the second brood emerges.

The weather in March determines when the overwintering larvae will resume feeding, and consequently when the adults will emerge in May. Only in the final instar do ants sometimes feed on secretions from the larva's Newcomer's (dorsal nectary) gland on the seventh abdominal segment. Secretion rate is dependent on plant quality (high nitrogen) and whether the larva has been attacked. This in turn controls the number of ants in attendance and level of protection. The larva also possesses a pair of retractile tubercles, which omit a bad odour and are thought to be defensive.

Common Blue male. **FK**

Diapause is controlled by daylight length. Some of the first brood enter diapause and do not pupate until the following spring, while the rest pupate to create the second brood.

The pupa secretes a substance that can stimulate ants to carry it into their nest. Ants associated with the Common Blue include: *Lasius alienus* (dry, sunny chalk grassland) and *Myrmica sabuleti* (dry, sunny sites), both of which prefer short turf; *Formica rufa* (woodland and open rides); *Lasius flavus* (abundant in pastures); and the garden black ant *Lasius niger* (sunny, medium-dry sites).

Common Blues form discrete colonies and can create new ones, but are not really wanderers like the Orange-tip. They fly only in sunshine and at night roost together head-down on grass stems, often with other Blues. The male is distinctly territorial, and either perches or patrols in search of females. The female takes great care in selecting a suitable foodplant, drumming her feet on the leaf, dipping her antennae and dragging her abdomen over the surface. Preference is for plants with flowers and high nitrogen content, isolated in a short sward, near to a path or taller vegetation.

The larvae create blotches in the leaves as they eat the lower layers. As they grow, they consume the whole leaf. On restharrow they prefer to eat the flowers.

■ *Common Blues at roost, page 211*

Common Blue female (blue-type individual) on fleabane. **KW**

Life cycle: bivoltine; winters as larva, which pupates in April, emerging in May. Eggs laid singly on upperside of foodplant. Larva pupates at base of foodplant attached by a few silk threads, but is often taken into an ant nest.

Larval foodplants: primarily common bird's-foot-trefoil; also other members of the family Fabaceae.

Phenology trend	**1990-2012**	earlier by 2 weeks	
Best transect day 2000-12	Aug 5, 2003	Sheepleas	127
Transects abundance	**1990-2012** loss 32%	**2000-2012** loss 34%	
UK transects abundance	**1976-2012** loss 15%	**10-year trend** loss 52%	
UK 4,361 10k squares	**2005-09** 2,147 = 49%	**10-year trend** loss 6%	

Flight weeks ▲High transect counts △Middle ^Low

Apr					May				Jun				Jul					Aug				Sep			
1	*8*	*15*	*22*	*29*	*6*	*13*	*20*	*27*	*3*	*10*	*17*	*24*	*1*	*8*	*15*	*22*	*29*	*5*	*12*	*19*	*26*	*2*	*9*	*16*	*23*
		^	^	^	^	△	△	▲	△	△	△	△	△	^	△	△	▲	▲	▲	▲	▲	△	△	△	^

Common Blue

weekly transect counts

Park Downs, Banstead TQ265585

Jill Hall

	WEEK	2000	2001	2002	2003	2004	2005	2006	2007	2008	2009	2010	2011	2012
29 April	5	-		-	-		-	-	-	-	-	-	4	-
6 May	6	-	-	-	-	-	-	-	-	-	-	-	44	-
13	7	-	-	1	-	-	-	-	4	-	4	-	28	1
20	8	7	-	2	-		-	-	**12**	1	17	5	**51**	3
27	9	7	-	3	12	3	13	3	**12**	4	10	24	16	2
3 June	10	10	2	1	10	**41**	18	18	4	3	11	52	8	1
10	11	**20**	11	5	4	9	14	23	5	6	5	19	4	3
17	12	**20**	4	8	4	6	9	5	1	2	1	11	-	-
24	13	8	8	7	1	7	6	10	1	4	5	12	-	-
1 July	14	5	6	1	-	-	-	13	-	-	-	5	-	-
8	15	-	1	2	-	-	-	2	-	-	-	-	-	-
15	16	1	-	-	8	-	-	-	-	-	1	-	2	-
22	17	-	-	-	9	-	-	51	1	-	6	21	6	-
29	18	-	5	1	36	-	4	37	4	4	29	74	15	-
5 August	19	-	7	3	**88**	23	7	**55**	1	**11**	**65**	63	16	3
12	20	3	17	12	68	14	18	49	-	10	26	**113**	4	**15**
19	21	11	**22**	6	29	14	**48**	34	1	9	47	55	1	2
26	22	10	12	**18**	17	26	15	26	5	4	4	19	2	7
2 September	23	8	6		5	9	13	14	-	2	1	15	4	14
9	24	3	2	9	5	-	3	3	1	2	4	-	1	2
16	25	-	1	3	5	-	-	-	-	2	-	-	-	3
23	26	1	-	1	8	-	1	-		-	-	-	-	-
Abundance index		114	104	96	301	134	169	340	49	67	227	517	224	56
Weeks recorded		**14**	**14**	**17**	**16**	**10**	**13**	**15**	**13**	**14**	**16**	**14**	**16**	**12**

Brown Argus female (left): underside shows colon spots on hindwing front margin and absence of spot closer to body on forewing. Compare Common Blue female (right). **Both FK**

Chalkhill Blue *Polyommatus* (formerly *Lysandra*) *coridon* — Ken Willmott

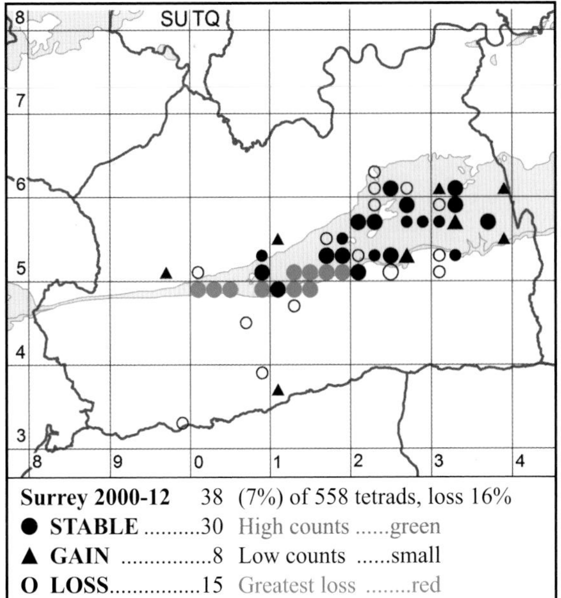

Surrey status: abundant on south-facing slopes of the North Downs with plentiful horseshoe vetch.

Flies: mid-July to September.

Conservation: protected from sale; BC 2010 Red List: near-threatened.

Trends: increasing; despite the wet weather, 2012 population was notably high in most Surrey locations. Some losses and gains relate to wanderers.

Wingspan: 33-40mm.

Identification: male is pale blue with black margin. Brown female is difficult to separate from second-brood Adonis Blue, which also flies on the North Downs in August.

Variations/aberrations: Bright & Leeds (1938) devoted a book to aberrations of this species. Percy Bright, once Mayor of Bournemouth, had a massive collection of pinned Chalkhill Blues. Nowadays rare aberrations such as ab. *tithonus*, the all-blue female, and ab. *ultraradiata*, with extreme rayed underside spotting, should only be photographed.

Confusion species: female Adonis is usually a darker chocolate-brown and on the wing a little later in August. Adonis might be expected to be fresher in appearance, but the Chalkhill has a protracted emergence, so fresh specimens of both species can be seen together. The chequered fringes of female Chalkhill Blue are paler; hindwing marginal spots are edged with white rather than blue. Chalkhill has a pale marginal band on the

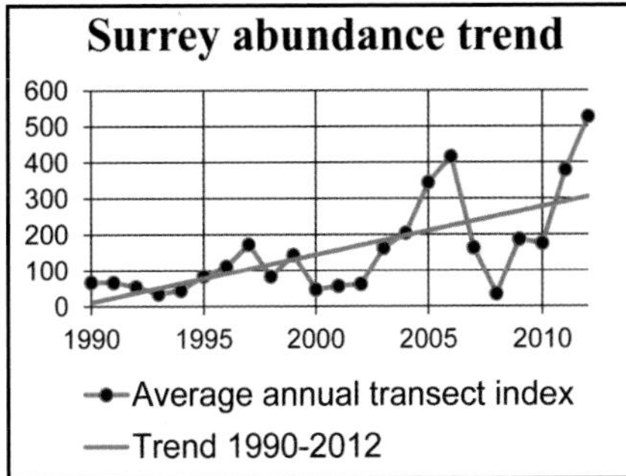

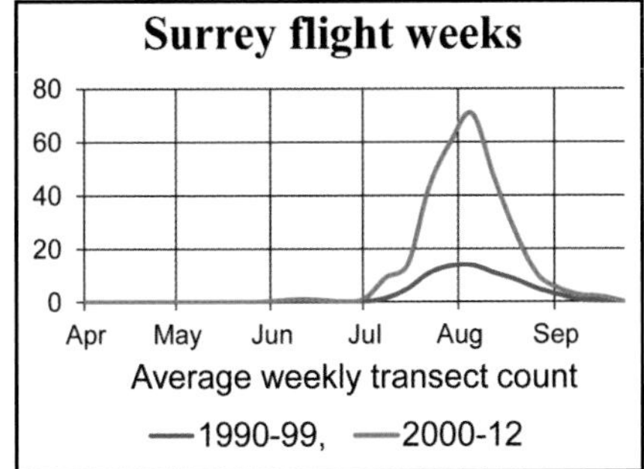

Chalkhill Blue *continued* **Ken Willmott**

forewing, sometimes with variable red spotting, which gives the appearance of the underside spotting showing through. This band becomes paler and more apparent with age. Adonis forewings are a uniform brown with the exception of marginal red spotting. Common Blue and Brown Argus females lack chequering on fringe.

Habitat: south-facing downland.

Top transects: Denbies Landbarn B, Pewley Down, Box Hill, Park Downs.

Life cycle: univoltine (unlike fellow horseshoe vetch feeder, Adonis Blue); winters as egg. Females lay on or in the vicinity of horseshoe vetch. Chalkhill eggs are most commonly on the underside, Adonis eggs on the upperside. Eggs hatch in late March or early April. Even though Chalkhill and Adonis larvae can share the same plant, the latter pupates and emerges far earlier (May) in its first brood. Chalkhill larvae begin to pupate mid-June among roots or underground (have been found buried by ants in constructed chambers). As with the Adonis, ants are important to the Chalkhill, and larvae can be located (avoid sunny days) by searching for ant gatherings rather than the larva itself, which will be close by. Both Chalkhill and Adonis males regularly gain nutrition from urine or faeces.

Chalkhill Blue males taking minerals from animal faeces. **KW**

Larval foodplant: exclusively horseshoe vetch.

Phenology trend	**1990-2012**	earlier by 0.5 weeks	
Best transect day 2000-12	Aug 8, 2012	Denbies Landbarn B	1,681
Transects abundance	**1990-2012** gain 2,838%	**2000-2012** gain 466%	
UK transects abundance	**1976-2012** gain 14%	**10-year trend** gain 13%	
UK 4,361 10k squares	**2005-09** 208 = 5%	**10-year trend** loss 1%	

Flight weeks ▲High transect counts △Middle ^Low

Apr					May				Jun				Jul					Aug				Sep			
1	8	15	22	29	6	13	20	27	3	10	17	24	1	8	15	22	29	5	12	19	26	2	9	16	23
									^	^	^	^	△	△	△	▲	▲	▲	▲	△	△	△	△	△	^

SURREY's 2012 Chalkhill Blue population was enormous, despite England's wettest summer since records began. The high rainfall resulted in the grasses and other downland plants that surround the horseshoe vetch growing more vigorously and thus attaining a taller sward than in most years.

Chalkhill Blue pair on wild basil, aberrant male above. **KW**

Unlike the Adonis Blue, which has the same larval foodplant, Chalkhill Blue does not require the higher ground temperatures for eggs, larvae and pupae, so was less affected by the lower temperatures provided by the shade of the taller vegetation. This is probably not the only factor influencing the population explosion of Chalkhill Blue but they must have thrived on the lush growth of horseshoe vetch, which in some years can be affected by drought. Conversely the Adonis Blue population in August plummeted.

Chalkhill Blue male. **KW**

Where its larval foodplant is in low density and restricted to small isolated areas, as it once was on Banstead Downs, Chalkhill populations can comprise only a few individuals and are therefore vulnerable to inappropriate management.

The Chalkhill Blue has good dispersal qualities, particularly in years of abundance. In both 2011 and 2012 I recorded single males in the clay woodlands of Chiddingfold Forest. Female dispersal is less-easily observed and I know of no records at such a distance from their breeding areas. The female is less active than the male and, once mated, concentrates on egg-laying activities and therefore stays within the location of larval foodplants, avoiding the attention of males.

During the 2012 super abundance, innumerable mating pairs were receiving attention from multiple frustrated males. Perhaps male dispersal in years of abundance is a result of being unable to locate their own receptive females due to the higher ratio of males in the population. Male Chalkhill Blues find females by the sexual strategy of "patrolling". Some females are mated so soon after emergence that their wings are not fully inflated. Sitting on an inactive ant-hill, with the downland turf shimmering with patrolling male Chalkhill Blues, must be one of the best experiences of a butterfly enthusiast's year.

Chalkhill Blue *continued* **Ken Willmott**

Searching for larvae in May or June is most productive on cloudy days, mid-morning until early afternoon. Do not look for the green and yellow-striped larvae among the horseshoe vetch plants. Look for red (*Myrmica*) or black (*Lasius*) ants. Both types can adopt a larva and when several ants together are busily moving to and fro, the reason is, more often than not, a Chalkhill Blue larva. Patiently watch the ants tending the larva for the sweet liquid droplets that emanate from its honey glands and look out for the white, eversible tubercular organ, which may be an attractant or a pacifier.

Where Chalkhill and Adonis Blues share the same habitat, as on Denbies Hillside, it is important that any conservation management, usually by means of domestic stock grazing, takes into account the differing needs of each species. Consequently the whole site should not be grazed in exactly the same manner.

The Chalkhill Blue can thrive with horseshoe vetch in lower temperatures with a slightly higher sward. If neglected, sward can become too high and ground temperatures too low, so grazing is an important conservation tool. However grazing should be a little more intensive when applied to the habitat of the Adonis, which requires a warmer environment for its early stages.

In my 40 years of visiting the Dorset coast I have documented a huge collapse in the Chalkhill Blue population, but the Adonis Blue still thrives. In my opinion overgrazing has destroyed the Chalkhill Blue habitat niche; Adonis Blue survives, but might have failed through undergrazing. We need to understand how both species coexist in the same general habitat, and appropriate management planning is crucial to secure the future of these iconic downland species in Surrey.

Chalkhill Blue weekly transect counts

Denbies Landbarn B TQ135499 **Gail Jeffcoate, Robert Cramp**

	WEEK	2000	2001	2002	2003	2004	2005	2006	2007	2008	2009	2010	2011	2012
1 July	14			-	1	-	1	-	1	-	13	3	1	
8	15			1	35	1	5	-	1	5	78	14	44	4
15	16			1	82	2	88	47	19	12		137	115	
22	17			13	160	39	383	651	53	63	**228**		458	820
29	18				257	122	**780**	**832**	119		190		634	816
5 August	19			**123**	**342**	618		581	**157**	**152**	207	**255**	**1050**	**1681**
12	20			88	205	**626**	382	240	26	53	76	129	166	774
19	21			53	70	212	251	108			68	88	76	366
26	22			18	25	32	92	30	4	26	15	29	9	59
2 September	23			5	3	21	25	10	2	4	7	19		11
9	24			2	1	11	3	8	1	3		-	-	1
16	25			2	2	-	3	-	-	2	3	-	2	3
23	26			1	-	-	-	-	-	-	1	-	-	-
Abundance index				424	964	1684	2705	2611	410	NI	976	NI	2648	4462
Weeks recorded				**11**	**12**	**10**	**11**	**9**	**10**	**9**	**11**	**8**	**10**	**10**

Adonis Blue *Polyommatus* (formerly *Lysandra*) *bellargus* — Ken Willmott

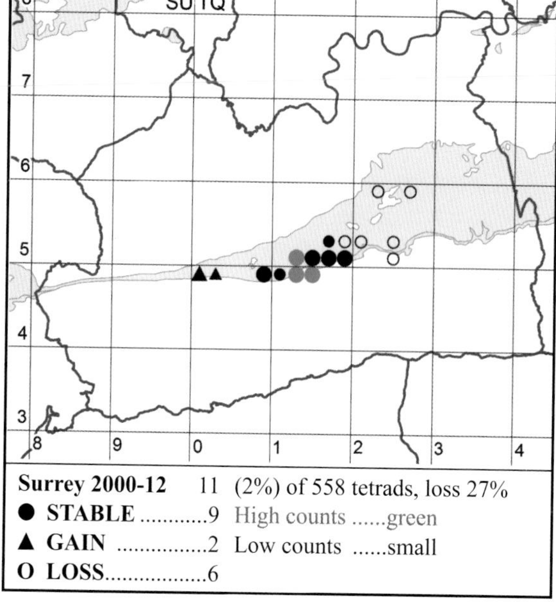

■ ***Map note**: the two gains are at Pewley Down, where the Adonis was recorded 2004-2007 but not 2008-2011. The site has experienced unofficial releases, which may explain records of males in May 2012 (one) and June 2013 (two).*

Surrey status: vulnerable; on the edge of its European range in southern England; restricted in Surrey to Denbies Hillside and Box Hill. Not as widespread as the Chalkhill Blue, more prone to population fluctuation, and requiring a different domestic livestock management regime.
Flies: May and June, August and September.
Conservation: protected from sale; BC 2010 Red List: near-threatened.
Trends: formerly in severe decline and now termed a "recovering" species nationally. This is not the case in Surrey due to the effect of bad weather on the spring brood in 2011 and 2012, resulting in low numbers in August and September. Hopefully this is a temporary situation. First-brood males can emerge in April during a fine spring, often within periods of drought and after particularly dry winters. In a fine summer, second-brood males can fly from mid-July.
Wingspan: 30-40mm.
Identification: male has dazzling, iridescent-blue wings with chequered fringe. Dark-brown female is difficult to separate from Chalkhill Blue where they fly together in August.

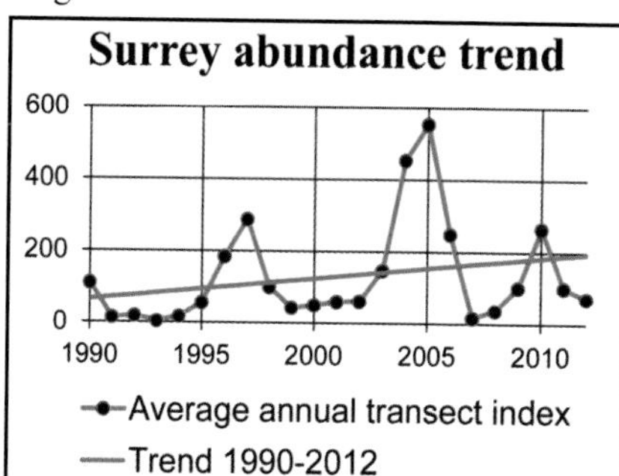

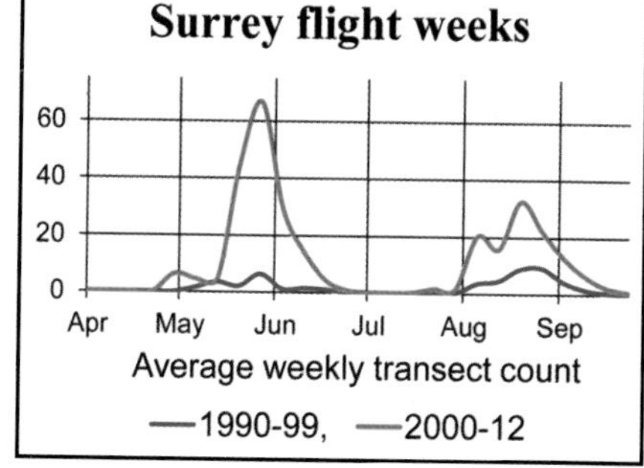

Adonis Blue *continued* **Ken Willmott**

Adonis Blue female. **BH**

Variations/aberrations: ab. *krodeli*, lacking most underside spotting, can be common on Denbies Hillside in a good year such as 2011 when a significant percentage showed varying degrees of wing-pattern modification. One remarkable asymmetrical aberration lacked spotting on one underwing only. Females can have varying amounts of blue on the upperside: ab. *ceronus* is entirely blue, with the exception of the red marginal crescents; ab. *semiceronus* is partially blue. A natural Adonis/Chalkhill hybrid, ab. *polonus*, was captured at Denbies Hillside on June 13, 2004.

Confusion species: hindwing crescents on female Adonis are red, edged with blue near the fringe; on Chalkhill they are edged with white and often less distinct. Fresh Adonis females appear darker than Chalkhill females, especially the chequered fringes. Chalkhill males have pale-blue scaling towards the thorax and body. Common Blue and Brown Argus, which often fly with Adonis Blues, lack the fringe-chequering.

Habitat: south-facing downland with horseshoe vetch and appropriate grazing levels (domestic livestock or rabbit populations) to maintain short turf.

Top transects: Denbies Landbarn B, Box Hill.

Life cycle: bivoltine; winters as larva. Emergence dates affected by weather, with poor summers usually producing low autumn numbers. From Surrey observations (2011-12) the second brood may be partial in some years, with July larvae having the potential to hibernate early and not pupate. This has yet to be proven, but even after a disastrous second brood, adults can be surprisingly numerous in the following spring.

Females, especially in the second brood, lay in warmer situations than those selected by the Chalkhill Blue. Adonis eggs are often on the upperside of the horseshoe vetch leaf at the petiole (where the leaf joins the stem) and easier to find than those of the Chalkhill. In May and June females avoid the hottest spots and deposit on cooler plants. Larvae mature by mid-July and pupate to produce a late-summer brood. Larvae from second-brood females overwinter at the base of horseshoe vetch plants and resume feeding the following spring. They are tended by *Myrmica* or *Lasius* ants, like Chalkhill larvae, and can be located by searching for ant activity rather than the camouflaged larva. I was able to photograph one wild pupa by carefully opening the mud chamber that ants had constructed around it. Males take nutrition from faeces and urine.

Larval foodplants: exclusively horseshoe vetch.

Adonis Blue male on bird's-foot-trefoil. **GW**

THE Adonis Blue ranks second only to the Wood White as a Surrey rarity. It is similarly dependent on the management of a restricted and specialised habitat, making it both vulnerable and a challenge to conservationists toiling to preserve its populations.

Fortunately, most remaining and potentially future Adonis habitat, including Denbies Hillside, is owned by the National Trust. I have advised on this site since 1970, and my comments here reflect my long-term monitoring of this important location.

The Adonis thrives in sward of 1-6cm, which can be controlled through grazing. Domestic stock used at Denbies has included escaping goats, Exmoor ponies, various breeds of sheep and, most recently, cattle. Despite this variety, the Adonis Blue persists, albeit currently in low numbers, and grazing procedures need regular assessment to ensure appropriate conditions are maintained.

Significantly, one of the most stable compartments at Denbies for the Adonis Blue and other species, including the Silver-spotted Skipper, has not been domestically grazed for many years. This area is probably maintained by a stable rabbit population and this natural procedure is recommended as a fall-back option.

In the light of the work of Roy and Thomas (2003), grazing to produce a uniformly short turf for both broods is no longer recommended. They found that first-brood females avoided the shortest, hottest turf, and laid in cooler sites with a maximum turf height of around 6cm. This provided a wider choice of egg-laying sites. In contrast, second-brood females selected sites only in the warmest micro-climates.

A grazing regime that provides short turf in March and April, with little or no grazing from May to late July, is now prescribed. This will help defoliated horseshoe vetch to recover in time for the summer brood of Adonis Blue females to deposit their eggs, and allow other downland plants to flower and seed. Grazing should resume from late July, aiming for an average turf height of 3cm.

Adonis Blue *continued* **Ken Willmott**

Adonis Blue larva attended by Myrmica ants. **BH**

Our challenge is to maintain a suitable habitat for the Adonis Blue without adversely affecting other species through under- or over-grazing. The latter is apparently linked to a decline in Lulworth Skipper numbers on Adonis Blue sites in Dorset.

The Adonis Blue range along the North Downs has certainly contracted within the past three decades. Some sites that supported Adonis and Chalkhill Blue in the early 1990s have subsequently lost both species, together with horseshoe vetch. I can only suggest that the loss of the host plant was connected to drought conditions and the high rabbit population.

Successful, lasting introductions are uncommon. They should be attempted only as a final resort, after exhaustive research, and after all attempts to encourage natural recolonisation have failed. The safety of the donor colony should be assured and permission obtained from the landowner before the beginning of such a project.

The Adonis Blue has twice been introduced to Old Winchester Hill in Hampshire. In 1981, 65 adults were released and the colony survived until 1989. In 2002, under the auspices of English Nature (now Natural England), another introduction was attempted. Despite a grazing scheme and other preparations, the butterfly was last seen in 2008 – two in the summer and six in the autumn.

There are Adonis strongholds in Hampshire, Isle of Wight, Dorset and Wiltshire; Sussex and Kent have good numbers, with the Chiltern Hills being its northern limit.

Phenology trend	**1990-2012**	earlier by 1.5 weeks	
Best transect day 2000-12	May 27, 2005	Denbies Landbarn B	600
Transects abundance	**1990-2012** gain 201%	**2000-2012** loss 14%	
UK transects abundance	**1979-2012** gain 146%	**10-year trend** loss 46%	
UK 4,361 10k squares	**2005-09** 125 = 3%	**10-year trend** gain 30%	

Flight weeks ▲High transect counts △Middle ^Low

Apr					May				Jun				Jul					Aug				Sep			
1	8	15	22	29	6	13	20	27	3	10	17	24	1	8	15	22	29	5	12	19	26	2	9	16	23
				△	△	△	▲	▲	▲	△	△	^	^		^	△	^	△	△	▲	▲	△	△	△	^

Adonis Blue pair, browner female on left, on salad burnet. **HC**

Adonis Blue
weekly transect counts

Denbies Landbarn B TQ135499 **Gail Jeffcoate, Robert Cramp**

	WEEK	2000	2001	2002	2003	2004	2005	2006	2007	2008	2009	2010	2011	2012
29 April	5			-		-	-	-	3	-	-		70	-
6 May	6				-	-	-	-	**18**	-	5	-	**100**	-
13	7			6	14	2	-	3	1	1		-	46	
20	8			29	40	160	399		2	9	22	217	49	80
27	9			**43**	44	**279**	**600**	296	-	12	10	**222**	5	**120**
3 June	10				18	160	208	**318**	2	**17**	5	152	3	8
10	11			11	-	44	141	155		5	-	18	-	1
17	12			1	-	-	21	72	-	-	-	8		-
24	13			1	1	-	1	-	-	-	1	-	-	1
1 July	14			-	-	-	-	-	-	-	-	-	-	
8	15			-	-	-	-	-	-	-	-	-	-	-
15	16			-	-	-	-	-	-	-		-	-	
22	17			-	-	-	-	-	-	-	-		-	-
29	18				11	-	-	1	-		-		-	-
5 August	19			-	27	95		1	-	4	6	10	14	-
12	20			-	72	164	23	13	-	1	**84**	39	43	1
19	21			30	**97**	203	298	26			52	62	40	3
26	22			25	64	44	156	22	-	7	24	67	11	4
2 September	23			8	12	47	111	4	3	4	3	48		7
9	24			2	8	32	35	5	-	2		2	3	7
16	25			1	-	8	8	1	-	2	3	2	1	-
23	26			-	-	-	3	-	-	-	-	2	-	-
Abundance index				178	408	1238	2005	920	36	76	250	849	397	232
Weeks recorded				**11**	**12**	**12**	**13**	**13**	**6**	**11**	**11**	**13**	**12**	**10**

Holly Blue *Celastrina argiolus* **Ken Willmott**

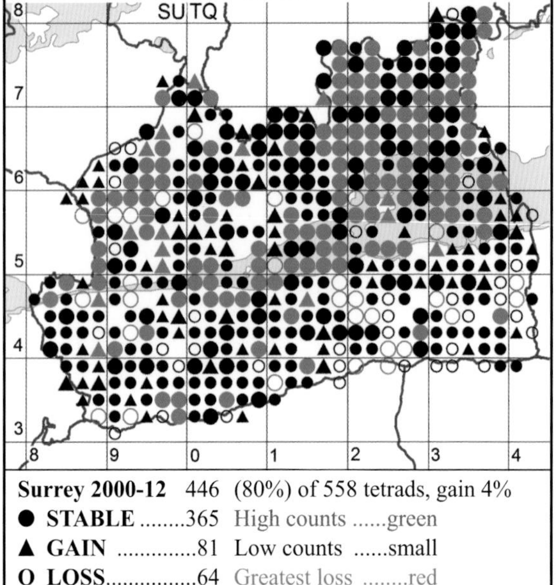

Surrey status: common; population expansion and contraction linked to that of host-specific parasitoid wasp, *Listrodromus nycthemerus*. Fluctuations must also be influenced by effect of weather patterns on the fecundity of both spring and summer females.

Flies: mid-April to June; July to September.

Trends: stable; can be a late March butterfly in a favourable spring.

Wingspan: 26-34mm.

Identification: sexually and seasonally dimorphic. Male is silvery blue, with traces of lilac, and thin black marginal line; fringe is chequered black and white. Female is usually a darker blue; black margin, broad and extended, is widest and darkest at the apex, which in summer-brood females increases in size and depth of colour; her hindwing has marginal black spotting, more intense in second brood. Second-brood males show slight increase in the marginal line and are perhaps a little darker blue. Undersides are pale blue, almost white, with black flecks, affording excellent camouflage among shiny holly leaves.

Variations/aberrations: amount of black on female upperside is variable; blue, particularly on males, can be paler.

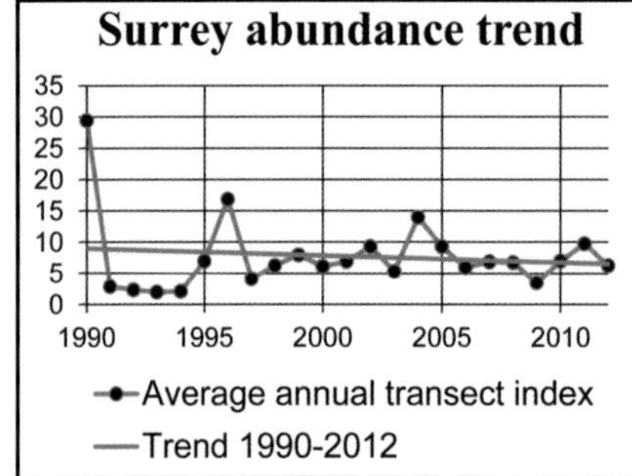

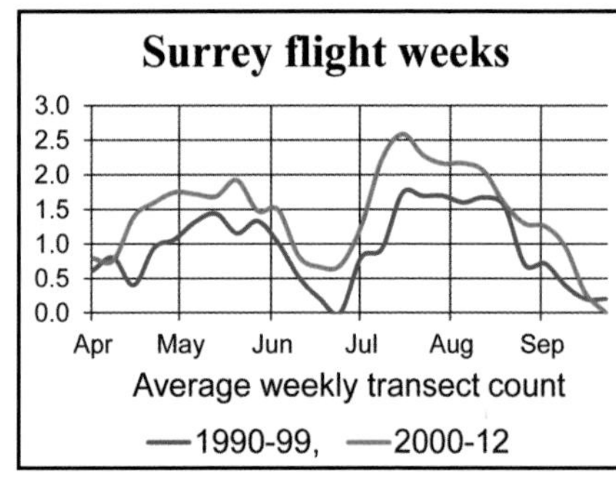

Holly Blue on ragwort. **MB**

Confusion species: habitat and underside different from brighter Common Blue; underside of Small Blue has spots rather than flecks. Any blue butterfly flying above head height in the garden or scrubby areas is likely to be a Holly Blue. Most other Blues are low-fliers.

Habitat: well-loved garden and parkland butterfly; frequents churchyards, woodland, downland, heathland and even the city. In 2011 I saw one flying towards Covent Garden market over a throng of people and traffic.

Top transects: London Wetland Centre, Wimbledon Common, Pewley Down.

Other key sites: Kew Gardens, RHS Garden Wisley, churchyards including Leatherhead, John Innes Recreation Ground SW19 (part of Merton Park Conservation Area).

Life cycle: bivoltine; winters as pupa. Males establish territories, but appear to employ the two regular sexual strategies: perching to await arrival of females, and patrolling. These strategies may be linked to unreliable April weather or protandry (females emerge notably later than males). Females lay throughout May on the unopened flower buds of several shrubs, primarily holly, which is dioecious (male and female reproductive organs on separate individuals of the same species). On male trees the larva feeds on the tender new terminal leaves; on female trees it feeds on the green berries. The summer brood, which Frohawk (1924) suggested is partial in some years, has a protracted emergence and resulting females lay almost exclusively on the unopened flower buds of ivy. The larva burrows its head into the flower bud and devours the contents, as did the earlier brood with holly, leaving a tell-tale hole. Autumn pupae, which have been found among tangled ivy roots and suckers, overwinter from late September through to the following spring; summer pupae hatch within 21 days.

Larval foodplants: holly (1st brood), ivy (2nd brood); I can also confirm cotoneaster, box, alder buckthorn, ling, dogwood.

ON the first warm day of April I usually visit a large holly tree in Leatherhead churchyard. If the Holly Blue is on the wing it always heads for this particular tree, which is in sunshine from mid-morning to early afternoon. It has become a "master tree", with sun orientation being the most important factor, allowing the butterfly to raise its body temperature to 32-35ºC in order to fly successfully. The Leatherhead tree is a great indicator of the first day of the Holly Blue season.

Holly Blue *continued* **Ken Willmott**

Even more striking are the July Holly Blues that choose as their summer master tree an old gnarled hawthorn at a high point on Bookham Common, where males regularly perch and jostle. High in the canopy above them is the Purple Emperor territory. These master trees attract males not only of these two species but also of Speckled Wood and Red Admiral, in a congregation guaranteed every year along High Point Path.

Holly Blue: spring female. **GE**

The host-specific parasitoid, *Listrodromus nycthemerus*, is an ichneumon wasp with a yellow and black body and legs. Look out for this wasp in August on unopened flower buds of ivy, jiggling its antennae, and seeking the tiny first-instar larvae into which it injects its eggs. The larva matures into a pupa from which the wasp emerges instead of the butterfly.

From a substantial number of larvae collected by Richard Revels in Bedfordshire in the early 1990s the number of wasps emerging from pupae of both broods increased from 8% to 99%, clearly showing how Holly Blue populations can go from boom to bust. In September 2012 I could find no evidence of eggs or larvae on an expanse of ivy near Leatherhead Church, but only two *Listrodromus nycthemerus* wasps scanning the flower buds.

Spring females need unopened flower buds of holly, and the irregular timing of the bud-burst can impact on female activity. They always lay on the thick green bud sheath, which will not fall to the ground. If the holly flowers too early, females will have to spend more time, sometimes in short spells of April sunshine, searching for unopened flowers.

My early observations led me to believe that larvae would only be successful on a female, berry-producing tree. My marked eggs all failed to mature on male trees, but the sample was too small and it was Ernie Pollard (who devised the transect recording method) who located larvae on male holly trees, feeding on the tender new terminal leaves.

The Holly Blue larva, despite not being found at ground level, and indeed sometimes at a height of 2-3 metres, is attended by *Myrmica* (red) and *Lasius* (black) ants. It has three colour forms, the most common being entirely green with a black shiny head (invisible when feeding on berries!). The second form has a basic green colour, with discontinuous maroon stripes on its sides and back. The most attractive form shows a deep rose-pink in continuous stripes and is similar to the larva of the Small Copper.

Holly Blue

weekly transect counts

London Wetland Centre TQ228770

Richard Bullock

	WEEK	2000	2001	2002	2003	2004	2005	2006	2007	2008	2009	2010	2011	2012
1 April	1	-	-	2	1	-	1	-	1	-	-	-	2	3
8	2		-	1	1	-	3	-	1	-	-	-	4	2
15	3	-	-	3	2	-	3	1	**6**	-	1	1	**6**	-
22	4	-	1	5	1	2	4	2	3	3	**3**	2	5	
29	5	2	1	2	1	2	**7**	2	4	4	2	-		2
6 May	6	2	1	1	2	1	4	2	2	2	2	1	3	1
13	7	3	2	3	1	3	2	1	-	**6**	1	1	-	2
20	8	1	-	-	-	3	1	-	-	2	-	2	-	**6**
27	9	1	-	1	-	1	2	-	-	1	-	1	-	4
3 June	10	-		-	-	-	-	-	-	-	-	-	-	
10	11	-	-	-	-	-	-	-	-	-	-	-	-	-
17	12	-	-	-	-	-	-	-	2	-	-	-	1	-
24	13	-	-	-	1	-	-	-		-	-	-	4	-
1 July	14	-	-	-	2	2	-	-	1	2	-	-	2	-
8	15		-	1	2	4	2	2	1	2	-	**3**	3	1
15	16	5	4	4	**4**	**7**	5	2	4	2	1	2	5	3
22	17	**8**	3	5	2	5	4	**3**	3	3	1	2	3	2
29	18	**8**	**11**	4	3	6	3	**3**	2	5	1	1		
5 August	19	7	3	**8**	1	4	5	1	1	3	-	2	2	3
12	20	4	6	3	1	3	3	1	2		1		1	1
19	21	2	3	1	1	1	1	-	1	2	1		1	-
26	22	1	2	-	2	-	3	-		1	-	1	1	-
2 September	23	1	1	1	1	1	1	-	-	-	-	1	-	1
9	24	2	-	-	1	1	-	-	-	-	-	-	-	-
16	25	-	-	-	1	-	-	-		-	-	-	-	-
Abundance index		50	38	46	31	44	54	21	38	40	14	NI	49	36
Weeks recorded		**14**	**12**	**16**	**20**	**16**	**18**	**11**	**15**	**14**	**10**	**13**	**15**	**13**

Phenology trend	**1990-2012**	earlier by 1.5 weeks	
Best transect day 2000-12	Aug 14, 2004	Sheepleas	18
Transects abundance	**1990-2012** loss 27%	**2000-2012** loss 14%	
UK transects abundance	**1976-2012** gain 145%	**10-year trend** loss 23%	
UK 4,361 10k squares	**2005-09** 1,409 = 32%	**10-year trend** loss 3%	

Flight weeks ▲High transect counts △Middle ^Low

Apr					May				Jun				Jul					Aug				Sep			
1	8	15	22	29	6	13	20	27	3	10	17	24	1	8	15	22	29	5	12	19	26	2	9	16	23
^	^	△	△	△	△	△	△	△	△	^	^	^	△	▲	▲	▲	▲	▲	▲	△	△	△	△	^	

White Admiral *Limenitis camilla*

Ken Willmott

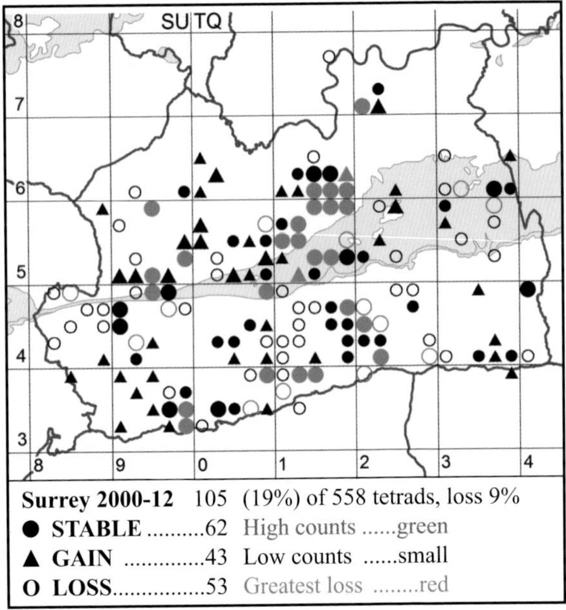

Surrey status: resident in most larger, suitable woodlands.
Flies: mid-June to August.
Conservation:
UK Biodiversity Action Plan priority species;
BC 2010 Red List: vulnerable.
Trends: expanding range but subject to population fluctuations, particularly in poor May and June weather when the larvae are exposed to predation for a longer period. Egg-laying can also be reduced during a dull, cool July, resulting in fewer larvae to face the rigours of winter. Emergence has advanced well into June in recent years, usually correlating with the flowering of bramble, the primary nectar source.
Wingspan: male 54-64mm, female 58-66mm.
Identification: sizeable black butterfly with white wing bands (broken on forewings) that inspired its naval name. When fresh, the larger female has russet patches above the dark spotting on the hindwing inner angle and near the apex. Spectacular underside has white bands surrounded by copious orange, spotted with black.
Variations/aberrations: renowned for its aberrations, with excessive black scales covering the white bands, making a most unusual sight in flight. Ab. *obliterae* is partially melanistic; the rarer ab. *nigrina* is all black. These aberrations have been frequent on Bookham Common, but are rare when the population is low, as it was in 2012 when I saw only one *obliterae*.

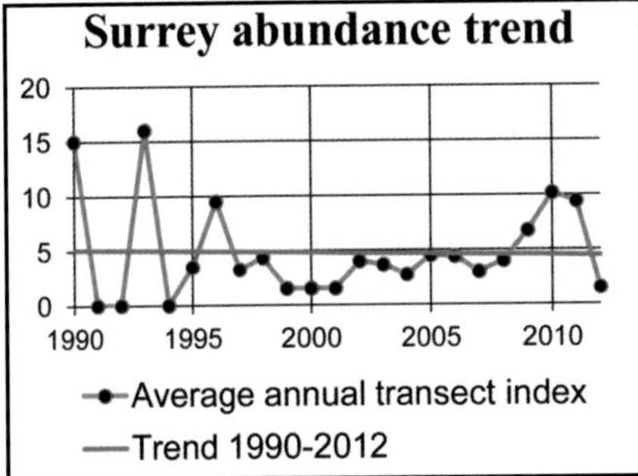

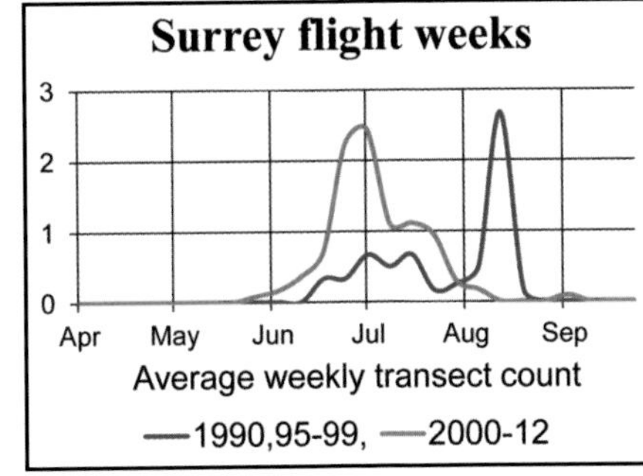

White Admiral. **KW**

Confusion species: Purple Emperor is larger and has orange spot near inner angle of upper hindwing; male Emperor has purple/blue sheen on upperside.

Habitat: deciduous high forest with a wealth of honeysuckle growing in dappled shade; honeysuckle in a sunny situation is shunned. White Admiral survives within conifer plantations until the dappled shade deteriorates into cooler full shade, and maintains smaller populations in suitable remnant, deciduous, high forest within commercial woodland complexes, such as Chiddingfold Forest.

Top transects: Epsom Common, Oaken Wood, Ashtead Common.

Other key sites: Bookham Common, Holmwood Common and Highridge Wood, Whitmoor Common.

Life cycle: univoltine; winters as larva. Males patrol lower branches of oaks in sunshine, attempting to locate a female that has just emerged from tangled honeysuckle in dappled shade. Females deposit a single egg on the edge of a honeysuckle leaf; it hatches a week later. The tiny larva creates a platform at the very tip of the leaf, eating the soft parts either side of the midrib, which then acts as its resting place to which it always returns after feeding. Both larva and platform become adorned with frass, which greatly enhances the camouflage of the larva.

In early September, after moulting twice, the larva builds a hibernaculum. Firstly it secures the stalk of the honeysuckle leaf onto the woody stem with silk, to prevent it falling to the ground during the winter. It then constructs an envelope by biting through one side of the leaf and pulling it across to the other before securing it with silk. The larva then hibernates until the following March/April, when it begins feeding on the fresh leaves. It moults twice more before pupating in early June, underneath a leaf or on the woody stems. It hatches a fortnight or so later.

Larval foodplants: exclusively honeysuckle.

White Admiral *continued*

Ken Willmott

A 1970s study by Ernie Pollard found a correlation between White Admiral abundance and temperatures in June, when the larvae are ready to pupate. If their development was expedited by fine weather, their period as larvae and pupae was shortened and they were therefore less available for bird predation, leading to a more successful emergence.

White Admiral final instar larva on honeysuckle. **KW**

My own studies of the White Admiral at Bookham Common and Chiddingfold Forest (conservation and commercial forest habitats, as contrasting settings) have shown remarkable instances of population crashes followed by considerable increases, mostly due to differing spring and summer weather conditions. The great storms of 1987 and 1990 did not bode well for a species that requires dappled shade for the females to lay on the spindly honeysuckle growths. Unlike other woodland butterflies, such as the Pearl-bordered Fritillary and Wood White, the White Admiral does not choose the wider, sunny rides and open spaces. It prefers the less disturbed areas, as long as rides and tracks are not too shaded or narrow and there is some sunny bramble growth.

The severe decline of the Pearl-bordered Fritillary was hastened by the abandonment of the coppice industry, but this proved beneficial to the White Admiral. Lessons should be learned from this: never overdo the creation of clearances, nor allow shaded conditions to continue through neglect. The removal of a single, large tree along a ride can make a considerable difference to the light/shade ratio. If the woodland area is large enough, a balance should be struck to maintain the populations of species that require sunny conditions and those that need dappled shade. It is imperative to cater for the precise needs of both these woodland specialists.

In Chiddingfold Forest the harvesting of conifer plantations created spaces that initially deterred White Admirals. As new plantations matured, after some ten years growth, the sun-loving butterflies declined. They were replaced by the White Admiral, which now thrives along the wider, timber-extraction routes as the honeysuckle climbs among the trunks of Corsican pine, creating the dappled shade that they seek. Eventually there will be too much shade even for the White Admiral; as temperatures around the honeysuckle

Phenology trend	**1990-2012**	earlier by 3.5 weeks	
Best transect day 2000-12	Jul 4, 2010	Epsom Common	19
Transects abundance	**1990-2012** loss 13%	**2000-2012** gain 252%	
UK transects abundance	**1976-2012** loss 57%	**10-year trend** loss 44%	
UK 4,361 10k squares	**2005-09** 428 = 10%	**10-year trend** gain 14%	

White Admiral male on bramble. **GW**

drop, the butterfly will seek other remnant habitats.

Similarly, the White Admiral will abandon honeysuckle opened up to the full sun by the removal of nearby scrub and oak. Thinning operations must take this into account. In contrast to the White Admiral, the rare, day-flying Broad-bordered Bee Hawk-moth prefers honeysuckle in a sunny location. Maintaining honeysuckle growth in diverse habitats is vital to the success of such specialist species.

I have monitored White Admirals in a particular woodland ride on Bookham Common for several years, checking numbers against weather records. This helps management planning. When the population is low, there should be less intervention where the supporting honeysuckle environment is prolific. The measurement of light values where females are laying offers useful information for the development of egg-laying sites, but must be conducted on days of continuous sunshine when the results will be more conclusive. Egg-laying females fly deliberately among the shady honeysuckles and can be easily monitored on a suitable sunny day.

Current populations of White Admirals in Surrey are low due to the record-breaking cool, wet summer of 2012. The species made a remarkable recovery from record low numbers in the 1980s and I am hopeful it will do so again, given that suitable habitat remains. Weather predictions for an increase in extreme events and the threat from ash dieback, *Chalara fraxinea*, threaten to change our woodland habitats. This must pose a threat to White Admiral stability, as sun will replace the shade of the ash trees.

White Admiral *continued*

White Admiral — weekly transect counts

Oaken Wood, Chiddingfold SU990338 — **John Buckley**

	WEEK	2000	2001	2002	2003	2004	2005	2006	2007	2008	2009	2010	2011	2012
27 May	9	-	-	-	-	-	-	-	-	-	-	-	1	-
3 June	10	-	-	-	-	-	-	-	-	-	-	-	2	
10	11	-	-	-	-	-	-	-	-	-	-	-	3	-
17	12	-	-	-	-	-	-	-	1	1	-	-	2	-
24	13	-	-	1	3	1	1	6	-	2	2	7	2	-
1 July	14	-	-	2	4	2	4	3	-	-	1	6	-	
8	15	-	-	-	-	2	-	3	1	-	1	5	2	
15	16	1	-	-	-	1	-	2	2	1	1	5	-	
22	17	1	2	-	-	-	-	-	-	2	-	3	-	1
29	18	-	-	-	2	-	-	-	-	1	-	1	-	-
5 August	19	-	-	1	-	-	-	-	-	-	-	-	-	-
Abundance index		2	2	4	9	6	5	13	4	7	6	NI	12	NI
Weeks recorded		**2**	**1**	**3**	**3**	**4**	**2**	**4**	**3**	**5**	**4**	**6**	**6**	**1**

Epsom Common TQ189605 — **Alison Gilry**

	WEEK	2000	2001	2002	2003	2004	2005	2006	2007	2008	2009	2010	2011	2012
3 June	10										-		3	
10	11										-		5	-
17	12										-	-	5	-
24	13										7		8	-
1 July	14										5	19	2	
8	15										1	6	2	
15	16										1	3	-	
22	17										-	2	1	2
Abundance index											15	30	24	NI
Weeks recorded											**4**	**4**	**7**	**1**

Flight weeks — ▲High transect counts △Middle ^Low

Apr					May				Jun				Jul					Aug				Sep			
1	8	15	22	29	6	13	20	27	3	10	17	24	1	8	15	22	29	5	12	19	26	2	9	16	23
								^	△	△	△	▲	▲	△	▲	△	△	△				^			

Purple Emperor *Apatura iris*

Ken Willmott

Surrey status: elusive, high-flying, canopy species. Probably occurs in most suitable woodlands but difficult to monitor (not suited to transects).

Flies: late June to late July and beyond if emergence delayed by poor weather.

Conservation: protected from sale; BC 2010 Red List: near-threatened.

Trends: stable.

Wingspan: male 70-78mm, female 76-92mm.

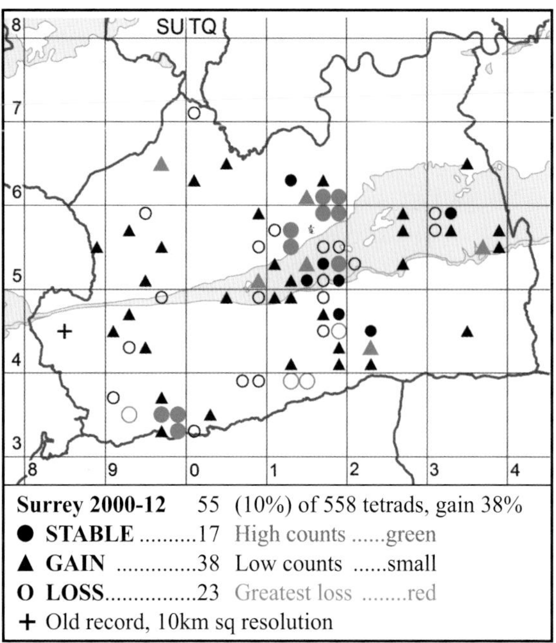

Identification: smaller male is unmistakable with its purple/blue sheen, visible on all four wings if viewed at certain angles to the sun. The sheen is often only partially seen and photographs may show no purple at all, just dark brown or black with white bars on both fore- and hindwings. There is an embellishment of orange in the form of an eyespot near the inner angle of the hindwing and variably scattered elsewhere, especially along the front margin of the forewing. Females can be notably bigger, with larger white bands and marks on the upperside; they show no trace of the purple sheen.

Variations/aberrations: similar to those found in the White Admiral – a diminution of the white bands and marks on the wings due to excessive covering with black/brown wing scales (melanism), possibly in response to low temperatures at a critical time in the pupal state (possibly when soft and vulnerable after shedding larval skin).

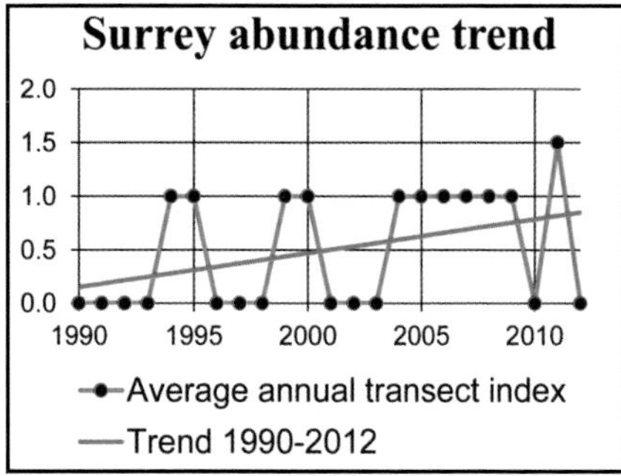

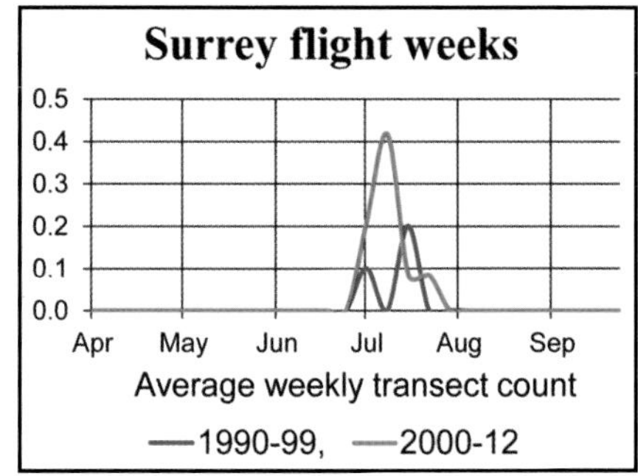

Purple Emperor *continued* **Ken Willmott**

The semi-black ab. *iolata* and the all-black ab. *lugenda* are the most well-known aberrations. Matthew Oates (National Trust) has photographed the ultimate all-black variety in central England; only two have been recorded at Surrey's Bookham Common during the last four decades of observation.

Confusion species: White Admiral, which comes to ground less often, has more rounded forewings. In-flight White Admirals rarely occupy the Emperor's high canopy and glide among the trees at a lower elevation. The Emperor has a more powerful "jizz".

Habitat: deciduous high forest with a wealth of larval food plants, wide rides and clearings. It will also inhabit partly-coniferous woodland that has remnants of deciduous forest, as at Chiddingfold, where females will lay on surviving sallows for several years until they are finally shaded out.

Key sites: Bookham Common, Ashtead Common, Chiddingfold Forest, Sheepleas.

Life cycle: univoltine; winters as larva after moulting twice, feeding again the following spring, normally in early April but variable depending on the timing of bud expansion and leaf break on the sallows; pupates from mid-May onwards.

Larval foodplants: goat willow (*Salix caprea*; broad-leaved), grey willow (*Salix cinerea*; narrower-leaved) and their hybrids, collectively known as sallow; also crack willow (*Salix fragilis*). *Salix* species are difficult to separate, but these three are well used by Surrey Purple Emperors.

Feeding: there is a Surrey record (J M Tucker) of one perched on the flowers of sweet chestnut. Otherwise they enjoy a variety of animal faeces, with dog and fox the most popular and horse the least. They are also attracted to sap runs (mostly wounded oak) and sometimes can be seen at such sites in threes and fours, agitating wasps, flies, Red Admirals, Commas and Speckled Woods.

THREE "events" in adult behaviour in July give opportunities to find Purple Emperors. The first is when freshly emerged males descend to the ground seeking mineral salts, which they lose when fertilising females. They use a variety of sources, animal faeces being the most common. A wounded, sticky, sweet-smelling oak can also attract several adults, which can target even small wounds from a considerable distance.

The greatest chance of an observation is on a warm, cloudless day, up to 7pm but rarely before 9am. Morning, 9.30-11.30am, is the best time to observe the phenomenon of grounded males and is dependent on weather conditions. It is unusual to find them after midday. A 6.30pm sighting in Wiltshire in 1984 followed a mostly cool and cloudy day. The first week or two after emergence is the period to target; otherwise, this activity ceases as many males will have mated and no longer need to replenish mineral salts.

The second opportunity to locate Purple Emperors is at their "master trees", where males congregate to establish their territory high in the canopy. This is not exclusively on tall oaks. Study an Ordnance Survey map with woodland in mind and concentrate on the contour lines to find the highest points in your search area. A GPS is also an important tool, not only to record your grid reference but also to confirm height.

In brief, the sexual strategy of the Purple Emperor male is to establish a territory and

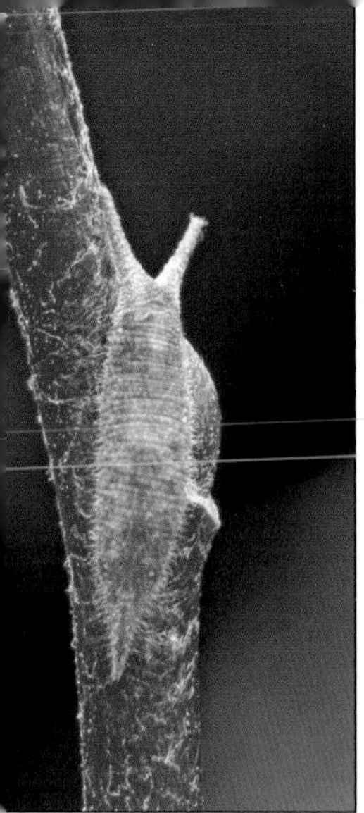

Purple Emperor wintering larva. **BH**

Male taking minerals. **FK**

await the arrival of a female. Males of several British butterflies use the same strategy, known as perching, or hilltopping. Research in the USA showed a high percentage of females captured on hilltop territories were virgins, while fertilised females stayed away.

In some localities the sexual strategy of Purple Emperor has been known to change, with males seeking presumably freshly-emerged females on appropriate sallow trees. This "patrolling" strategy is rarely seen in Surrey but on one notable occasion I encountered a grounded female (a relatively rare find) on Bookham Common below a fine goat willow. She had obviously emerged that morning and her maiden flight was somewhat weak. After becoming a film star for half an hour, she took to the air again and landed close by on a young oak facing the grassy ride. This was at 11am, a time when males are eager to make their way to the high ground.

A male arrived on the scene and soared up and down the ride several times in a short period, each time passing the resting female, but never showing interest or awareness. There seemed to be no visual or olfactory processes in action and both eventually went their separate ways.

The Hill Farm territory on Bookham Common (see site account on page 190) has survived for over 30 years and is still one of the best places in the country to observe

Purple Emperor *continued* **Ken Willmott**

territorial behaviour. This survival is despite the vagaries of the British weather, including the two great storms of 1987 and 1990, which impacted on the Purple Emperor territories and its *Salix spp.* larval foodplants. Bookham Common is thought to produce one of England's earliest emergences, but it is still variable: e.g. 2011 – June 14; 2012 – June 29; 2013 – July 8. Such accurate information is due to the ease of access and observation at the Hill Farm territory, which is cared for by the National Trust warden.

In 1983 chasing groups of nine and three were observed in one vista across the canopy gap in the territory, with the larger group being led by the all-black variety ab. *lugenda*. This has never been repeated and the most common modern vista is between three and six, depending on the success of the season.

The third and perhaps most inspirational observation opportunity is when a huge female glides into the depths of a sallow tree to lay eggs. The majority of eggs are deposited high up, but a small proportion may be within hand's reach, and these are findable with careful searching and without the need to damage the sallow. An egg-laying spree by an individual female can produce a number of eggs on a single sallow - one in Hampshire had a dozen.

The female selects a sallow leaf in full or dappled shade but will cease laying on the disappearance of sunshine. One of the lowest found eggs, in Chiddingfold Forest, was on a windblown goat willow. I watched the female laying at knee height (0.5-1.0m).

At Bookham Common on July 22, 1986, I marked an egg within four hours of its being laid; it hatched 16 days later on August 7. Many believe that good weather in July, leading to a large number of eggs being laid, means a bumper year will follow. This is not necessarily the case, as flocks of foraging tits become more expert at finding eggs and young larvae when many are available. A poor year for egg-production means that birds are unable to find them so easily.

First-instar larvae do not possess the iconic horns that appear after the first moult. A second moult occurs before the larva enters hibernation in late October or early November, depending on the weather conditions. Pre- and post-hibernation larvae position themselves at the very tip of a sallow leaf with a distinctive arched resting pose. The larva travels down the midrib of its "seat" leaf to eat portions of both edges, making a clear feeding pattern. The earlier searching is undertaken, the greater chance of success, as larvae suffer high mortality before hibernation.

Hibernation sites vary, favourites being the fork of a twig or pressed up against a newly formed leaf bud. The larva emerges from hibernation early the following April as the sallow leaves begin to expand and burst. The magnificent final-instar larva, which has changed its skin twice more since hibernation, can crawl some distance from its final feeding leaf. It then pupates on the underside of a sallow leaf between mid-May and mid-June, again depending on April-May temperatures and location.

The Purple Emperor's southern distribution ranges from south Wiltshire and Hampshire, in the west, to Surrey, West Sussex and Kent in the east. Central England distribution includes Oxfordshire and Hertfordshire, where new locations have been discovered. Northamptonshire is much visited by Purple Emperor worshippers.

Purple Emperor male taking minerals. **BH**

Purple Emperor		weeks with English transect record											
	WEEK	2000	2001	2002	2003	2004	2005	2006	2007	2008	2009	2010	2011	2012
17 June	12								✓					
24	13					✓		✓	✓	✓	✓		✓	
1 July	14		✓		✓	✓	✓	✓	✓	✓	✓	✓	✓	✓
8	15	✓	✓		✓	✓	✓	✓	✓	✓	✓	✓	✓	✓
15	16	✓	✓	✓	✓	✓	✓	✓	✓	✓	✓	✓	✓	✓
22	17	✓	✓	✓		✓	✓	✓	✓	✓	✓	✓	✓	✓
29	18	✓	✓	✓	✓	✓	✓	✓			✓			✓
5 August	19		✓			✓					✓	✓		✓
12	20													✓
Weeks recorded		4	6	3	4	7	5	6	6	5	7	5	5	7

Phenology trend	**1990-2012**	insufficient data	
Best transect day 2000-12	Jul 2, 2011	Chobham Common NE	2
Transects abundance	**1990-2012**	insufficient data	
UK transects abundance	**1979-2012** gain 43%	**10-year trend** loss 55%	
UK 4,361 10k squares	**2005-09** 131 = 3%	**10-year trend** gain 44%	

Flight weeks (all records)																									▲High counts △Middle ^Low
Apr					May				Jun				Jul					Aug				Sep			
1	*8*	*15*	*22*	*29*	*6*	*13*	*20*	*27*	*3*	*10*	*17*	*24*	*1*	*8*	*15*	*22*	*29*	*5*	*12*	*19*	*26*	*2*	*9*	*16*	*23*
											^	△	▲	▲	▲	▲	△	△	^						

Red Admiral *Vanessa atalanta* — Ken Willmott

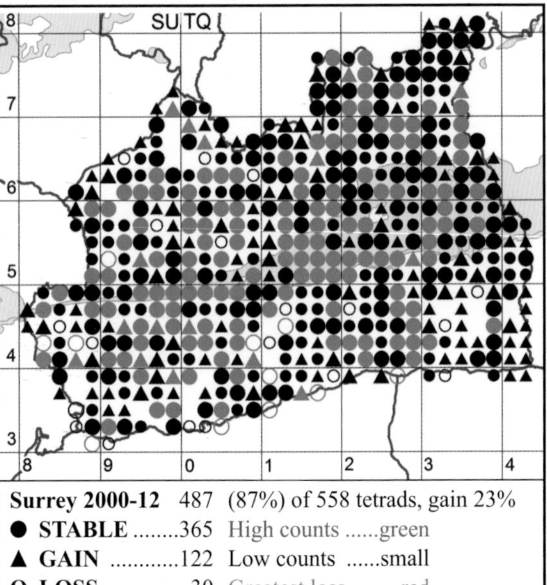

Surrey status: common migrant in fluctuating numbers and now a proven British hibernator; variable percentages engage in a return autumn migration; wintering larvae recorded as surviving the British winter.

Flies: almost throughout the year, especially from sunny March days into November, via combination of hibernators, migrants and summer emergents; more ready to fly in low temperatures than other hibernating vanessids; peaks July and autumn.

Trends: varies annually, according to severity of winter (for overwintering success rate) or clemency of spring and early summer (for migrants).

Wingspan: male 64-72mm, female 70-78mm.

Identification: a large, dark butterfly in rapid flight; forewing has bright-red band, with white markings in the apical area; marginal area of hindwing also has a red band with black spots, plus a blue patch closest to the body. The ornate underside is multi-coloured in bright light, but more sombre in dull conditions, allowing good camouflage for roosting and hibernating. Only when the forewings are raised does the band on the forewing upperside become visible from beneath.

Variations/aberrations: approximately one in six Red Admirals has a white spot within the red band on the forewing. Aberrations are mostly confined to the tone of the red, ranging to straw yellow, ab. *flavescens*. In ab. *fracta* the red bands are discontinuous.

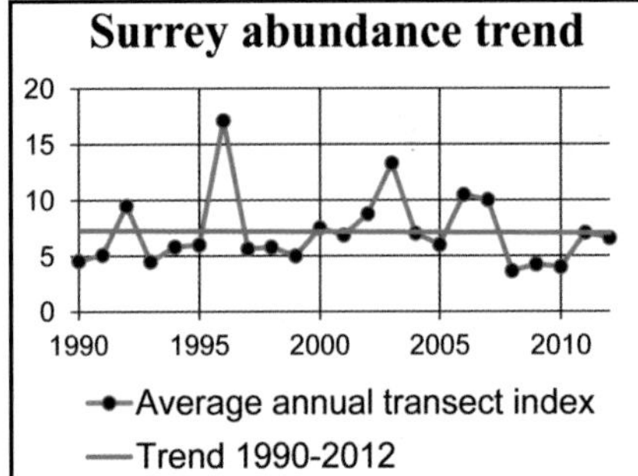

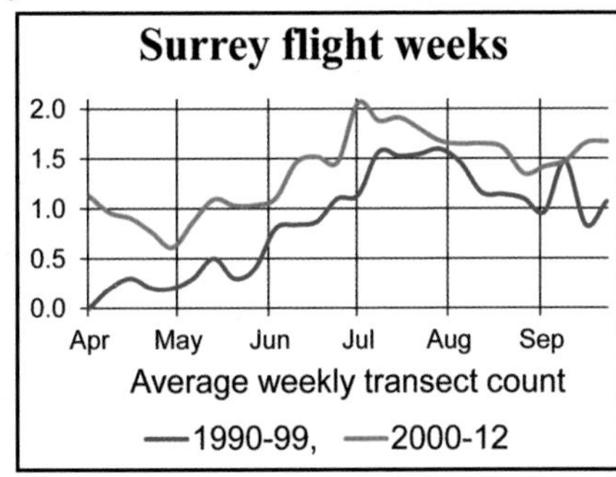

Red Admiral on bramble leaf. **FK**

Confusion species: none.

Habitat: diverse; a common garden butterfly in late summer and autumn. Early spring adults, especially males, are particularly frequent in woodland. Fertile females can be seen virtually anywhere with nettles.

Top transects: London Wetland Centre, Sheepleas, Wimbledon Common.

Life cycle: a single egg is deposited on the upperside of a nettle leaf. The developing larva constructs an abode by drawing leaves together with silken threads. As the larva matures these structures become larger and consist of more than a single leaf. The fully grown larva chews the main stem of the plant, causing it to collapse onto the larger leaves below to create a pupal chamber, again secured by silk. This provides enough space for the pupa to hang, and the adult to crawl from the chamber to dry out and expand its wings. Eggs hatch in 10 days. The larva can mature in just 23 days and the pupa hatches in 2-3 weeks, subject to ambient temperatures. However larvae suffer high mortality and are vulnerable to parasitoids in their early stages, especially when they need to construct a new abode. The journey from egg to butterfly takes about 50 days.

Larval foodplants: common nettle; less frequently small nettle, pellitory-of-the-wall, hop.

Feeding: as well as flowers, the Red Admiral enjoys sap-runs from wounded trees, especially oaks, and fallen apples in late autumn – visit RHS Garden Wisley.

Red Admiral *continued* **Ken Willmott**

THE Red Admiral's ability to hibernate in Britain was discussed by Frohawk (1924) based on records from the early 1900s, and more recently by Collins (1995) and Tucker (1997).

Collins admitted that hibernation may occur occasionally, but suggested that examples in March and April might equally represent early immigration. He was also convinced that the Red Admiral's survival here was dependent on continual migration.

There is now much evidence that Red Admiral overwintering in Britain is becoming commonplace, at least in south-east England. As climate change impacts further, the species may well survive without regular large-scale immigration, although there is no indication that natural immigrants are declining.

Red Admiral pupa on nettle. **BH**

I have seen Red Admiral every March (and sometimes earlier) for the last 15 years at the highest point of Bookham Common. This is now a predictable occurrence in the same woodland ride, on the same patch of midday-sunlit ground, with a butterfly awaiting the arrival of a female or chasing away another male interloper. There is little chance of 15 successive March months having favourable weather for immigration. Appearances earlier than March are further evidence of overwintering.

Frohawk also noted that there was no evidence of any hibernated females having deposited eggs in this country. However I observed a female laying on Bookham Common on March 8, 2007, when earlier weather conditions had not been favourable for immigration.

Proof of survivors in severe winters is less certain. The end of 2010 had one of the coldest spells on record followed by the mildest February since 2002, but it was a cloudy month, especially in the south and east, and certainly not conducive to immigration. Despite these conditions, on the first mild day of February with lengthy sunny spells (Feb 24, 2011, 11.5°C) I recorded a Red Admiral at the Bookham Common high point.

Phenology trend	**1990-2012**	earlier by 0.5 weeks	
Best transect day 2000-12	Jul 13, 2003	Sheepleas	12
Transects abundance	**1990-2012** loss 3%	**2000-2012** loss 39%	
UK transects abundance	**1976-2012** gain 318%	**10-year trend** loss 25%	
UK 4,361 10k squares	**2005-09** 2,402 = 55%	**10-year trend** loss 2%	

Red Admiral taking minerals. **BH**

These records from the end of the season seem too late for return migration to the continent, in view of shorter daylight hours, lower temperatures and less settled weather:

Oct 24, 2010	Stoke D'Abernon Garden Centre: flying around black plastic hanging basket, seeking dark hibernating site?
Oct 29, 2000	Stoke D'Abernon: seeking exit from Garden Centre glasshouse.
Oct 27 & 30, 2001	Merton Park SW19: egg-laying females on south-facing fence.
Nov 1, 2001	Leatherhead: male and female courting on top of privet hedge.

The following records are more likely to indicate an early awakening from hibernation:

Jan 27, 2003	Bookham Common: two males on territories.
Feb 4, 2004	Bookham Common: male on territory.
Nov 9, 2005	Leatherhead garden: feeding from yellow buddleia.
Dec 6, 2006	RHS Garden, Wisley: trunk of apple tree.

In Surrey I have often witnessed incoming Red Admirals in varying numbers, flying fast and direct, overcoming all obstacles. Tall trees are no barrier to their relentless and determined flight. Every year at Denbies Hillside, from lunchtime onwards on a suitably promising day, I enjoy seeing the occasional Red Admiral flash past on its northward journey.

On August 30, 2003, on the Dorset coast, I observed an amazing Red Admiral immigration, second in my experience only to the massive Painted Lady invasion of 2009. Red Admirals were streaming in from the sea, with 15 counted in just 10 minutes. At that time of the year they should have been flying in the opposite direction! The majority were flying steadily in a straight line and at head height.

Red Admiral *continued*

Red Admiral — weekly transect counts

London Wetland Centre TQ228770 — **Richard Bullock**

	WEEK	2000	2001	2002	2003	2004	2005	2006	2007	2008	2009	2010	2011	2012
1 April	1	-	1	1	-	-	1	1	1	-	-	1	-	1
8	2		-	-	-	-	-	1	-	-	-	-	-	1
15	3	-	-	-	-	1	-	-	-	-	-	-	-	-
22	4	-	-	-	-	1	-	1	-	-	-	-	-	
29	5	-	-	-	-	-	-	-	2	-	-	-		-
6 May	6	-	-	-	-	-	-	1	2	-	-	-	1	-
13	7	1	2	-	-	-	-	1	1	-	-	1	-	-
20	8	-	-	1	-	-	-	-	2	-	-	-	-	-
27	9	-	-	1	-	-	-	-	-	1	-	-	-	-
3 June	10	-		-	1	1	-	-	1	-	1	-	-	
10	11	1	-	-	1	1	-	1	1	-	1	1	-	-
17	12	2	-	1	2	1	1	-	2	-	**3**	**3**	2	-
24	13	1	-	1	4	1	2	1		-	1	1	2	-
1 July	14	**5**	-	-	2	2	2	1	1	1	1	**3**	2	-
8	15		1	**4**	3	2	2	1	2	-	1	2	4	**2**
15	16	1	**4**	2	2	2	2	2	**3**	-	1	2	**6**	**2**
22	17	2	2	1	4	-	**3**	4	2	-	-	2	3	1
29	18	-	2	1	3	**3**	1	**5**	-	1	-	1		
5 August	19	-	-	2	6	**3**	1	3	-	**2**	-	1	2	**2**
12	20	-	1	-	**7**	2	-	2	-		-		1	-
19	21	1	-	-	**7**	-	2	1	1	1	-		1	-
26	22	1	1	1	6	-	-	-		1	1	-	1	-
2 September	23	1	1	1	2	-	-	-	-	1	-	-	1	-
9	24	2	-	2	2	-	-	1	1	1	-	-	-	1
16	25	-	-	1	1	-	-	-		1	**3**	-	2	1
23	26	-			2	-	1	2	-	-	1	-	1	1
Abundance index		20	15	21	55	20	18	29	24	11	14	NI	31	13
Weeks recorded		**11**	**9**	**14**	**17**	**12**	**11**	**17**	**14**	**9**	**10**	**11**	**14**	**9**

Flight weeks — ▲High transect counts △Middle ^Low

Apr					May				Jun				Jul					Aug				Sep			
1	*8*	*15*	*22*	*29*	*6*	*13*	*20*	*27*	*3*	*10*	*17*	*24*	*1*	*8*	*15*	*22*	*29*	*5*	*12*	*19*	*26*	*2*	*9*	*16*	*23*
△	^	^	^	^	^	△	^	^	△	△	△	△	▲	▲	▲	▲	▲	△	△	△	△	△	△	▲	▲

Painted Lady *Vanessa cardui*

Harry E. Clarke

Surrey status: common, if irregular, migrant, usually from late May; 2009 was a spectacular year.

Map notes: map inevitably volatile for such a mobile, unpredictable migrant.

Trends: 1996 was the previous big year before 2009.

Wingspan: male 58-70mm, female 62-74mm.

Identification: upperside salmon-pink with black markings; female's outer margin is more rounded than male's.

Confusion species: when wings closed, other vanessids.

Habitat: almost any, including gardens.

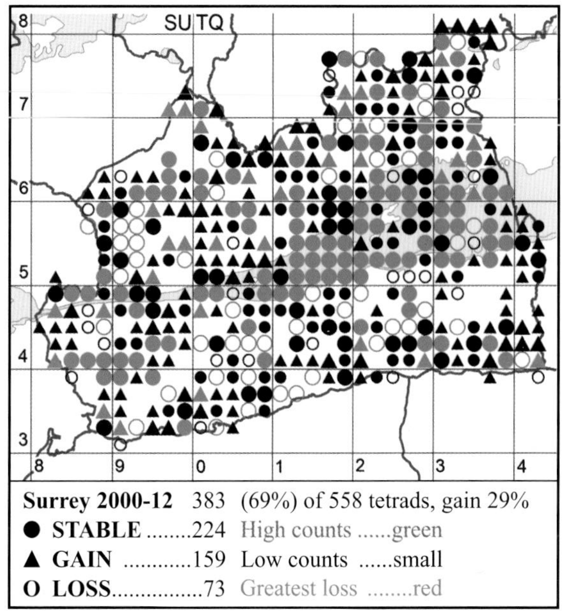

Top transects in 2009: London Wetland Centre, Nore Hill, Juniper Hill, Brentmoor Heath, Sheepleas.

Life cycle: c. six generations per year, migrating between West Africa and Northern Europe. Female lays a single egg on upperside of foodplant; larva creates a tent, which it uses until the last instar; pupates beneath vegetation. Depending on temperatures, the cycle from egg to adult takes 7-9 weeks; adults live 10-24 days.

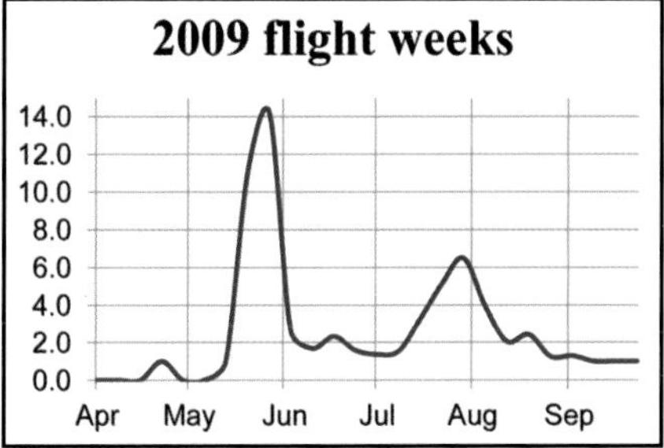

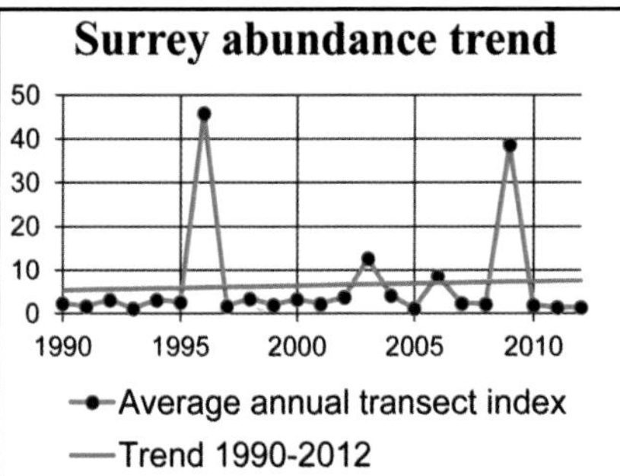

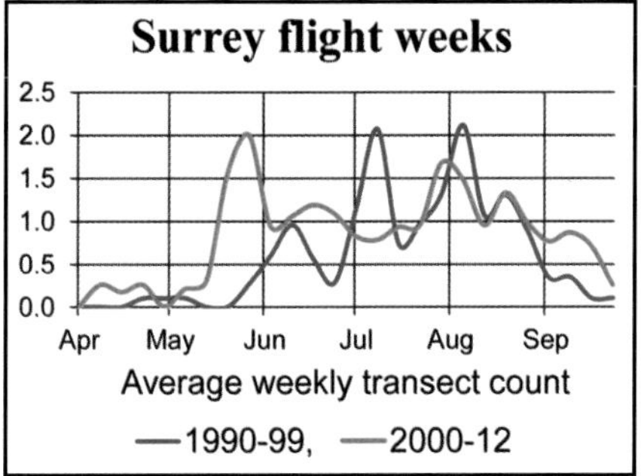

Painted Lady *continued* **Harry E. Clarke**

THE record-breaking Painted Lady migrates further than any other insect. Over some six generations in one year it completes a 15,000km round trip between Africa and Northern Europe. It can travel close to the ground but the main migration occurs at a height of 150-1,200m. Numbers in Britain fluctuate greatly from year to year, depending on suitable winds from North Africa.

Painted Lady on ivy. **FK**

The year 2009 was remarkable not only for Painted Lady abundance, but also for the research across Europe and North Africa into their migration.

During April, a few Painted Ladies arrived from Morocco, including one at Mitcham Common on 24 April. However, most of the Moroccan generation were still breeding around the Mediterranean. Towards the end of May the new generation emerged and migrated north. On May 25 radar detected about 2.3 million crossing the English Channel, with a further 1.7 million on May 29. The London Wetland Centre recorded 81 on May 26 and 148 on May 28. Nore Hill had 140 on May 29. Many other Surrey sites also experienced this invasion.

These migrants produced a new Surrey generation, emerging in mid-July. Some of these stayed to start a second generation, but most started to migrate south. Emigration peaks were August 7, when radar observed 1.2m, September 5 (1m) and September 19 (1.6m). Larvae and pupae of the second Surrey generation would have been subjected to increased levels of parasitism, and perished when temperatures dropped to 5°C.

Other great years for the Painted Lady in Surrey were 1952, 62, 64, 66, 70, 80 and 96.

Phenology trend	**1990-2012**	no change	
Best transect day 2000-12	May 28, 2009	London Wetland Centre	148
Transects abundance	**1990-2012** gain 42%	**2000-2012** gain 75%	
UK transects abundance	**1976-2012** gain 224%	**10-year trend** loss 94%	
UK 4,361 10k squares	**2005-09** 2,419 = 55%	**10-year trend** gain 10%	

Painted Lady London Wetland Centre TQ228770		weekly transect counts **Richard Bullock**											
	WEEK	2000	2001	2002	2003	2004	2005	2006	2007	2008	2009	2010	2011	2012
6 May	6	-	-	-	3	-	-	-	-	-	-	-	-	-
13	7	-	-	-	-	-	-	-	-	-	-	-	-	-
20	8	-	-	1	-	1	-	1	1	-	81	-	-	-
27	9	-	-	1	**15**	-	1	-	-	-	**148**	-	-	-
3 June	10	-		-	6	-	-	1	-	-	-	-	-	
10	11	**2**	-	-	4	-	-	1	1	-	2	-	-	-
17	12	**2**	-	1	2	-	-	-	1	-	2	-	-	-
24	13	**2**	-	1	2	-	-	-		-	2	-	-	-
1 July	14	1	-	-	1	-	-	-	-	-	1	-	-	-
8	15		-	-	-	-	-	-	-	-	1	1	-	-
15	16	1	-	-	2	-	-	-	-	-	1	-	-	-
22	17	-	1	-	2	-	-	2	-	-	-	-	-	-
29	18	1	**2**	-	3	-	-	**4**	-	-	7	-	-	
5 August	19	1	-	**3**	4	-	-	2	-	-	4	-	-	-
12	20	-	-	1	6	-	-	-	-		1			-
19	21	-	-	-	4	1	-	-	**2**	-	4		-	-
26	22	**2**	-	-	1	-	-	-		-	1	-	-	-
2 September	23	-	-	-	1	-	-	-	-	-	2	-	-	-
9	24	1	-	-	3	-	-	-	-	-	-	-	-	-
16	25	-	-	-	-	-	-	-		-	1	-	-	-
23	26	-			1	-	-	-	-	-	1	-	-	-
Abundance index		14	3	9	60	2	1	10	7		206	NI		
Weeks recorded		**9**	**2**	**6**	**17**			**6**	**4**		**16**	**1**		

However, in 1951, 53, 56, 59, 60, 81 and 84 there were no favourable winds, and consequently no immigrants were observed in Surrey.

Unlike its relative the Red Admiral, the male Painted Lady does not maintain a territory but waits for a female in a prominent position such as a bare patch of ground or hilltop. This is thought to be due to the Painted Lady's usually occurring in large numbers, so it is not cost-effective to defend a territory.

The female lays singly onto the leaf upperside, preferably near to nectar sources. Each female produces c. 500 eggs. The parasitoid wasp *Cotesia vanessae* kills larvae, *Pteromalus puparum* kills pupae. Predation by birds and spiders also takes its toll.

Larval foodplants: thistles; many others used, including mallow, nettle, viper's-bugloss.

Flight weeks ▲High transect counts △Middle ^Low																									
Apr					May				Jun				Jul					Aug				Sep			
1	8	15	22	29	6	13	20	27	3	10	17	24	1	8	15	22	29	5	12	19	26	2	9	16	23
	^	^	^		^	^	▲	▲	△	△	▲	△	△	△	△	△	▲	▲	△	▲	△	△	△	△	^

Small Tortoiseshell *Aglais urticae* **Ken Willmott**

Surrey status: still common and widespread but has declined massively, both nationwide and especially in south-east England.

Flies: March (or earlier) to September and even October.

Trends: Surrey transects abundance 1990-2012 has dropped by a staggering 96%. Large gatherings on autumn flowers, such as Michaelmas-daisy in September, are now a less common occurrence where they used to be a frequent event, for example in my local parks. In some years there can be a substantial continental influx.

Wingspan: male 45-55mm, female 52-62mm.

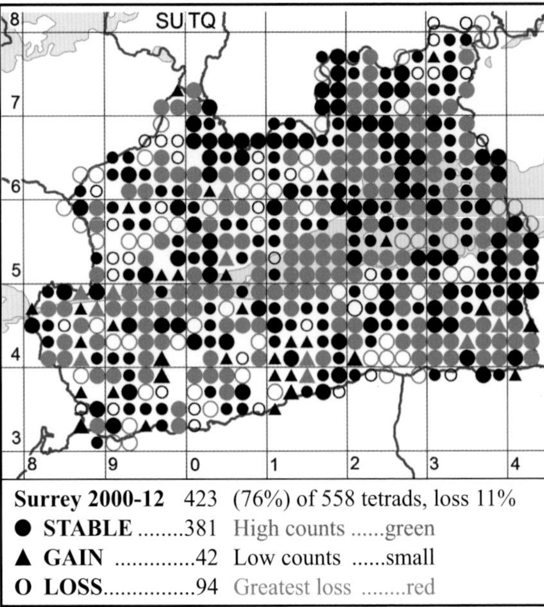

Identification: often confused with the very different Red Admiral by the general public; one of our most attractive butterflies, with bright-orange base colour, distinctive black central spots in its forewing pattern, and brilliant blue crescents along the outer margins of both fore- and hindwings. The drab underside affords camouflage for hibernating in dark places.

Variations/aberrations: no two Small Tortoiseshell wing markings are exactly the same. The blue crescents around the wing margin vary in size and intensity, as do the black spots on the forewing, which can be absent. The ground colour can vary in shade. The palest variety, a creamy colour, is ab. *brunneoviolacea*. Perhaps the most extreme and well known aberration is ab. *semi-ichnusoides*, which has the two forewing spots

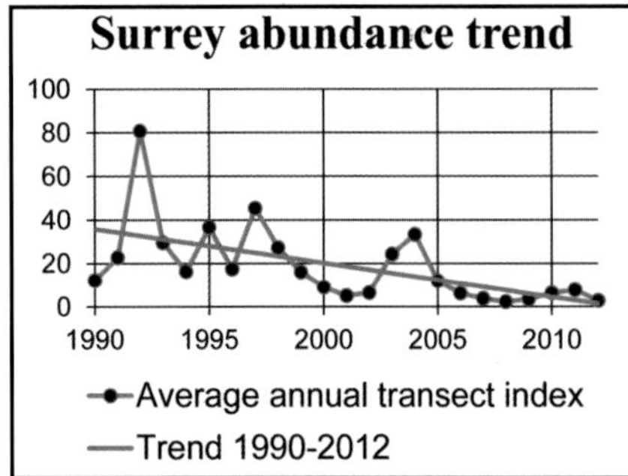

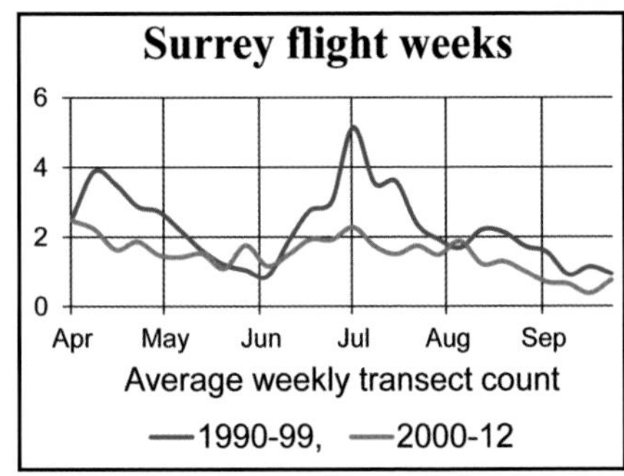

Small Tortoiseshell pair (male on right) on bramble. **FK**

missing, the two black square markings along the front margin of the forewings joined, and little or no orange on the hindwing. This aberration can be created by temperature experiments in captivity, but I have observed it on the Dorset coast.

Confusion species: Large Tortoiseshell, a rare migrant to woodland, has a bigger wingspan and is a less bright orange; hindwing underside has a distinct white mark.

Habitat: diverse, with those emerging from hibernation seeking the yellow flowers of spring and young, maturing nettle beds. Although it is unusual to find the species in woodland, I have recorded the occasional individual feeding on sallow blossom (Chiddingfold Forest 2010). First-brood adults emerging in June seek a variety of nectar resources and prefer young, recently cut nettles. Many visit gardens as buddleia comes into flower, as do second-brood adults in July and August, seeking to feed on the wealth of flowers prior to hibernation. My observations of the Small Tortoiseshell on Michaelmas-daisies at Wisley suggest they prefer *Aster novae-angliae* to *novi-belgii*.

Top transects: Hutchinson's Bank, Sheepleas, Riddlesdown, Quarry Hangers.

Small Tortoiseshell *continued* **Ken Willmott**

Life cycle: bivoltine hibernator; can awake as early as February, given a mild, sunny day with temperatures above 10ºC. I have even seen an individual from an indoor hibernating site flying during a Christmas Carol service as the room temperature increased.

The majority emerge in March or April and seek warm, sunny, sheltered nettle beds for courtship and egg-laying. Egg batches, varying in number, are deposited in April (before Peacocks use the same environment), hatch in May, and then produce a new brood of adults in mid-June/early July. Their offspring emerge from August to mid-October and enter hibernation.

Hatching is a protracted affair: at Sheepleas on July 21, 2012, I located both newly-hatched larvae and others in the third of their four instars. Although I have found the golden-coloured pupa on the stem of a nettle leaf, most larvae crawl away from the nettles for their pupation.

Larval foodplant: nettles.

Small Tortoiseshell female on creeping thistle. **KW**

THE Small Tortoiseshell is in dramatic decline in Surrey and generally in south-east England from a peak in 1992. It was formerly a widespread and common garden butterfly, especially on buddleia and Michaelmas-daisies at the height of their season. We need to monitor not only adults on transect routes, but also activity on nettles regarding egg-laying and the larval survival rate.

Nettles remain common, but this species requires the larger beds with a sunny aspect. Nettle beds have a distinctive odour on the warmer days of spring, which may help males to locate them and establish their territories, and females to find their mates before laying on the underside of the leaves.

The management of nettles, despite their importance for butterflies, is rarely incorporated into management planning on nature reserves or other sites of wildlife value. I have witnessed nettle beds damaged by conservation-biased organisations allowing fairs and circuses on their property.

Summer grazing can be a favoured management regime for some conservation organisations, but cattle in particular will trample through nettle beds at a time when they are being used by the Small Tortoiseshell and other species. Nettles do need to be cut, but the timing should vary each year depending on their growth rate and the critical periods when they are about to be used for egg-laying or larval-feeding. June is usually the best month to cut nettles. But if preliminary inspection reveals that Peacock and late Small Tortoiseshell larvae are still feeding, enough plants should be left for them to complete their cycle. The blades should not be set to cut too close to the ground.

A single pass with a tractor pulling a gang mower has been successful at Sheepleas, leaving narrow rows of nettles still standing and others bruised but able to recover. I have recorded larvae surviving such a cut and feeding on new growth. The cut material can usually be left *in situ*, as I believe it was at the Sheepleas site.

New growth after the cut emulates the spring freshness and should attract Small Tortoiseshell females, who lay close to the terminal leaves where there is a higher concentration of nitrogen. I have also observed a female laying on uncut, older nettles in July on Bookham Common, but the significance of this is not clear.

One reason suggested for the Small Tortoiseshell's decline in the south-east is the arrival, perhaps due to climate warming, of a European tachinid fly, *Sturmia bella*, which was first recorded in Britain in 1998. This parasitoid, which targets Small Tortoiseshell and other nettle-feeders, is difficult to separate in the field from *Phryxe vulgaris*. The latter emerges from the larva of its host, whereas the European invader hatches from the pupa.

Sturmia bella lays single eggs on the upper surface of nettle leaves and these are ingested by the feeding larva. Once inside they hatch and feed but avoid the larva's essential organs, thus allowing it to pupate before the fly emerges from the pupa. This new parasitoid has probably contributed to the Small Tortoiseshell's decline, but other factors are likely to be involved. It is crucial that we make every effort to assist the survival of these brightly coloured butterflies, which are great ambassadors and inspire the interest of the general public.

My personal favourite Small Tortoiseshell experience came when I stumbled into a bed of nettles, disturbing an egg-laying female, who flew off and settled some distance away. As I contemplated a search for her eggs, she flew over me and straight onto the leaf she had left, where she continued building her batch of eggs! Did she do this by sight, by smell? Incredible!

Phenology trend	**1990-2012**	earlier by two weeks	
Best transect day 2000-12	Aug 5, 2003	Sheepleas	47
Transects abundance	**1990-2012** loss 96%	**2000-2012** loss 71%	
UK transects abundance	**1976-2012** loss 74%	**10-year trend** loss 77%	
UK 4,361 10k squares	**2005-09** 2,470 = 57%	**10-year trend** loss 3%	

Small Tortoiseshell *continued*

Ken Willmott

Small Tortoiseshell

weekly transect counts

Hutchinson's Bank TQ380617

Martin Wills

	WEEK	2000	2001	2002	2003	2004	2005	2006	2007	2008	2009	2010	2011	2012
1 April	1	**4**	-	-	4	**26**	4	-	-	-	-	-	1	**2**
8	2	3	**2**	-	-	6	**8**	**2**	-	-	-	-	2	-
15	3	1	-	-	-	4	6	-	-	-	-	2	-	-
22	4	1	-	-	-	3	-	-	-	-	-	-	-	-
29	5	2	1	-	-	2	-	1	-	-	-	-	-	-
6 May	6	-	**2**	-	2	-	1	-	-	-	-	-	-	1
13	7	1	-	-	-	1	-	-	-	-	-	-	-	-
20	8	-	1	-	-	-	-	-	-	-	-	-	1	-
27	9	-	-	-	-	-	-	-	-	-	-	-	3	-
3 June	10	-	-	-	1	-	-	-	-	-	-	-	3	-
10	11	-	-	-	**6**	-	4	-	1	-	-	-	**7**	1
17	12	-	-	-	5	-	2	-	-	-	-	-	3	-
24	13	-	-	1	3	3		-	-	-	-	-	1	**2**
1 July	14	-	-		4	5	-	-	-	-	-	**4**	-	-
8	15	-	-	-	-	10	2	1	-	-	-	1	-	-
15	16	1	-	**2**	-	6	1	-	1	-	1	-	-	-
22	17	2	-	-	2	1	-	-	-	-	-	-	-	-
29	18	-	-	-	3	-		-	-	-	-	-	-	-
5 August	19	1	-	-	-	1		-	-	-	-		-	-
12	20	-	-	-	-	-				-	-	-	-	-
19	21	-	-	-	1	-				-	-	-	-	-
26	22	-	-	-	-	-				-	-		-	-
2 September	23	-	-	-	-	-				-	-	-	-	-
9	24	-	-	-	-	-				-	-	-	-	1
16	25	-	-	-	1	-				-	-	-	-	1
Abundance index		15	6	4	32	68	35	5	2	-	1	7	23	8
Weeks recorded		**9**	**4**	**2**	**11**	**12**	**8**	**3**	**2**		**1**	**3**	**8**	**6**

Flight weeks

▲High transect counts △Middle ^Low

Apr					May				Jun				Jul					Aug				Sep			
1	*8*	*15*	*22*	*29*	*6*	*13*	*20*	*27*	*3*	*10*	*17*	*24*	*1*	*8*	*15*	*22*	*29*	*5*	*12*	*19*	*26*	*2*	*9*	*16*	*23*
▲	▲	△	▲	△	△	△	^	△	^	△	▲	▲	▲	△	△	△	△	▲	△	△	^	^	^	^	^

Peacock *Aglais* (formerly *Inachis*) *io*

Malcolm Bridge

Surrey status: common and widespread.

Flies: emerges from hibernation during the first warm days of March and flies to early June. Fresh brood emerges in July, peaking in early August, with a few stragglers flying into September.

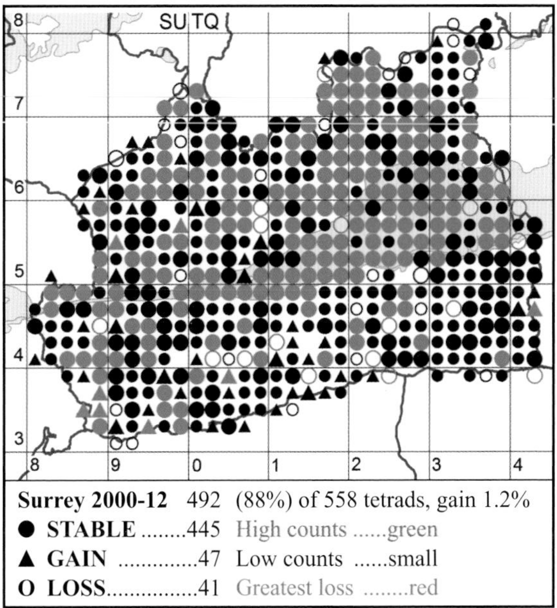

Trends: has undergone lengthy periods of scarcity but for the greater part of the last century has experienced a strong recovery phase and is now common throughout the whole county, including suburban and urban areas. The one concern is that this species, to a lesser extent than the Small Tortoiseshell, has suffered from a newly arrived parasitoid, the tachinid fly *Sturmia bella*. This may explain the reduced Surrey transect counts.

Wingspan: male 63-68mm, female 67-75mm.

Identification: rich, rusty red, with four large eyespots; underside almost black. Were the Peacock a rarity, it would inspire butterfly lovers to travel far and wide to enjoy it.

Variations/aberrations: best known aberration, ab. *belisaria*, the "Blind Peacock", lacks the blue/black eyespots, with only the grey ground colour present. An example was photographed by Geoff Eaton (see next page) on Horsell Common in 2007 (Eaton, 2011b). Other aberrations feature large dark areas close to the eyespots, or a greyish-violet ground colour, giving the impression of transparency.

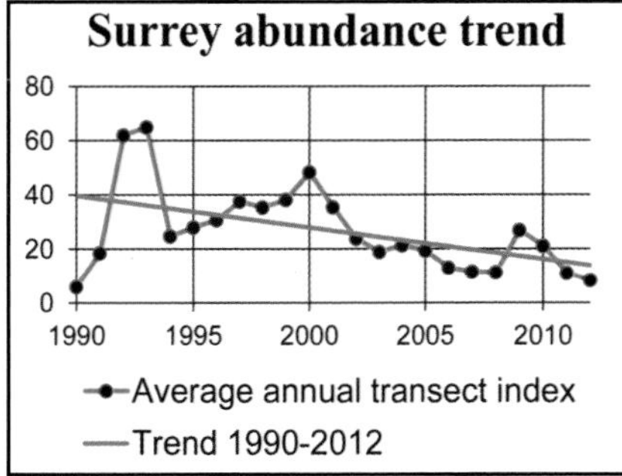

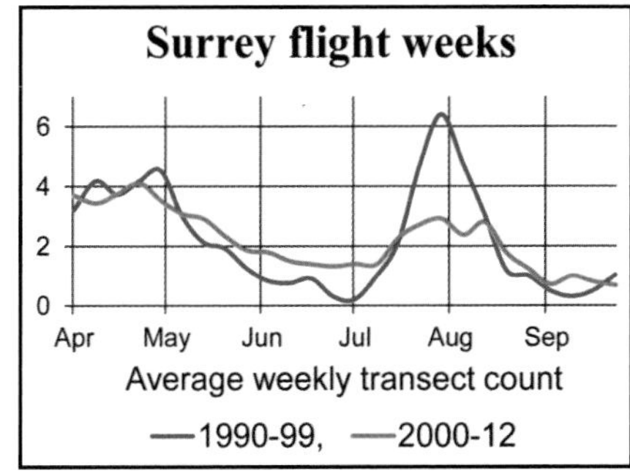

Peacock *continued* **Malcolm Bridge**

Confusion species: none.
Habitat: although in every sense a wider countryside species, this free-flying and powerful butterfly is commonest in and around woodland. It is also a common garden butterfly, where it relishes feeding from the flowers of buddleia in late July and early August.
Top transects: Hutchinson's Bank, Coulsdon Common, Happy Valley, London Wetland Centre, Mitcham Common, Roundshaw Downs.

"Blind Peacock", ab. belisaria, Horsell Common, July 2007. **GE**

Life cycle: essentially a univoltine hibernator, with evidence of an occasional second brood. Female lays a large batch of often several hundred eggs, piled several layers deep on the underside of a nettle leaf. They are usually laid at about midday and the nettles chosen will be in full sun at that time. The larvae feed gregariously within the shelter of a silky pavilion spread over several leaves. They warm up by basking on the sunny side of this construction, which soon becomes decorated by shrivelled larval skins. Larvae abandon the web in early July when fully fed and can be conspicuous when trekking along bare ground to a pupation site. The pupation phase lasts 2-3 weeks. Fresh adults appear in July and hibernate from early August.
Larval foodplants: common nettle; occasionally hop.

WE are fortunate to live in a period of Peacock prosperity and many of our forebears did not enjoy its splendid presence as readily as we do year on year. The Peacock seems to delay egg-laying until May, some weeks later than Small Tortoiseshell or Comma, which may explain why it escapes the worst predations of the parasitoid fly, *Sturmia bella*, which was first recorded in Britain in 1998.

In parts of their European range Peacocks are bivoltine or even trivoltine. There is growing evidence that in our area in a good summer there is a small second brood which emerges in late September. I saw this at first hand in 2009 when fully grown Peacock larvae were characteristically wandering along pathways towards a pupation site in early September. I collected three and left a similar number. The three pupated within a couple of days and two adults emerged 16 and 18 days later. The third was parasitised. Colleagues also reported late-September Peacocks and I suspect that some were second brood rather than late hibernators from the first brood.

Peacock on ragwort in July. **MB**

Transect counts for Peacocks are always higher in spring, when sightings are spread over several weeks. In summer, the interval between individual emergence and hibernation is barely a week.

The Peacock has remarkable defence strategies. Each wing surface carries a pronounced vein near the base and the butterfly can emit a very audible hiss by rubbing forewings and hindwings together when alarmed. To complete the charade of danger the butterfly flicks open its wings to reveal four large "eyes" to a potential assailant. Thomas has described some research by Vallin *et al.* (2006) which suggests that these strategies are more effective than the camouflage strategy of fellow hibernators like the Small Tortoiseshell and the Comma. When caged with hungry Blue Tits the Peacock experienced the least predation of the three despite the Comma's seemingly better camouflage.

Cool airy buildings, garden sheds or holes in trees offer the most usual hibernation sites. The brick and concrete pillboxes along the brow of the North Downs are chosen every year by hibernating Peacocks and by mid-August three or four "black triangles" can be found suspended from the ceiling rather than the walls at the start of their lengthy hibernation. Even at the height of summer these pillboxes are cool and they are only a little colder in the depths of winter. Even so, winter predation is high, especially in the early weeks before the predators have in their turn hibernated. Second-brood Peacocks would seemingly have a far better chance of surviving a winter than the main brood.

Peacock *continued*

Peacock Hutchinson's Bank, New Addington TQ380617		weekly transect counts											**Martin Wills**
WEEK		2000	2001	2002	2003	2004	2005	2006	2007	2008	2009	2010	2011	2012
1 April	1	**23**	13	2	7	8	**10**	-	6	2	9	2	7	1
8	2	19	7	1	**11**	**11**	3	-	**10**	2	2	9	6	3
15	3	18	11	6	4	6	7	7	6	**5**	10	15	4	-
22	4	16	15	**7**	9	9	-	**8**	2	4	8	4	5	5
29	5	**23**	**19**	4	6	4	-	**8**	2	3	4	**19**	2	**6**
6 May	6	13	16	2	5	5	1	1	5	1	5	2	**12**	5
13	7	17	7	4	3	8	-	-	3	3	6	3	2	1
20	8	3	1	1	3	9	-	-	1	-	1	2	4	3
27	9	10	4	1	2	2	3	1	1	1	1	2	1	1
3 June	10	6	5	-	1	4	1	3	3	-	-	3	2	-
10	11	-	3	3	-	-	-	-	-	-	1	2	1	-
17	12	-	4	4	1	-	-	2	1	2	1	2	-	1
24	13	-	-	-	-	-		-	-	-	-	-	-	-
1 July	14	-	2		-	-	-	1	-	1	-	-	-	-
8	15	-	-	-	1	-	-	-	1	-	-	-	-	-
15	16	-	-	-	1	-	-	-	-	-	6	-	-	-
22	17	-	-	-	1	-	-	3	-	-	-	-	8	-
29	18	-	-	-	3	3		-	1	-	**12**	-	5	-
5 August	19	6	1	-	1	-		-	1	-	3		2	-
12	20	4	-	2	-	-					-	-	1	-
19	21	-	1	-	-	-					-	-	-	3
26	22	-	-	-	-	-				1	-		-	1
Abundance index		153	109	39	59	71	28	33	44	26	69	66	59	30
Weeks recorded		**12**	**15**	**12**	**16**	**11**	**6**	**9**	**14**	**11**	**14**	**12**	**15**	**11**

Phenology trend	**1990-2012**	no change	
Best transect day 2000-12	Aug 11, 2000	Happy Valley	32
Transects abundance	**1990-2012** loss 65%	**2000-2012** loss 75%	
UK transects abundance	**1976-2012** gain 15%	**10-year trend** loss 30%	
UK 4,361 10k squares	**2005-09** 2,492 = 57%	**10-year trend** gain 17%	

Flight weeks				▲High transect counts								△Middle									^Low		
Apr					May				Jun				Jul					Aug				Sep			
1	*8*	*15*	*22*	*29*	*6*	*13*	*20*	*27*	*3*	*10*	*17*	*24*	*1*	*8*	*15*	*22*	*29*	*5*	*12*	*19*	*26*	*2*	*9*	*16*	*23*
▲	▲	▲	▲	▲	▲	△	△	△	△	△	^	^	△	△	△	△	▲	△	△	△	^	^	^	^	^

Comma *Polygonia c-album* — Ken Willmott

Surrey status: common and widespread.
Flies: mid-March to May; late June to October; peaks in spring and July.
Trends: between 1830 and 1929 there were fewer than six records from a group of southern counties including Surrey, and the stronghold was in the Welsh Borders. A switch in larval foodplant from hop (then declining in commercial cultivation) to nettle is thought to have allowed recolonisation through dispersal of autumn populations. It is now a well-loved garden butterfly.

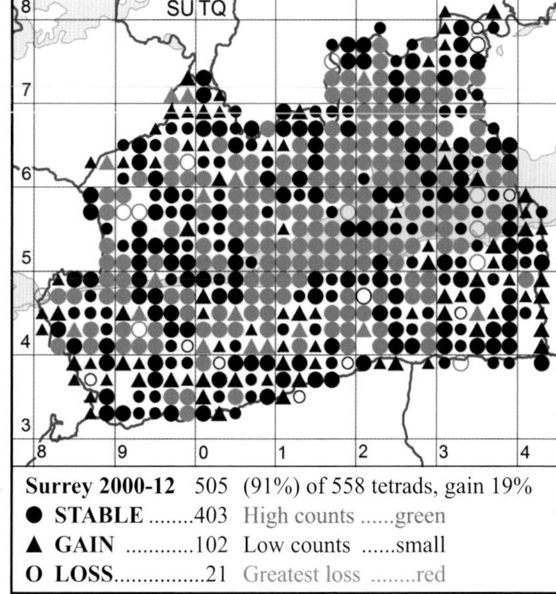

Wingspan: 50-64mm.
Identification: unmistakable ragged wings; female slightly paler, less ragged, fewer wing indentations. Eponymous white "comma" on underside is unique.
Variations/aberrations: a variable species, including the seasonally-dimorphic form *hutchinsoni*. On Bookham Common I have recorded ab. *suffusa*, in which the dark markings on the forewing upperside are confluent and the hindwings are almost black; also ab. *o-album*, in which an O replaces the comma. In ab. *extincta* the comma symbol is missing altogether. An unnamed aberration with virtually black hindwings established a summer territory in my Leatherhead garden in 2010.
Confusion species: none.

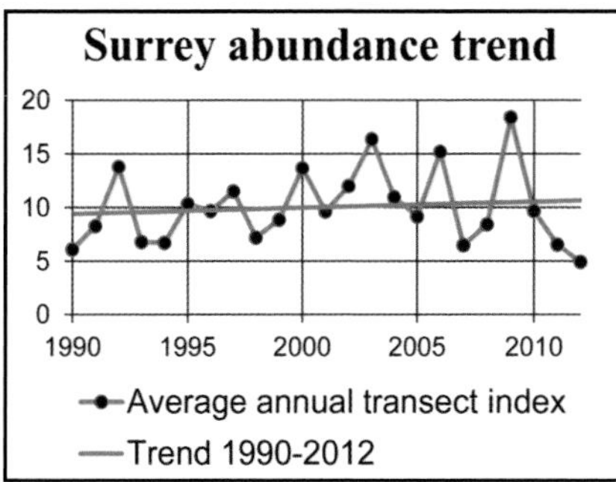

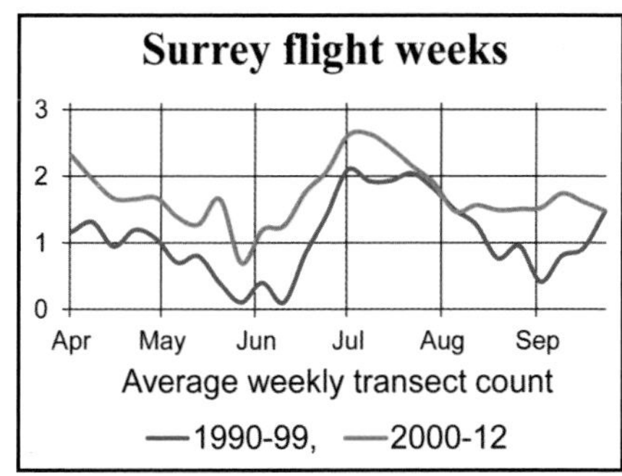

Comma *continued* **Ken Willmott**

Comma: hutchinsoni female on creeping thistle. **FK**

Habitat: a woodland butterfly in spring, when males establish territories along the wider sunny tracks, glades and intersections. The autumn brood in particular visit gardens.

Top transects: Wimbledon Common, Mitcham Common, Ashtead Common.

Other key sites: Bookham Common, Chiddingfold Forest, RHS Garden Wisley.

Life cycle: bivoltine hibernator. Frohawk (1924) believed that the first dozen or so eggs laid in spring would reach the pupal stage before midsummer's day (June 21), thus taking advantage of the lengthening hours of daylight and producing the form *hutchinsoni* (Pale Comma). However Harper & Waller (1950) found that the key factor is nettle succulence: the larval period of *hutchinsoni* averaged 33 days from more succulent nettles, whereas low succulence increased the larval period by almost three weeks and produced the dark form.

Form *hutchinsoni* is short-lived. It emerges and mates in July, with females laying throughout July and into August. Larvae from *hutchinsoni* females develop faster than those from the dark Commas, which emerge slightly later from mid-July well into August. These dark Commas evidently enter hibernation after only a short period of intense nectaring and do not mate until the following spring. In contrast, the *hutchinsoni* forms produce a second brood of adults in late summer and autumn. These are also of the dark form, and are on the wing until October, visiting late flowers such as ivy and Michaelmas-daisy before joining the earlier dark Commas already in hibernation.

The majority of larvae pupate away from their foodplant, but I have found a few on nettle leaves or stems and also underneath a nearby slate-coloured windowsill. The attractive grey-brown pupa, adorned with gold droplets, resembles a withered leaf. Hibernating sites vary, but the underwing markings and shape suggest the sheltered branches of trees and bushes. I have found a roosting Comma on the branches of an apple tree and was shown a remarkable example of one individual successfully overwintering on a sheltered wrought-iron gate!

Larval foodplants: common nettle; also elms, willows, hazel, currant, hop.

THE first warm days of spring prompt Commas to emerge from hibernation and quickly command woodland rides, glades, junctions and roadside scallops to await the arrival of a female. At this time of the year, unless it is exceptionally warm, the Comma does not fly much before midday.

A 100m stretch of woodland ride can contain several male territories, some rather too close together, triggering lengthy aerial disputes in which both males can soar high above the treetops in fast and combative flight. On separation, one of the males will tumble from the sky, often returning to his original perch, or another close by. In the only wild pairing I have witnessed, a male followed a female into a waist-high patch of bramble, where they joined and remained motionless, safely underneath a leaf.

Once mated, the female lays on a daily basis when the weather is suitable. A slow flying, frequently settling Comma near its larval foodplant is almost always an egg-laying female. On landing on the upper surface of a nettle leaf, she carefully lays a single egg on the apex of a leaf serration, although I have seen an egg on nettle flowers. A variety of nettle sites are chosen but it is uncommon for a Comma to share with Small Tortoiseshell and Peacock, although I saw one *hutchinsoni* doing so in 2012 at Sheepleas. The Comma prefers smaller, sheltered patches of nettles, perhaps at the base of hedgerows or wood edges where they are not averse to partial shade.

The standard dark Comma (top, male) and the paler form, hutchinsoni (female). **KW**

I have found a larva on grey willow on Denbies Hillside, and on hazel in Chiddingfold Forest. Larvae can also be located on elm in July underneath the lower leaves. The resting larva forms a C-shape and its shadow is not too difficult to discern, along with feeding evidence of perforations in the leaf.

The final-instar larva is handsome with orange spines and a white "saddle" on its back that resembles a bird-dropping, thus affording camouflage protection. Fully grown larvae do considerable damage to an elm leaf, adding to the perforations by eating large chunks of leaf edge. In 2012 I observed a female laying on elm shoots emanating from the base of a hedge. The female positioned the eggs at the edge of a slightly serrated leaf, as with nettles. Elm suckers continue to be a foodplant for the Comma; in Surrey at least, the 1970s outbreak of Dutch elm disease has not had a major impact on Comma populations.

Comma Wimbledon Common TQ220720														**Gay Carr**
	WEEK	2000	2001	2002	2003	2004	2005	2006	2007	2008	2009	2010	2011	2012
1 April	1						1	-	-	-	-	1	1	-
8	2						-	-	-		2	2	1	-
15	3						-	1	-	1	1	5	3	-
22	4						1	1	-	-	-	1	-	-
29	5						-	1	-	-	-	5	-	-
6 May	6						-	1		-	-	-	-	1
13	7						-	-	-	-	-	1	-	-
20	8						-	-	1	-	-	-	-	-
27	9						-	-	-	-	-	-	-	-
3 June	10						-	-	-	-	1	-	-	-
10	11						-	-	4	-	1	-	1	-
17	12						-	2	1	-	4	-	1	-
24	13							3	5	1	6	2	3	
1 July	14						2	1	**7**	4	10	3	3	1
8	15						**4**	**6**	-	**7**	12	3	1	3
15	16						2	2	2	**7**	**15**	**8**	1	**9**
22	17						3	-	1	3	3	2	**4**	5
29	18						1	2	2	3	8	3	-	1
5 August	19						-	-	-	-	3	4	1	1
12	20						-	-	-	-	2	1	1	-
19	21						-	-	-	-	1	1	1	1
26	22						-	-	-	-	1	1	-	-
2 September	23						-	-	-	-	1	1	2	-
9	24						-	1	-	4	-	1	3	1
16	25						-	-	-	-	-	1	-	2
23	26						-		-		1	-	-	3
Abundance index							15	19	21	33	70	46	26	27
Weeks recorded							**7**	**11**	**8**	**8**	**17**	**19**	**15**	**11**

Phenology trend	**1990-2012**	no change	
Best transect day 2000-12	Jul 15, 2009	Wimbledon Common	15
Transects abundance	**1990-2012** gain 13%	**2000-2012** loss 38%	
UK transects abundance	**1976-2012** gain 262%	**10-year trend** loss 39%	
UK 4,361 10k squares	**2005-09** 1,599 = 37%	**10-year trend** gain 8%	

Flight weeks ▲High transect counts △Middle ^Low

Apr					May				Jun				Jul					Aug				Sep			
1	8	15	22	29	6	13	20	27	3	10	17	24	1	8	15	22	29	5	12	19	26	2	9	16	23
▲	▲	△	△	△	^	^	△	^	^	^	△	▲	▲	▲	▲	▲	△	^	△	△	△	△	△	△	^

Dark Green Fritillary *Argynnis aglaja* **Ken Willmott**

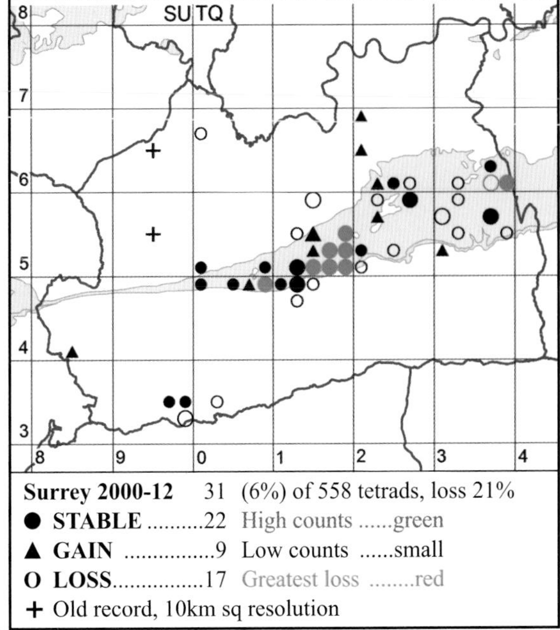

Surrey status: thinly spread on downland, with stronghold on Box Hill.

Flies: late June to August.

Trends: formerly abundant in suitable habitats on Denbies Hillside and Banstead Downs, as well as Box Hill, where it still remains in reduced numbers. Since about 2007 it appears to be recolonising, on a small scale, some of its former haunts on Denbies Hillside, where in 2012 I observed two females seeking egg-laying sites.

Wingspan: 58-68mm.

Identification: large, strong-flying butterfly with bright orange-fulvous ground colour chequered with black spots. Hindwing underside has silver spots and eponymous green flush. Larger female is darker and more strongly marked.

Variations/aberrations: in the hot, dry summer of 1976 I observed the melanic ab. *wimani* on Denbies Hillside. In 1971 I recorded the less extreme ab. *nigrans* in a new plantation at Chiddingfold Forest. A fine aberration in which the silver spangles on the underside of the wings join to form large blotches is ab. *charlotta*. Females in Surrey are occasionally as dark as subspecies *scotica*, which is found in the Scottish Isles.

Confusion species: Silver-washed Fritillary lacks underside spots, and the male upper forewing has strong sex brands. Dark Green and Silver-washed occasionally share the same woodland habitat, although Dark Green will seek more open areas.

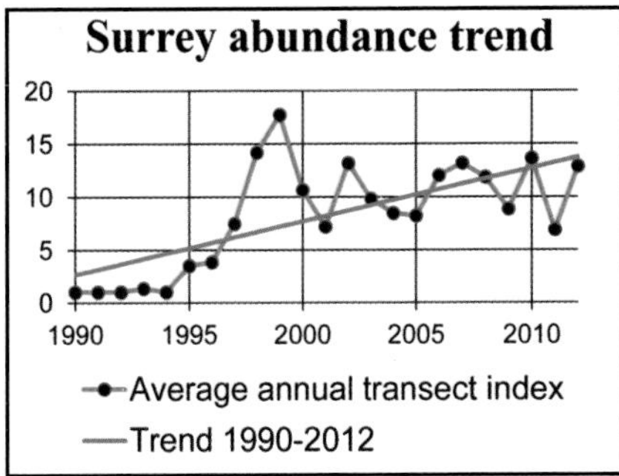

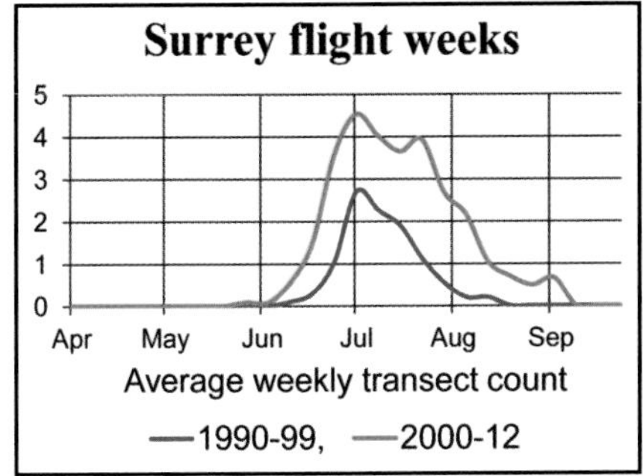

Dark Green Fritillary *continued* — Ken Willmott

Habitat: mostly associated with downland in Surrey. However, in the early 1970s I saw females laying close to violets in sunny, sheltered situations in the young woodland plantations of Chiddingfold Forest where the shade had yet to eradicate their foodplant. I recorded a couple, including a female, in Chiddingfold Forest in 2011, but suspect them to be artificial releases. I did not see any offspring there in 2012. The distance between Chiddingfold Forest and downland breeding areas is probably too far for natural dispersal. Thomas considered that most adults remain within the boundaries of their clearly defined breeding grounds, with the occasional individual flying 2-3km to a neighbouring site.

Top transects: Box Hill, Nower Wood.

Other key sites: Denbies Hillside, Happy Valley (Mickleham).

Life cycle: univoltine; winters as larva. Males locate females by the sexual strategy of patrolling, usually finding fresh females at ground level. Females lay singly, more often on plant litter in close proximity to a violet rather than on the plant itself. They can venture into the vegetation where they use chemical receptors on their feet to locate a suitable plant. The tiny larva emerges in about a fortnight, and eats nothing but eggshell before entering hibernation within the surrounding plant litter. It feeds for the first time during the latter part of March or early April. It moults five times and becomes fully grown in late May when it may be found on a warm day racing across the ground to locate another violet, or basking on a dried leaf. Look for nibbled leaves of the hairy violet on calcareous soils in early May. The larva pupates low in the vegetation after constructing a flimsy chamber of grass and other plant material.

Larval foodplants: hairy violet on downland; common dog-violet in woodland.

THE male is hyperactive on sunny days, flying low across the downs in search of females waiting in the vegetation. Records from my early notebooks include:

1969 Jul 13 Banstead Downs: common.

1970 Jun 27 Denbies Hillside: common, including a mating pair.

1974 Jul Denbies Hillside: very common.

1985 Jul 3 White Downs: numerous males.

1987 Jul 13 White Downs: numerous, females egg-laying.

1990 Jul 11 Denbies Hillside: 6, including 2 females.

1991 Jul 10 Denbies Hillside: **none.** Three days earlier on Salisbury Plain I saw 200+, showing the sort of numbers that are possible in a good year.

Interestingly on July 6, 1989 Dark Green Fritillary was recorded as numerous at the western end of the Denbies escarpment (Lamb's Leys); four days later I saw only one female and no males on the main slope. The Denbies collapse seems to have begun around then and could be linked to the droughts and increased rabbit populations of that period. It survives today, but only just, and is doing much better at Box Hill.

My recent Denbies records include:

2011 Jun 29 Steer's Field: 3 males nectaring.

2012 Aug 6 Allotments east and west: 3 females, 2 seeking egg-laying sites.

Dark Green Fritillary pair, male on right. **BH**

Surrey's downland supports a wide range of species, some of which are habitat specialists occupying a specific niche. Some need a taller sward (Marbled White, Ringlet); others need a shorter turf, which produces a higher ground temperature for their early stages (Adonis Blue, Silver-spotted Skipper).

Dark Green Fritillary is somewhere in the middle, preferring patches of low to medium height scrub, with large-leaved hairy violets growing in some shelter but not completely exposed. The management of downland therefore must take into account all these niches. Extensive scrub-clearance programmes, while advantageous for some species in the long term, do not favour Dark Green Fritillary. Scrub thinning, with the removal of aged scrub to allow sunny gaps, is beneficial.

Grazing by domestic animals is a common conservation tool. However overgrazing can harm the Dark Green Fritillary as it exposes the foodplants in the same way that the rabbit explosion did in the late 1980s and early 1990s. My observations of many females laying among hairy violets show that they do not select those plants that are exposed by either chainsaw or livestock. They like some shelter but not heavy shade. Such suitable plants are often found around the edges of scrub such as hawthorn.

Surrey's remaining downland, thankfully in the hands of conservation organisations, should be carefully assessed before the implementation of management plans. Climatic conditions, both current and historical, rabbit population, and the use of rotational rather than annual grazing schemes, should be taken into account in conservation planning for all species, including the Dark Green Fritillary.

Dark Green Fritillary on thistle. **GW**

Dark Green Fritillary										weekly transect counts				
Box Hill, Zig Zag TQ177520							**Janet Cheney, Steve Gallis, Sue Harris**							
	WEEK	2000	2001	2002	2003	2004	2005	2006	2007	2008	2009	2010	2011	2012
10 June	11	-	-	-	-	-	-	-	7	-	-	-		-
17	12	1	-		**9**	-	2	-	10	-		-		2
24	13	-	-	8		4	2	4	4	7	7			6
1 July	14	4	**8**	4	4	5	2	13	**12**	10	**10**	**16**		11
8	15		4	**11**	1	4	**12**	**19**		**11**	4	13		7
15	16	**5**	2	9	3	-	10	12	7	5	6			**14**
22	17	**5**	-	9	1	**6**	1	11	3	**11**	3	8		
29	18	2	-	2	-	4	4	5	6	1	4			
5 August	19	2	-	-		1	3	5	3	-	3	5		
12	20	-	-	-	-		1	3	-	1	-			1
19	21	-	-	-	-	-	-	2	-	-	-	5		
26	22		-	-	-	-	-	1	-	-	-	3		
Abundance index		23	14	47	24	36	37	77	63	49	38	NI		NI
Weeks recorded		**6**	**3**	**6**	**5**	**6**	**9**	**10**	**8**	**7**	**7**	**6**		**6**

Phenology trend	**1990-2012**	later by 0.5 weeks
Best transect day 2000-12	Jul 12, 2006	Box Hill Zig Zag 19
Transects abundance	**1990-2012** gain 417%	**2000-2012** gain 15%
UK transects abundance	**1976-2012** gain 153%	**10-year trend** gain 12%
UK 4,361 10k squares	**2005-09** 931 = 21%	**10-year trend** loss 1%

Flight weeks ▲High transect counts △Middle ^Low

Apr					May				Jun				Jul					Aug				Sep			
1	*8*	*15*	*22*	*29*	*6*	*13*	*20*	*27*	*3*	*10*	*17*	*24*	*1*	*8*	*15*	*22*	*29*	*5*	*12*	*19*	*26*	*2*	*9*	*16*	*23*
								^	^	^	△	△	▲	▲	▲	▲	△	△	△	△	^	^			

Silver-washed Fritillary *Argynnis paphia* **Ken Willmott**

Surrey status: a great rarity in 1973 and completely absent from many current locations 1974-1980; now common in suitable woodland.

Flies: late June to August, peaking in July.

Trends: expanding in both distribution and abundance, with the poor July of 2012 being hopefully only a temporary setback.

Recent earliest sightings at Bookham Common:

2010 Jun 25 8 males
2011 Jun 14 2 males
2012 Jun 23 1 male

Surrey 2000-12 168 (30%) of 558 tetrads, gain 25%
● **STABLE**..........92 High counts ......green
▲ **GAIN** ....76 Low counts ......small
O **LOSS**................42 Greatest loss ....red

Wingspan: male 69-76mm, female 73-80mm.

Identification: sexually dimorphic. Male is a bright orange-fulvous colour, with black spots decreasing towards apex of forewings, which each have four distinct black sex brands. Female is less bright and more heavily spotted, especially on the forewings. Underside "washed" or striped with silver.

Variations/aberrations: female has a beautiful greenish-blue form called *valesina*, which is rare in Surrey but can be up to 15% of the population in other southern counties such as Hampshire and Wiltshire. I have seen this variety on Bookham Common and in Chiddingfold Forest along with ab. *nigricans*, nearly all black; ab. *ocellata*, black spotting joined; ab. *confluens*, black markings enlarged.

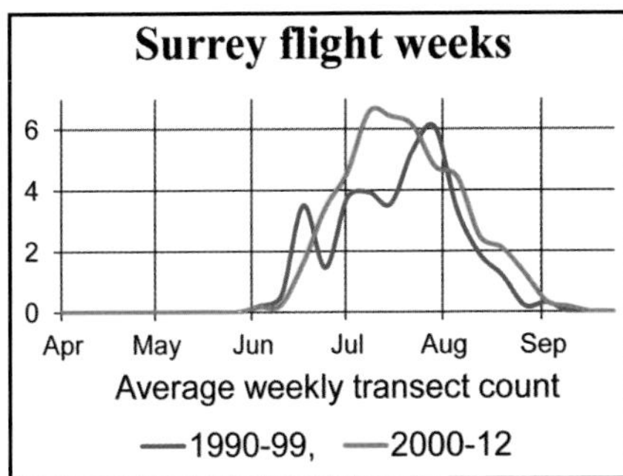

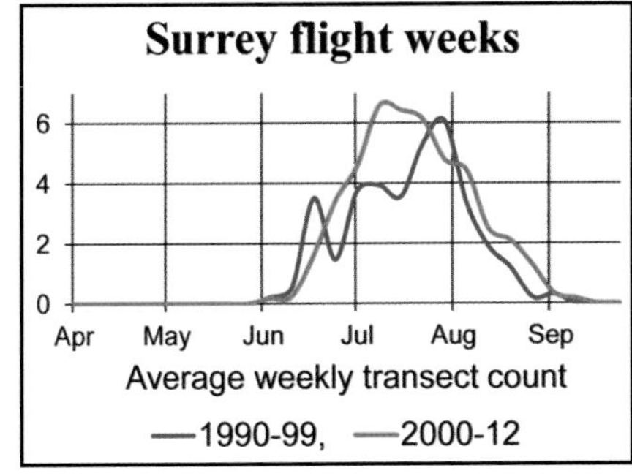

Silver-washed Fritillary *continued* **Ken Willmott**

Confusion species: male Dark Green Fritillary lacks the black sex brands. Penultimate row of spotting on upperside is rounded on Silver-washed, triangular on Dark Green; underside of Dark Green is green with silver spots.

Habitat: larger woodlands, both deciduous high forest, as on Bookham Common, or conifer mix as in Chiddingfold Forest. Has good dispersal ability in years of abundance. I have recorded a male on my garden buddleia in Leatherhead and there have been similar sightings some distance from woodlands. I have observed dispersal across downland on both Denbies Hillside and Box Hill, when they can be mistaken for Dark Green.

Silver-washed Fritillary pair, male above. ***FK***

Top transects: Oaken Wood, Witley Common, Epsom Common, Ashtead Common, Nower Wood, Sheepleas.

Other key sites: Bookham Common, Chiddingfold Forest, Ranmore Common, Whitmoor Common.

Life cycle: univoltine; winters as larva. Usually appears a little later than the White Admiral, which shares similar habitat. Male loops female in courting flight as he disseminates pheromones in the form of androconial scales from the sex brands. Female seeks violets on the forest floor, but rather than laying on the actual foodplant, flies onto nearby tree trunks of usually, but not exclusively, oak. Corsican pine can sometimes be used, as in Chiddingfold Forest. At a height of 1-5m she deposits single eggs on either moss (north side), or in a bark crevice. The eggs hatch within a couple of weeks, but the larva eats only the remnant shell of the egg before going into hibernation.

The following spring the 3mm larva apparently drops to the ground, rather than making a hazardous journey down the trunk, and finds the violets in dappled shade located by the female the previous summer. Poor spring weather will extend the larval period, leaving larvae vulnerable to predators on the forest floor for a longer time, and this can reduce adult populations in July. The pupa hatches in about three weeks, varying according to the June weather.

Larval foodplants: common dog-violet.

Silver-washed Fritillary male on bramble. **GW**

WHILE the Dark Green Fritillary has dramatically contracted its range and population in Surrey, the Silver-washed Fritillary has increased in both. The Silver-washed always had a relatively stable population in Chiddingfold Forest although this was influenced by the commercial activities of the Forestry Commission, which can be temporarily negative (early-aged plantations, over-thinning) or temporarily positive (maturing of conifer plantations before too little sunlight penetrates). Since 1973 I have recorded the colonisation (or recolonisation, as there are records from 1949) of Bookham Common as follows:

1973 Jul 10 & 26: one male.

1974-1980 none, despite regular visits during flight period.

1981 none on three visits; abundant Chiddingfold Forest.

1982 none; five recorded to the west of Denbies Hillside.

1983 none on four visits; fine summer.

1984 Jul 29: one male.

1985 Jul 21: two males; Jul 24: six males.

1986 Jul 15: one male; Jul 27: first female.

1987 Jul 8: two males; Jul 11: one male; Jul 27: one female (same area as 1986).

1988 none.

1989 Jul 11: one male; several seen on North Downs sites.

1990 none; recorded again on North Downs sites.

1991-1992 none; increase in records from North Downs sites.

1993 Jun 30-Jul 2: one male; Jul 18: none.

1994 Jul 9: one male; Jul 17: none; Jul 20: one male.

Silver-washed Fritillary *continued* — Ken Willmott

1995 Six records of single males; Jul 8: four males with wider distribution.

1996 Jul 18: 20+ incl three females; **stable colony established.**

1997 Jul 2: 35+, three mating pairs; Jul 13: 25+, including **first egg-laying female.**

1998 Jul 19: 12+, incl three females, looping courtship observed.

1999 Jul 6: 8+, incl four males on bramble.

2003 Jul 12: first aberration recorded: extreme ab. *ocellata.*

The North Downs expansion began some seven years earlier than further north on the clay soils of Bookham Common. Small populations were being recorded on the North Downs in 1989 after an earlier record of five individuals west of Denbies Hillside in 1982. Other Surrey sites I saw being colonised at the time included the Norbury Park Estate (Jul 25, 1989) and Headley Warren (Jul 20, 1991).

One of probably several factors that contributed to the expansion was the improvement in habitat. This specialist requires violets in dappled shade, similar to the honeysuckle preferences of the White Admiral. Aerial photographs from 1949 show that Bookham Common used to be more open. As the woodland matured, the number of situations with dappled sunlight increased, as did the number of suitable violets. Shade can be a problem in itself, but tree-felling conducted by the National Trust in 1993 created ideal sun penetration and violet production. Three years later the Silver-washed Fritillary was established on Bookham Common after an expansion of its distribution in 1995.

In 2010 the National Trust began another large-scale felling programme on Bookham Common. Over 100 oaks were designated as veterans and space is being cleared around them for future young oaks to flourish. The project will be closely monitored and it is hoped that new sites with dappled sunlight will benefit the Silver-washed Fritillary.

In Chiddingfold Forest, the Corsican pine plantations, once the residence of the Pearl-bordered Fritillary, have developed into breeding habitat for the Silver-washed Fritillary (and also White Admiral). As the trees have matured they have cast their shadows onto the formerly sunny violets once used by the spring fritillaries. Soon the plantations will become too shady even for females of the Silver-washed Fritillary, which will have to become pioneers and search for new breeding grounds.

Phenology trend	**1990-2012**	earlier by 0.5 weeks	
Best transect day 2000-12	Jul 11, 2006	Sheepleas	40
Transects abundance	**1990-2012** gain 38%	**2000-2012** loss 26%	
UK transects abundance	**1976-2012** gain 106%	**10-year trend** loss 2%	
UK 4,361 10k squares	**2005-09** 586 = 13%	**10-year trend** gain 12%	

Flight weeks ▲High transect counts △Middle ^Low

Apr					May				Jun				Jul					Aug				Sep			
1	8	15	22	29	6	13	20	27	3	10	17	24	1	8	15	22	29	5	12	19	26	2	9	16	23
									^	^	△	△	△	▲	▲	▲	▲	△	△	△	△	^	^		

Silver-washed Fritillary female, form valesina, on burdock, **BH**.

Silver-washed Fritillary, ab. ocellata, on bramble. **KW**

Silver-washed Fritillary weekly transect counts
Oaken Wood, Chiddingfold SU990338 **John Buckley**

WEEK		2000	2001	2002	2003	2004	2005	2006	2007	2008	2009	2010	2011	2012
3 June	10	-	-	-	-	-	-	-	-	-	-	-	1	
10	11	-	-	-	-	-	-	-	1	-	-	-	1	-
17	12	-	-	-	-	-	2	-	6	-	-	-	5	-
24	13	-	-	-	6	7	**8**	10	1	-	6	28	12	-
1 July	14	5	-	5	16	12	1	7	**12**	13	12	14	**17**	
8	15	5	-	**18**	10	**17**	**8**	19	5	1	**20**	26	15	
15	16	14	**25**	4	9	15	6	15	1	6	16	**34**	6	
22	17	**19**	17	7	**23**	5	-	**23**	6	6	14	29	1	**5**
29	18	5	16	7	10	5	3	20	1	4	8	20	-	2
5 August	19	6	3	2	4	5	5	11	-	**17**	4	16	-	4
12	20	3	2	4	2	1	3	2	-	5	3	4	-	2
19	21	2	-	3	-	1	-	-	-	1			-	4
26	22	-	-	1	-	-	-	-	1	-	-	-	-	-
Abundance index		64	63	51	80	46	36	107	32	57	88	NI	56	23
Weeks recorded		**8**	**5**	**9**	**8**	**9**	**8**	**8**	**9**	**8**	**8**	**8**	**8**	**5**

Speckled Wood *Pararge aegeria*

Ian Cunningham

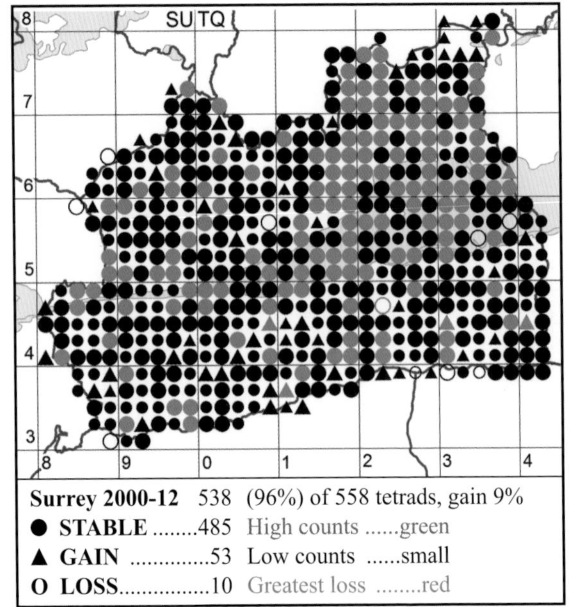

Surrey 2000-12 538 (96%) of 558 tetrads, gain 9%
● **STABLE** ....485 High counts ......green
▲ **GAIN** ....53 Low counts ......small
O **LOSS**................10 Greatest loss ....red

Surrey status: common and widespread.

Flies: unique in being reliably present throughout the season, peaking between late July and early September.

In London, with its warmer microclimate, the flight period can last from mid-March until November. In more rural Surrey these dates are respectively about one week later and two weeks earlier.

Trends: stable.

Wingspan: male 46-52mm, female 48-56mm.

Identification: upperside chocolate brown with creamy-yellow spots (bigger in female and whiter in adults from overwintered pupa); one black eyespot with tiny white centre near tip of forewing, and three along outer margin of hindwing. Underside hindwing is lighter.

Confusion species: Wall Brown, now essentially lost from Surrey, is more orange.

Habitat: deciduous woods, especially oak but not if 100% beech; more sparingly in rides in coniferous woods, even if sunlight is only dappled; also parks and gardens with only a few trees, provided there is suitable rough grass.

Top transects: Wimbledon Common, Epsom Common, Nower Wood, Wandsworth Common.

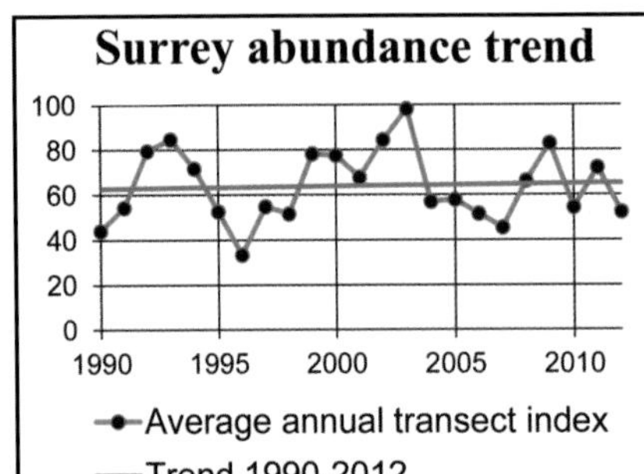

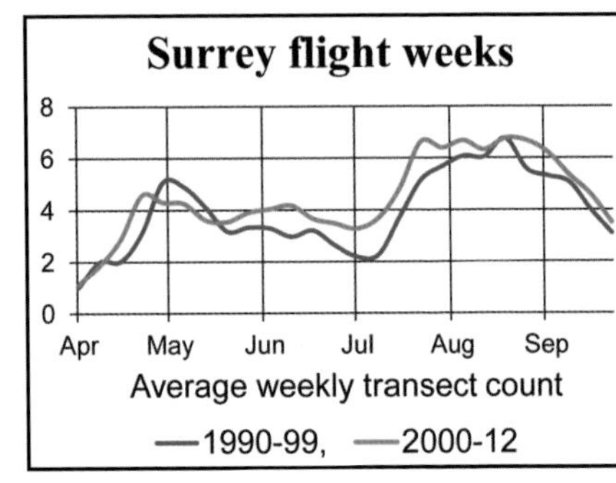

Speckled Wood. **GE**

Life cycle: uniquely overwinters as either larva or pupa, leading to overlapping broods. Eggs are laid singly on grass in warm, sheltered and (in summer) shady spots. Larva rests on the upperside of a grass blade and may move to adjacent vegetation to pupate. Adults feed on aphid honeydew as well as plant nectar.
Larval foodplants: grasses, including cock's-foot, common couch, false-brome.

THE Speckled Wood has not always been the success story it is today. A severe decline in the late 19th and early 20th centuries reduced its strongholds in the south to West Sussex and a few areas in the south-west and Wales. However it did not vanish entirely from Surrey. The reasons for its decline and subsequent resurgence from the 1920s to its current omnipresence are not clear.

Wandsworth Common Woodland in SE London is a key site of about a quarter sq km that produces a broadly stable mean annual count of 600+, with a maximum of 79 on a single visit.

With its relatively slow, fluttering flight, the Speckled Wood is easy to see and follow to its landing point. Males seeking females either patrol their territory or perch in wait. The fact that the butterfly is territorial does not prevent as many as half a dozen appearing in the same spot. Competing males, spiralling upwards in combat in rays of sunlight, are a thrilling sight.

Flight weeks ▲High transect counts △Middle ^Low

Apr					May				Jun				Jul					Aug				Sep			
1	8	15	22	29	6	13	20	27	3	10	17	24	1	8	15	22	29	5	12	19	26	2	9	16	23
^	^	^	△	△	△	△	^	△	△	△	△	^	^	△	△	▲	▲	▲	▲	▲	▲	▲	△	△	^

Speckled Wood *continued*

Speckled Wood — weekly transect counts

Wimbledon Common TQ220720 — **Gay Carr**

	WEEK	2000	2001	2002	2003	2004	2005	2006	2007	2008	2009	2010	2011	2012
1 April	1						-	-	-	-	-	-	-	3
8	2						2	-	-		1	-	3	2
15	3						-	-	5	1	4	1	4	6
22	4						1	-	7	1	9	2	6	2
29	5						2	1	8	6	10	7	14	4
6 May	6						3	2		7	12	7	13	1
13	7						7	4	6	8	11	9	16	1
20	8						4	3	8	6	12	6	11	5
27	9						2	2	4	4	12	6	12	9
3 June	10						-	3	4	8	15	9	5	11
10	11						3	5	4	10	14	9	8	16
17	12						9	6	5	15	7	9	6	15
24	13							5	2	8	6	5	4	
1 July	14						1	4	4	5	7	6	4	12
8	15						3	4	7	4	8	7	9	9
15	16						8	3	9	13	15	10	16	2
22	17						7	4	**11**	13	10	11	14	7
29	18						**12**	5	7	8	17	12	14	12
5 August	19						10	**9**	6	4	11	10	15	14
12	20						8	3	7	14	16	**22**	15	15
19	21						9	8	9	20	25	17	10	18
26	22						7	7	8	26	**34**	12	13	20
2 September	23						10	**9**	9	**30**	26	**22**	14	**24**
9	24						3	7	8	19	29	19	15	21
16	25						4	7	6	5	17	9	**17**	7
23	26						1	6	4	10	10	7	11	4
Abundance index							121	108	157	244	343	230	276	261
Weeks recorded							**22**	**22**	**23**	**24**	**25**	**24**	**25**	**25**

Phenology trend	**1990-2012**	earlier by 0.5 weeks	
Best transect day 2000-12	Jul 23, 2001	Wandsworth Common	79
Transects abundance	**1990-2012** gain 4%	**2000-2012** loss 25%	
UK transects abundance	**1976-2012** gain 128%	**10-year trend** loss 20%	
UK 4,361 10k squares	**2005-09** 1,932 = 44%	**10-year trend** gain 20%	

Marbled White *Melanargia galathea* **Malcolm Bridge**

Surrey status: locally common, especially on the Chalk.

Flies: second half of June and throughout July, peaking last week of June and first two weeks of July.

Trends: range increasing; decline in abundance has stabilised.

Wingspan: male 53mm, female 58mm.

Identification: bold black and white chequered markings discernible in languid flight; female underside creamy.

Confusion species: none.

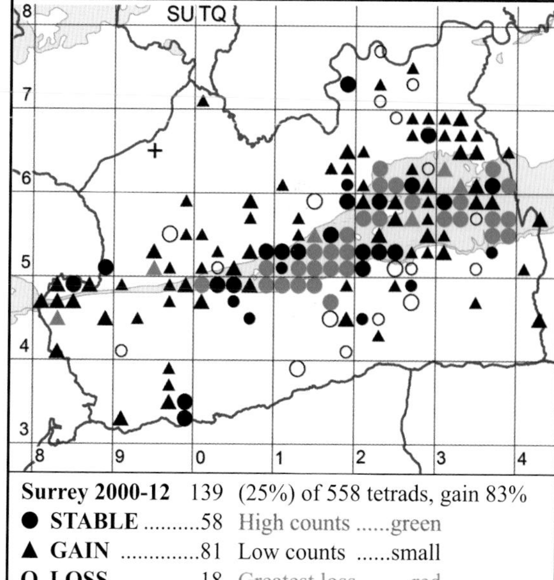

Habitat: unimproved grasslands with a tall sward. The presence of red fescue grass appears to be essential. The late Dame Miriam Rothschild, whose initial suspicions were aroused by the warning colour of the adults, considered the species to be toxic to birds and other predators. After years of research she was able to identify the source of the toxin as a red fescue fungus. By eating this, the larva makes itself highly unpalatable. The toxin offers the same protection to the pupa and adult butterfly.

Top transects: Denbies Landbarn B, Hutchinson's Bank, Pewley Down, Oaken Wood.

Other key sites: North Downs generally, Broadstreet Common.

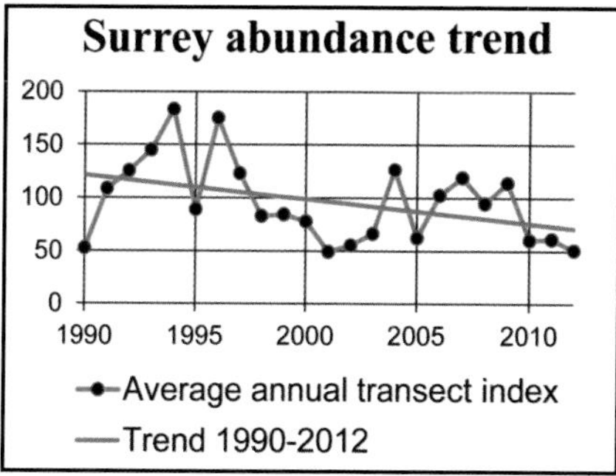

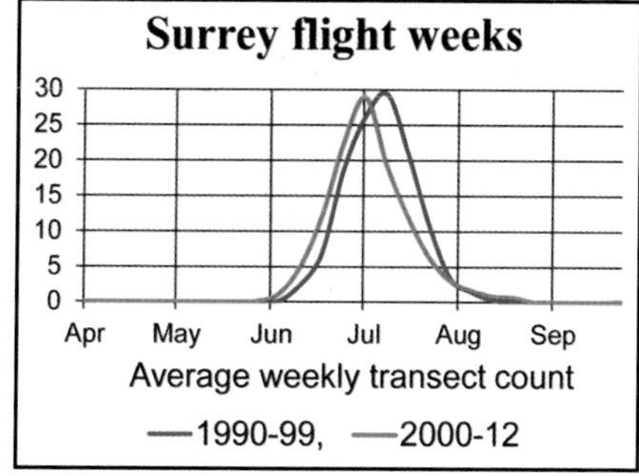

Marbled White *continued*

Malcolm Bridge

Life cycle: univoltine; winters as larva. The female perches on a tall plant and ejects an egg, which usually falls to the ground. The larva hatches after three weeks, eats most of the shell, and enters hibernation in adjacent dead vegetation. Feeding resumes in early spring when the young caterpillar nibbles the edges of blades of grass during the daytime. After its third and final moult the caterpillar is less choosy about which grass to eat but becomes a nocturnal feeder, hiding deep in grass tussocks during the day. The dumpy, yellowish pupa is formed during May, on the ground but lightly covered with moss or soil. Depending on June temperatures this stage will last for about three weeks until the adult emerges.
Larval foodplants: red fescue; other grasses also eaten, especially finer-leaved species.

IN Surrey and elsewhere in much of England and Wales the Marbled White has increased its range over the last three decades, often helped by a string of introductions. It is of interest that several successful introductions followed the release of only a small number of adults and with few or no subsequent releases.

If much of the range expansion is a natural occurrence, it is to be hoped that introductions will cease to be a factor in the future. However, many observers think that the Marbled White's dispersal capabilities are relatively poor and that the majority of unusual sites are due to translocations. Examples are Bookham Common, where it seems to have failed, and Oaken Wood.

Thomas noted that the Marbled White has experienced dramatic swings in population size over the last 250 years which correlate closely with climate fluctuations. Even over the short term, larval emergence in a warm August usually gives rise to a larger adult emergence in the following year, whereas a cool August yields a below average number of adults.

Unlike most Browns, whose males perch and wait, male Marbled Whites patrol continuously over open grassland in search of a female. Their chequered pattern, which warns predators that they are toxic, does not deter the larval stage of red mites, several of which may be carried. Mite larvae seem unaffected by the toxin. They infest many grassland species but seem not to cause any great harm.

Given that Collins (1995) described the Marbled White as an extinct resident and introduction, it is evidently a species that lends itself to human intervention. He recorded that in 1959, schoolmaster A E Collier, of Black Hairstreak fame, hoped that nobody's feelings would be hurt if he reintroduced the Marbled White to the North Downs. Clearly butterfly introductions have been a vexed issue for the greater part of the last 100 years, and continue to be so.

Flight weeks ▲High transect counts △Middle ^Low

Apr					May				Jun				Jul					Aug				Sep			
1	8	15	22	29	6	13	20	27	3	10	17	24	1	8	15	22	29	5	12	19	26	2	9	16	23
								^	△	△	△	▲	▲	▲	△	△	△	△	^	^					

Marbled White male on scabious. **FK**

Pair (male right) on pyramidal orchid. **HC**

Marbled White Denbies Landbarn B TQ135499											weekly transect counts **Gail Jeffcoate, Robert Cramp**			
WEEK		2000	2001	2002	2003	2004	2005	2006	2007	2008	2009	2010	2011	2012
3 June	10				-	-	-	-	1	-	-	-	-	-
10	11			-	-	-	-	-		1	-	-	21	-
17	12			1	9	33	-	1	**73**	2	12	-		-
24	13			15	**70**	**53**	46	45	36	19	19	14	**57**	5
1 July	14			28	55	48	**60**	**86**	46	**42**	**36**	**67**	24	
8	15			28	29	38	39	81	28	11	6	40	9	**17**
15	16			**33**	5	29	23	41	8	10		5	10	
22	17			10	1	8	1	8	3	5	-		1	5
29	18				-	1	3	1	-		-		-	-
Abundance index				112	201	210	172	241	253	98	78	127	167	NI
Weeks recorded				**6**	**6**	**7**	**6**	**7**	**7**	**7**	**4**	**4**	**6**	**3**

Phenology trend	**1990-2012**	earlier by one week	
Best transect day 2000-12	Jul 2, 2009	Pewley Down	190
Transects abundance	**1990-2012** loss 41%	**2000-2012** gain 4%	
UK transects abundance	**1976-2012** gain 46%	**10-year trend** loss 28%	
UK 4,361 10k squares	**2005-09** 668 = 15%	**10-year trend** gain 2%	

Grayling *Hipparchia semele* **Howard Street**

Surrey status: specialist of the western heaths, including the Thames Basin heaths shared with south-east Berkshire and north-east Hampshire.
Flies: mid-July to September.
Conservation:
UK Biodiversity Action Plan priority species;
BC 2010 Red List: vulnerable.
Trends: no longer found on downland; response to recent heathland restoration, as shown by monitoring for the Surrey Heathland Project, has been inconsistent, with the species increasing on some sites and disappearing from others. Healthy increase in transect abundance, although Chobham Common is the only current transect with good numbers.

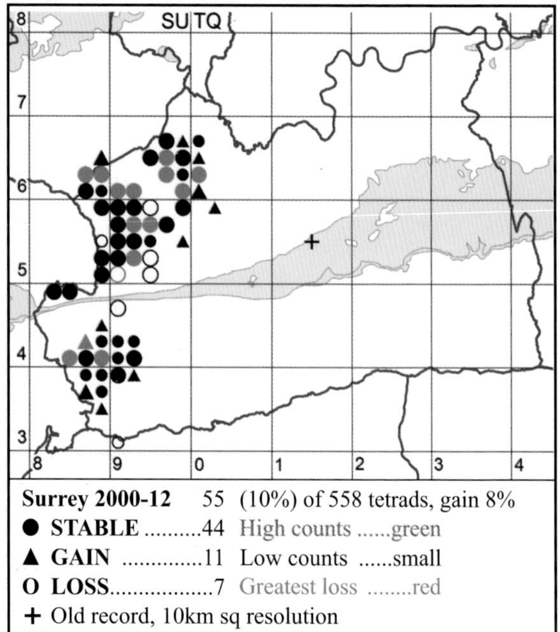

Wingspan: male 51-56mm, female 54-62mm.
Identification: largest of the Browns; female slightly larger and brighter. On landing the wings close to show an orange patch and eyespot on the underside of the forewing, visible only briefly before it is lowered behind the camouflaged hindwing. Brown and orange upperside, which has two eyespots on each forewing and one on each hindwing, is seen in flight, during courtship, and under certain circumstances when mating. The camouflaged underside of the hindwing makes the Grayling inconspicuous when settled on bark, bare soil or leaf litter and as it angles itself in relation to the sun to regulate its temperature. Erratic short flights are characteristic, and it often settles on skin or clothing.

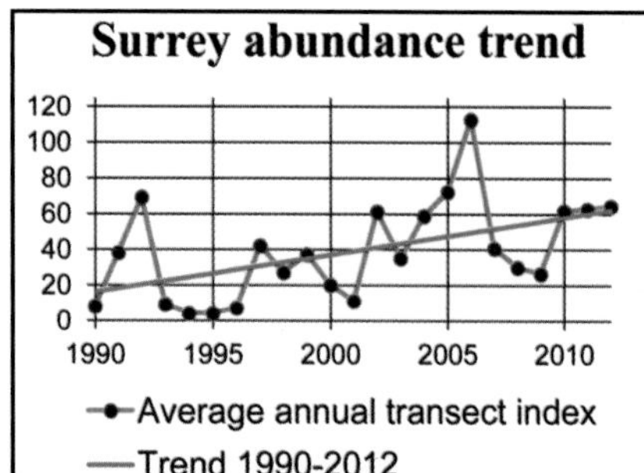

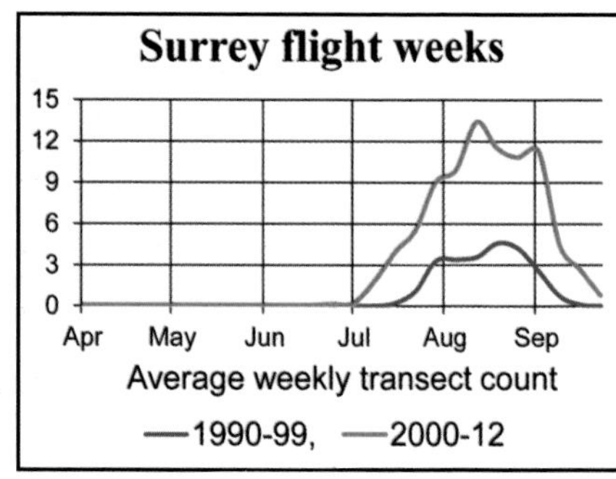

Grayling male on silver birch. **BH**

Variations/aberrations: regional differences in the Grayling have been classified as subspecies and treated as separate races. The most interesting, *thyone,* found only on Llandudno's Great Orme headland, is smaller and emerges a few weeks earlier than elsewhere. It is thought that isolation from the mainland thousands of years ago caused this variation. In Surrey there is conspicuous variation in the jagged band across the underside of the hindwing, from broad bright white to barely noticeable. This was once thought to be a difference between chalk and heathland forms but now the full range of variation is seen on the heaths.
Confusion species: Meadow Brown is smaller and behaves differently.
Habitat: only on heathland in Surrey, but elsewhere also on coastal dunes, undercliffs, calcareous grassland, quarries; well-drained soil and areas of bare ground are essential.
Top transects: Chobham Common NE, Brentmoor Heath, Frensham Common, Witley Common.
Other key sites: Dawney Hill, Horsell Common, Sheet's Heath, Thursley NNR, Staple Hill (Chobham Common); also the military ranges, and semi-developed sites such as Brookwood Cemetery and military vehicle test tracks on Curley Hill, Lightwater.
Life cycle: univoltine; winters as larva. Eggs are laid singly on sparse, fine grasses, or nearby wood litter. Larvae hatch after 2-3 weeks and are nocturnal. After hibernation they resume feeding in the spring, again only at night; during the day they hide deep in grass tussocks. The pupa is formed just below ground and the butterfly emerges after about a month.
Larval foodplants: various grasses, including bristle bent, tor-grass, false-brome, tufted and early hair-grass, rat's-tail fescue.

THE Grayling has benefited from Surrey County Council's Heathland project, set up in 1989 and incorporating Surrey's Last Wilderness programme (2002-2006), but not as consistently and predictably as the Silver-studded Blue. The Grayling can be found on sites with less than ideal conditions while deserting apparently favourable sites.

Based on research carried out on Dorset heaths, Anna Robinson analysed the habitat requirements of the Grayling and identified the variables that affect its density, either positively or negatively (Robinson & Brereton 2008). This study has been used as a basis for recording observations of Grayling habitats in Surrey. The results are not conclusive but my impression is that, while the Grayling is tolerant of cooler weather, as indicated by its northerly range, it is the condition of the soil that is critical for the survival of the

Grayling *continued* — Howard Street

burrowing larvae. Observations indicate that the ground must be fast-draining and friable, typically uneven or sloping with sandy soils disturbed by rabbits or erosion. There should also be areas of bare ground and trees for the butterfly to settle on.

The Grayling exhibits some unusual behaviour, including an elaborate courtship ritual which was documented by Tinbergen (1974). More recently Geoff Eaton has recorded his observations of unusual Grayling behaviour on Horsell Common together with some remarkable photographs as shown on facing page and in Eaton (2011a; 2012).

There is something unpredictable about the Grayling which, with the largely unexplained rapid decline and relatively recent disappearance from Surrey of the related Wall Brown, gives reason for concern.

Grayling — weekly transect counts

Chobham Common North-East SU977655 — **Audrey & David Moss**

	WEEK	2000	2001	2002	2003	2004	2005	2006	2007	2008	2009	2010	2011	2012
08-Jul	15					-	8	-	6	-	3	7	-	-
15	16						11	29		2	3	26	-	-
22	17					7	8	55	8	25	5	13	10	
29	18					12	5	23	8		25	33	25	10
5 August	19					**34**	32	**56**	6			**49**	37	10
12	20					16	**50**	40	**20**	11	19		**46**	43
19	21					6	28	24	6	18	**27**	12	35	**52**
26	22					6	23	17	15	**26**	24	11	9	37
2 September	23					13	23	24	8	9	14	23	30	**52**
9	24					-	17	11	5	7	12	12	12	2
16	25					-	1	8	8	1	3	6	1	3
23	26					-	2		-	2	2	-	2	
Abundance index						117	208	292	91	NI	157	NI	210	213
Weeks recorded						**7**	**12**	**10**	**10**	**9**	**11**	**10**	**10**	**8**

Phenology trend	**1990-2012**	no change
Best transect day 2000-12	Aug 5, 2006	Chobham Common NE 56
Transects abundance	**1990-2012** gain 285%	**2000-2012** gain 73%
UK transects abundance	**1976-2012** loss 60%	**10-year trend** gain 18%
UK 4,361 10k squares	**2005-09** 489 = 11%	**10-year trend** loss 18%

Flight weeks ▲High transect counts △Middle ^Low

Apr					May				Jun				Jul					Aug				Sep			
1	8	15	22	29	6	13	20	27	3	10	17	24	1	8	15	22	29	5	12	19	26	2	9	16	23
												^	^	^	△	△	△	△	▲	▲	▲	▲	△	△	^

Grayling behaviour, Horsell Common, Woking, August 2010: **GE**

1 *Male (right) mating with female (left); intruding male in attendance.*

2 *Intruding male attacks female.*

3 *Intruding male faces mating female (brighter wings).*

Gatekeeper *Pyronia tithonus*

Malcolm Bridge

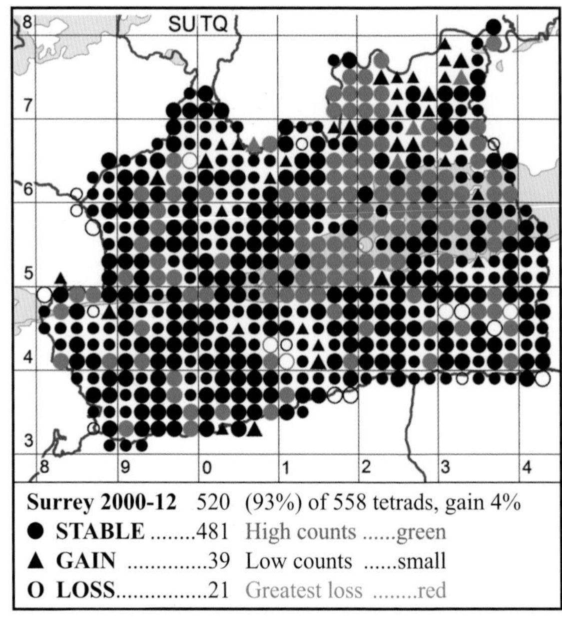

Surrey status: common and widespread.
Flies: early/mid-July to late August.
Trends: expanding range although transect numbers are down; south London has Gatekeeper records in nearly every tetrad, an impressive advance. The flight period has become more protracted and the Gatekeeper is now regularly seen, in reduced numbers, in late August.
Wingspan: male 37-43mm, female 42-48mm.
Identification: the smaller male's upperwings, bordered brown, are an intense orange broken by a large brown smudge of sex brand scales. The female shows a large area of paler orange inside a brown border. Underside: see "Confusion species" below.
Variations/aberrations: extra spots and eyespots are not uncommon. Pale and albino forms turn up infrequently. In one such form, *albo-marginata*, seemingly present in the gene pool at Hutchinson's Bank, the brown borders are bleached.
Confusion species: the larger female Meadow Brown shows a good deal of orange-bordered brown but the differences are clear. With wings closed there is a similarity between the two species but the underside hindwings of the Gatekeeper are dusted with white specks, those of the Meadow Brown with black specks. The black eyespot of the Gatekeeper usually holds two white spots, that of the Meadow Brown just one.

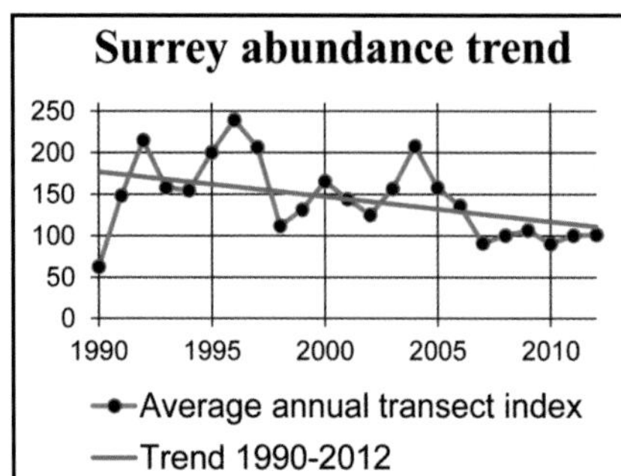

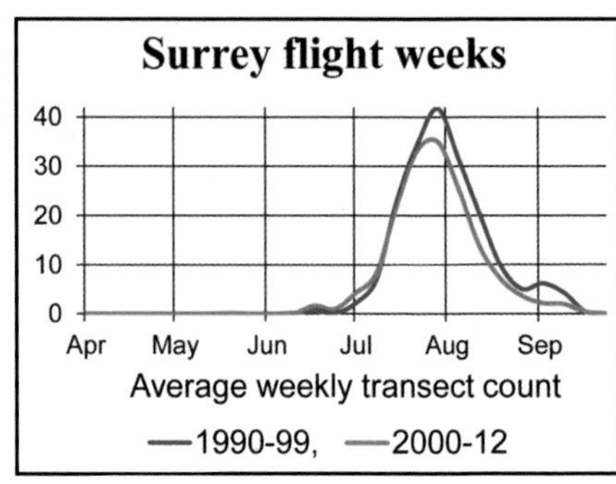

Gatekeeper male on round-headed rampion.
FK

Key habitat: warm, sheltered places with tall grasses bordered by shrubs and hedgerows. The species is equally at home on downland, heathland or light woodland.

Top transects: Park Downs, Fairmile Common, Mitcham Common, Nore Hill, Richmond Park.

Life cycle: univoltine; eggs are laid singly at the base of a shrub and hatch after three weeks. Larva hibernates after first moult, well before the onset of autumn, burrowing into the heart of a grassy clump; resumes feeding the following March or early April from dusk into the night. Pupation in June lasts 3-4 weeks. Adult has a short proboscis, only 6mm, which limits the choice of nectar plants to flat, simple flowers, notably bramble.

Larval foodplants: creeping bent, cock's-foot, sheep's-fescue, perennial rye-grass, annual and rough meadow-grass.

THE Gatekeeper is the last of the common and widespread species to appear each year and its emergence in early July is a sure sign that summer is moving towards the equinox. Also but now less frequently called the Hedge Brown, it was confusingly named the Large Heath by several authorities towards the end of the Victorian era. Goss (1902) noted that the Large Heath (i.e. Gatekeeper) was common throughout the county.

It is a species that defines the north-south divide in the UK. Its stronghold is southern England but it has a widespread distribution in much of Wales and the Midlands. In recent years it has edged north, with records from Lancashire, south Cumbria and Yorkshire. It is plentiful throughout Surrey but only in the past two decades has it become well established on the commons of south London. Good numbers are reported annually from Mitcham, Wimbledon and Tooting Commons and Richmond Park. The butterfly also thrives under the shadow of Canary Wharf at Stave Hill Park, Rotherhithe.

The butterfly was recorded at South Norwood Country Park for the first time in 1999. The warden, Dave Dack, saw it along the grassy hedgeline adjacent to Elmers End station, just inside Kent. This former sewage farm has been monitored by transect since 1998 and there were no previous records. Transect data picked up a few individuals in

Gatekeeper *continued* **Malcolm Bridge**

2000 and it took until 2005 for the Gatekeeper to reach most of the suitable habitat of this 125-acre site astride the county boundary.

Its success at colonising a large part of suburban south London is a pleasing advance on the observation by Collins (1995) that the species was absent only from built-up areas of London. According to Gail Jeffcoate *et al.* (2000), experienced recorders reported first sightings of Gatekeepers on the edge of London in the 1990s: Mitcham Common (Alan Wingrove) in 1992; Raynes Park, Barnes Common and Wimbledon Common in 1996. Gatekeepers were also seen in Rotherhithe and Bermondsey in the extreme north-east of our region in 1998. It now appears annually and breeds in quite small suburban gardens.

Gatekeeper — weekly transect counts

Park Downs, Banstead TQ265585 — **Jill Hall**

	WEEK	2000	2001	2002	2003	2004	2005	2006	2007	2008	2009	2010	2011	2012
24 June	13	-	-	-	-	-	-	-	1	-	-	-	-	-
1 July	14	-	-	3	7	2	-	-	14	-	1	-	-	-
8	15	8	8	4	49	5	89	17	17	7	21	7	1	-
15	16	21	82	42	147	106	115	135	**65**	52	41	84	34	1
22	17	126	116	56	132	170	168	**170**	46	**110**	91	**113**	33	34
29	18	**146**	**120**	**187**	**168**	**211**	**174**	145	48	93	**99**	94	**98**	65
5 August	19	-	51	122	56	151	55	11	42	65	48	56	96	**89**
12	20	20	33	65	5	33	38	7	14	11	14	13	20	18
19	21	15	7	5	-	2	12	1	-	2	5	6	25	3
26	22	-	-	4	-	2	-	-	1	2	1	-	-	6
Abundance index		336	417	490	564	374	651	517	260	338	336	385	327	216
Weeks recorded		**6**	**7**	**9**	**7**	**9**	**7**	**7**	**9**	**8**	**9**	**7**	**7**	**7**

Phenology trend	**1990-2012**	earlier by one week	
Best transect day 2000-12	Jul 18, 2006	Fairmile Common	222
Transects abundance	**1990-2012** loss 37%	**2000-2012** loss 46%	
UK transects abundance	**1976-2012** loss 37%	**10-year trend** loss 62%	
UK 4,361 10k squares	**2005-09** 1,372 = 31%	**10-year trend** loss 2%	

Flight weeks ▲High transect counts △Middle ^Low

Apr					May				Jun				Jul					Aug				Sep			
1	8	15	22	29	6	13	20	27	3	10	17	24	1	8	15	22	29	5	12	19	26	2	9	16	23
											^	^	△	△	▲	▲	▲	▲	△	△	△	△	△	^	^

Meadow Brown *Maniola jurtina*

Ken Willmott

Surrey status: common and widespread.
Flies: mid-June to late September.
Trends: abundance on transects is declining; individuals can emerge early, as shown by my record of May 31, 2011.
Wingspan: male 40-55mm, female 42-60mm.
Identification: sexually dimorphic; male usually darker brown, particularly when fresh, and with much less orange on upperside of forewings surrounding the single-dotted eyespot; male underside duller and markings less well defined.

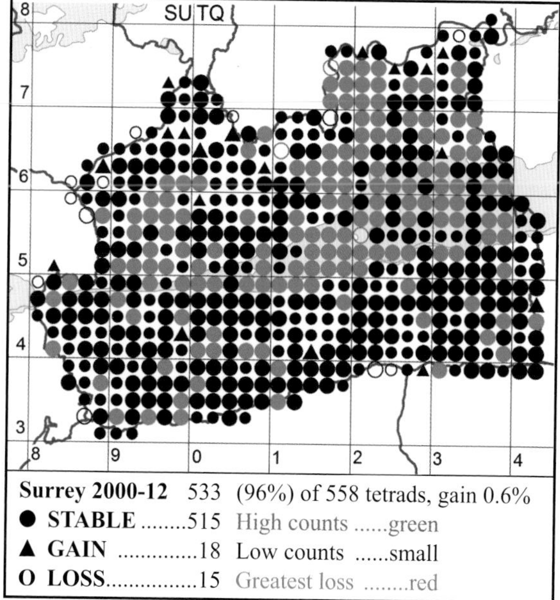

Variations/aberrations: amount of orange on wings of both sexes is variable; pathological deformation in the wing scales can produce white or cream patches. An albino male, ab. *cinerea*, on Denbies Hillside in 2003 resembled a Small White with just an orange patch. Ab. *anommata* lacks forewing eyespots.
Confusion species: Gatekeeper upperside has more orange; forewing eyespot has two white dots; underside has more prominent white spots and brighter, more distinct pale bands. Ringlet lacks orange markings.
Habitat: any suitable grassland, including gardens.
Transects with four-figure abundance index in 2012: Park Downs 1,662, Quarry Hangers 1,394, Riddlesdown 1,220, Farthing Downs 1,115, Denbies Landbarn B 1,092, Pewley Down 1,002.

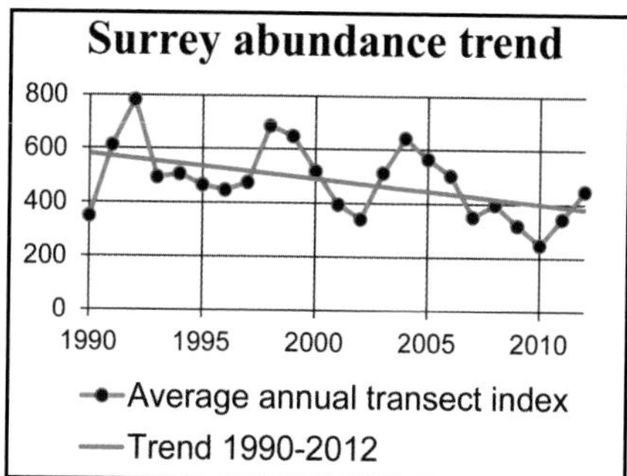

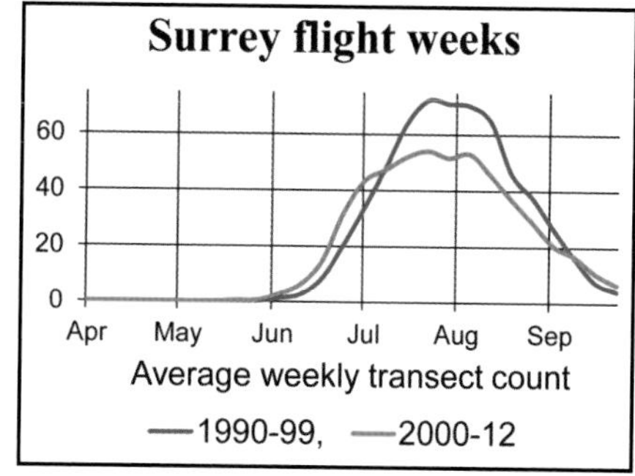

Meadow Brown *continued*

Ken Willmott

Life cycle: usually univoltine, with a protracted emergence, although Frohawk (1924) recognised a frequent, partial second brood, with freshly emerged specimens appearing from late August into September; winters as larva. Scores of males patrolling for females can be quite a spectacle. Females lay on grasses of short or medium height, often disappearing as they crawl around, opening and closing their wings to check the temperature. They will also lay on lawns and cut meadows, anticipating the regrowth for larvae to eat. After three moults before late October, the larva partially hibernates, and will often feed on mild winter nights. It moults twice more before pupating in spring for about one month.

Meadow Brown pair, female above. **BH**

Larval foodplants: wide variety of grasses. I have found innumerable larvae on false-brome at Denbies Hillside, and on cock's-foot in Chiddingfold Forest.

THE following records illustrate: 1 variable emergence dates; 2 existence of second brood; 3 longer flight period on the Chalk.

1 Chalk at Denbies Hillside:

2010, Jun 4 = none, **2011, May 31** = 10+ males, **2012, Jun 19** = 3 males.

The Meadow Brown exhibits protandry — where males fly for a period before the first females appear. In the wet summer of 2012 I did not record a female until June 30, 11 days after male emergence.

2 Mating pairs on Denbies Hillside in 2012: **Aug 23** = 3, **Sep 5** = 4, **Sep 19** = 1

The females were in perfect condition, and therefore freshly emerged.

2011 dates in clay woodland were significantly earlier: **Jun 26** = 1, **Jul 4** = 1, **Jul 11** = 1.

3 Denbies Hillside 2011:

First males (10+) **May 31**; last males (plus females) **Sep 29**.

That is a flight period of at least 122 days and no doubt a few were still on the wing in early October. Females were still emerging on the Downs throughout September, when populations in clay woodlands were in steep decline (Bookham Common, Sep 2: 12+ females, no males).

Meadow Brown male on bramble. **FK**

My study of a Meadow Brown population in a large meadow at Leatherhead provided data on habitat conservation for this common species. The grass on this site was cut for hay annually, usually in early July depending on the weather. As cutting proceeded, the butterflies moved to the field edges, but the females returned to the cut areas to lay on the remnant grass. This cut was not followed by grazing, and the next spring a wealth of grass and wild flowers had returned to greet another Meadow Brown emergence.

Ideally this cut would take place when the maximum number of females were on the wing, with minimal loss of female pupae during the cut, and a higher number of eggs laid post-cut. Also this cut would not be severe enough to adversely affect the larval foodplants of other species such as Common Blue and Small Copper.

Regular summer grazing by cattle on the open parts of Bookham Common has reduced the Meadow Brown population. In contrast, numbers remain good at Denbies Hillside because livestock is moved into different compartments after two or three weeks and grazing is less intensive. However it is important that habitats continue to be correctly grazed for the benefit of specialists, like Adonis Blue and Silver-spotted Skipper, rather than a generalist like the Meadow Brown.

Meadow Brown *continued*

Meadow Brown weekly transect counts
Park Downs, Banstead TQ265585 **Jill Hall**

	WEEK	2000	2001	2002	2003	2004	2005	2006	2007	2008	2009	2010	2011	2012
27 May	9	-	-	-	-	-	-	-	1	-	1	-	3	-
3 June	10	-	-	-	-	-	-	-	7	-	-	1	3	-
10	11	-	-	3	14	8	-	-	48	-	11	1	22	2
17	12	11	2	6	36	40	25	49	73	8	35	19	30	7
24	13	79	8	36	120	66	103	135	86	64	80	32	71	15
1 July	14	135	66	50	67	118	70	257	87	119	135	88	76	40
8	15	84	**140**	42	162	72	**296**	233	**99**	88	101	83	28	44
15	16	107	121	61	**194**	124	278	335	96	88	83	78	79	23
22	17	**163**	110	69	181	180	278	**384**	77	176	111	145	68	141
29	18	123	122	81	192	228	224	348	76	300	104	131	144	165
5 August	19	-	81	**90**	141	**311**	150	173	82	**310**	**147**	100	**247**	296
12	20	84	60	66	99	119	123	121	69	197	60	**171**	138	**321**
19	21	64	48	37	30	103	110	102	66	212	113	66	197	179
26	22	43	25	29	24	86	35	52	74	126	63	78	93	182
2 September	23	27	12		4	46	28	41	33	41	29	72	50	101
9	24	21	5	13	6	2	21	14	23	48	19	18	19	25
16	25	2	1	4	1	1	5	7	5	22	8	31	29	15
23	26	1	-	-	-	-	1	1		8	5	13	10	-
Abundance index		944	801	608	1271	1555	1747	2259	987	1901	1099	1136	1329	1556
Weeks recorded		**14**	**14**	**14**	**15**	**15**	**15**	**15**	**17**	**15**	**17**	**17**	**18**	**15**

Phenology trend	**1990-2012**	earlier by 0.5 weeks	
Best transect day 2000-12	Aug 7, 2004	Sheepleas	846
Transects abundance	**1990-2012** loss 34%	**2000-2012** loss 30%	
UK transects abundance	**1976-2012** gain 5%	**10-year trend** loss 31%	
UK 4,361 10k squares	**2005-09** 2,441 = 56%	**10-year trend** loss 2%	

Flight weeks ▲High transect counts △Middle ^Low

Apr					May				Jun				Jul					Aug				Sep			
1	8	15	22	29	6	13	20	27	3	10	17	24	1	8	15	22	29	5	12	19	26	2	9	16	23
						^	^	^	^	^	△	△	△	▲	▲	▲	▲	▲	△	△	△	△	△	△	△

Small Heath *Coenonympha pamphilus* — Gay Carr

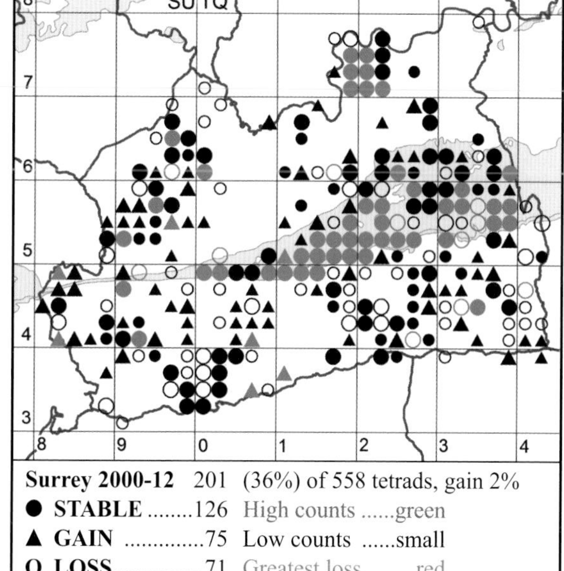

Surrey status: common and widespread on dry grassland.
Flies: overlapping broods from May to September, and even October.
Conservation: UK Biodiversity Action Plan priority species; BC 2010 Red List: near-threatened.
Trends: decline in transect abundance has stabilised.
Wingspan: male 29-33mm, female 34-37mm.
Identification: upperside pale orange-brown with distinct grey-brown margin. Forewing underside is orange with a small black eye-spot ringed in yellow. Hindwing underside has darker basal area, whitish band and understated eye-spots. It is the smallest of the browns, the female being larger and paler than the male. Its wings are always closed unless a laying female is assessing temperature.
Variations/aberrations: can vary in brightness, with both bright and dull individuals flying together in the same colony. Size of the spots can also vary.
Confusion species: Large Heath does not occur in southern Britain.
Habitat: grassland with fine grasses and where the sward is short and sparse; particularly favours dry, well-drained grassland, especially heathland and downland, but colonies may also be found from roadside verges to woodland rides.

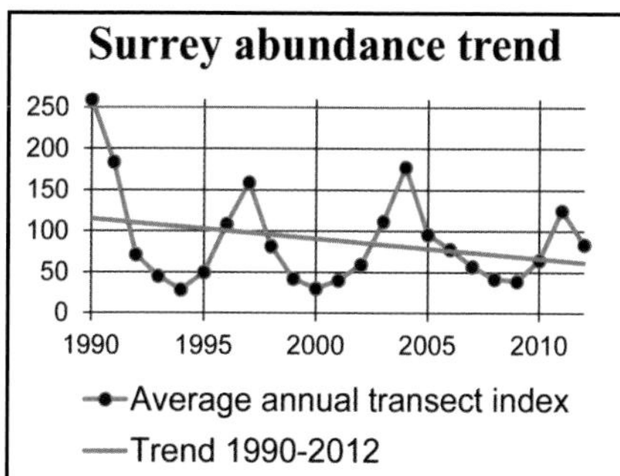

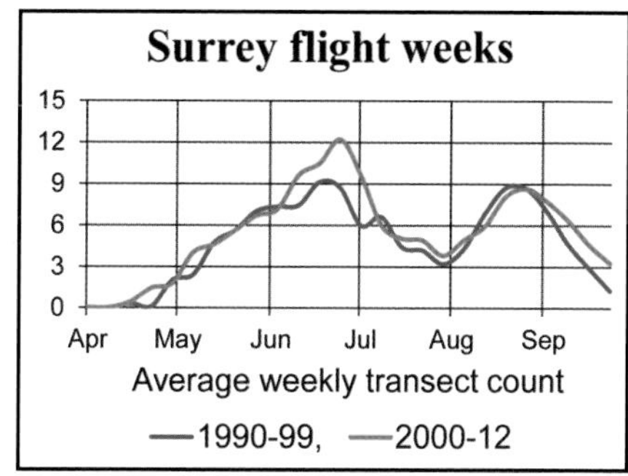

Small Heath *continued* **Gay Carr**

Top transects: Denbies Landbarn B, Box Hill, Colekitchen, Farthing Downs, Headley Heath, Hutchinson's Bank, Nore Hill, Park Downs, Quarry Hangers, Richmond Park.

Other key site: Newlands Corner.

Life cycle: typically bivoltine; winters as larva. Eggs are laid singly on fine grasses. The larvae feed together, mainly at night, and are beautifully concealed among the fine grasses. The larva moults four times, with the majority overwintering after three moults. However a varying percentage from later eggs hibernate at an earlier stage and in spring only the larger ones are ready to pupate.

Larval foodplants: fine grasses such as various bents, fescues, and meadow-grasses.

Small Heath. **GE**

■ *Mating pair: page 199*

THE Small Heath rarely settles more than a metre above the ground, where males gather in territories to await passing females. It appears much brighter in flight than when basking in the sun, tilted to one side.

The number of broods and the flight period are variable and adults may be seen continuously from spring to autumn on some sites in southern England. There is usually one brood in the north and two or even three in the south. In Surrey two broods are the norm unless it is a particularly hot summer.

The Small Heath is found throughout the county but colonies have been lost due to intensive agriculture and changing land use. Although the species favours dry soils, it is not restricted to this habitat, but is often seen in ones and twos on heavy clays and marshes, although in these places breeding is probably restricted to local dry spots. Thomas found many larvae in the glades of a swampy wood in the Surrey Weald, but only on the sides of ant hills protruding as islands above the waterlogged ground.

A key Surrey stronghold of the Small Heath away from the Chalk is the acid grassland of Richmond Park, which has held good numbers in both broods. However, although numbers were increasing from 2004 until 2006, they declined by more than half in 2007 with a disastrous year in 2008. They have been slowly increasing since then, and 2012 was a good year, particularly for the second brood. Wimbledon Common, which has a much smaller area of similar habitat, has shown much the same trend, but the increase has been slower and numbers are nowhere near to matching those of the early 90s.

Small Heath

weekly transect counts

Denbies Landbarn B TQ135499 — **Gail Jeffcoate, Robert Cramp**

	WEEK	2000	2001	2002	2003	2004	2005	2006	2007	2008	2009	2010	2011	2012
15 April	3			-	-		-	-	-	-	2	-	-	
22	4			-	10	-	-	-	5	-	1	-	-	
29	5			-		1	-	-	4	-	3		10	3
6 May	6				42	5	4	3	5	4	12	3	16	5
13	7			16	14	27	12	4	1	16		2	23	
20	8			4	23	38	11		11	12	8	18	15	29
27	9			21	28	36	11	6	6	6	10	11	23	41
3 June	10				12	30	16	1	**17**	17	5	23	36	21
10	11			19	34	59	14	29		15	1	26	12	27
17	12			15	53	43	25	32	16	8	6	36		28
24	13			**66**	39	**74**	**47**	**37**	5	**23**	3	**42**	15	**70**
1 July	14			50	35	38	38	28	6	18	4	22	11	
8	15			48	9	22	25	19	1	5	1	16	5	46
15	16			35	7	20	11	11	4	3		4	3	
22	17			23	16	8	3	3	2	5	1		12	15
29	18				56	7	2	2	3		2		12	-
5 August	19			8	36	14		5	2	3	2	4	42	1
12	20			2	43	25	1	1	-	-	12	7	36	-
19	21			17	47	14	1	2			**17**	10	47	10
26	22			24	**80**	22	2	3	3	6	3	12	**53**	10
2 September	23			20	52	36	14	12	9	4	12	19		12
9	24			10	33	28	15	21	9	1		3	16	26
16	25			12	18	14	9	2	4	7	5	10	18	27
23	26			4	8	10	4	5	-	5	4	13	4	13
Abundance index				425	731	571	268	222	130	166	133	299	458	NI
Weeks recorded				**18**	**22**	**22**	**20**	**20**	**19**	**18**	**21**	**19**	**20**	**17**

Phenology trend	**1990-2012**	no change	
Best transect day 2000-12	Jun 24, 2005	Richmond Park	123
Transects abundance	**1990-2012** loss 46%	**2000-2012** gain 23%	
UK transects abundance	**1976-2012** loss 54%	**10-year trend** loss 22%	
UK 4,361 10k squares	**2005-09** 1,934 = 44%	**10-year trend** loss 9%	

Flight weeks

▲High transect counts △Middle ^Low

Apr					May				Jun				Jul					Aug				Sep			
1	*8*	*15*	*22*	*29*	*6*	*13*	*20*	*27*	*3*	*10*	*17*	*24*	*1*	*8*	*15*	*22*	*29*	*5*	*12*	*19*	*26*	*2*	*9*	*16*	*23*
		^	^	^	△	△	△	▲	▲	▲	▲	▲	▲	△	△	△	△	△	▲	▲	▲	▲	△	△	△

Ringlet *Aphantopus hyperantus* **Malcolm Bridge**

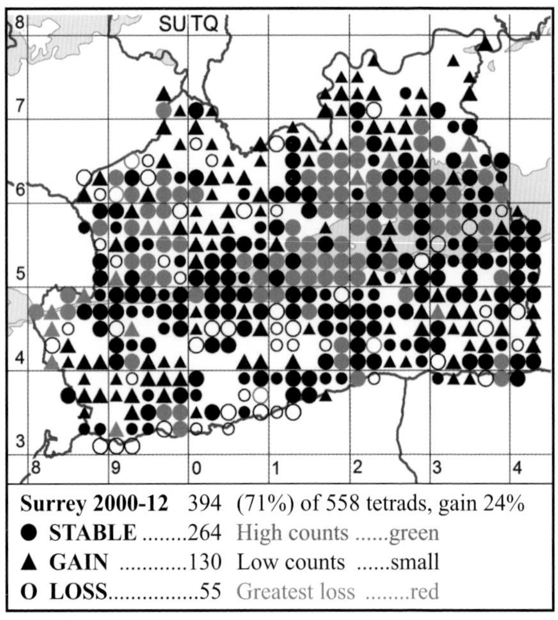

Surrey status: locally common and widespread, increasingly so in suburban south London from where it was lost in the late 19th century.

Flies: mainly a July butterfly, although smaller numbers, usually males, can be seen in the latter part of June; by early August it has largely gone.

Trends: expanding range.

Wingspan: male 42-48mm, female 46-52mm.

Identification: dark brown upperwings, which in fresh specimens appear almost velvety black and have a white fringe. At rest the underwings are unmistakable: a plain, mid-brown background adorned with a string of conspicuous eyes, rather like RAF roundels but with a white spot edged with black and enclosed in a yellow ring.

Variations/aberrations: underside eyespots vary in size, shape and numbers. The most striking form, ab. *lanceolata,* has large, elongated "eyes"; ab *obsoleta* lacks the yellow rings of the eyes and even the white pupil; ab. *arete* shows only the white spot with no surrounding black and yellow circle.

Confusion species: less pristine specimens in flight can resemble a male Meadow Brown, although the Ringlet has a distinctive bobbing style.

Habitat: any patch of unimproved grassland, particularly in damp situations.

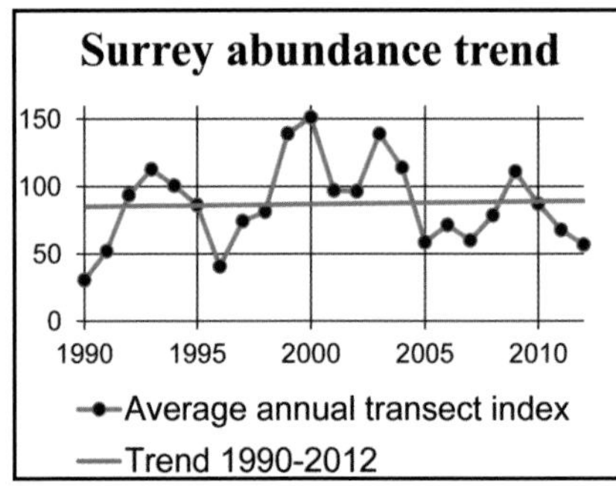

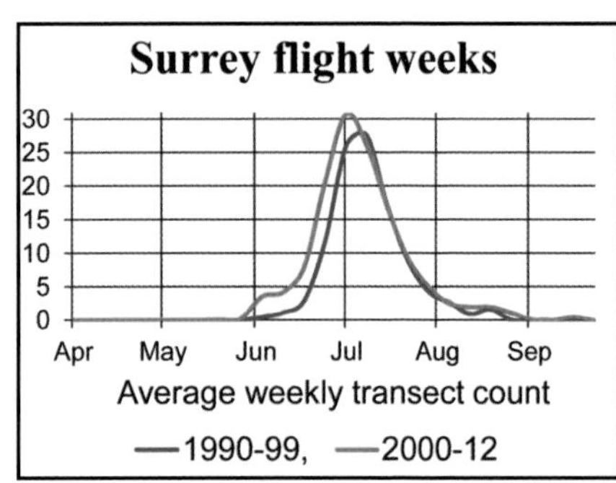

Ringlet pair, male on right. **BH**

Top transects: Hutchinson's Bank, Ashtead Common, Epsom Common, Happy Valley, Mitcham Common, Park Downs, Pewley Down, Swan Barn Farm.

Life cycle: univoltine; winters as larva. The female settles on or close to a larval foodplant, pulses her body in the manner of a Marbled White, and an egg appears at the tip of her abdomen. She then flies off, allowing the egg to drop to the ground. The larva hatches after about two weeks and wanders in search of a suitable grass clump. Well before the onset of autumn the third-instar larva finds a secure lodging, usually at the base of its foodplant.

Larvae resume feeding in April and are most readily found on warm May evenings when a torchlight search or use of a sweep net will usually yield a few final instars. The fully grown larva is pale brown with a dark dorsal stripe and pale pink and white stripes along its flanks. The larva pupates in early June in a loosely constructed silken chamber within the base of its grass clump.

Larval foodplants: grasses, including cock's-foot, false-brome, tufted hair-grass, couch.

Flight weeks ▲High transect counts △Middle ^Low

Apr					May				Jun				Jul					Aug				Sep			
1	8	15	22	29	6	13	20	27	3	10	17	24	1	8	15	22	29	5	12	19	26	2	9	16	23
							^	^	△	△	△	▲	▲	▲	▲	△	△	△	△	△	△	^			

Ringlet *continued*

Malcolm Bridge

THE Ringlet's return to suburban London after a century's absence is a welcome development. It is a "value for money" butterfly and seems as willing to fly on a dull and cheerless day, with no more than a hint of warmth, as it is in bright sunshine. Indeed even light rain does not ground this unfussy butterfly. It is an early riser and usually on the wing shortly after 9am. Males emerge some ten days before the females and can be seen alongside Meadow Browns, fluttering among grassy tussocks in search of a female.

The Ringlet's requirements are simple, but overzealous cutting and tidying of grassy commons will result in losses, with the recently established colony (mid 1990s) at South Norwood Country Park illustrating this. The park used to benefit from Ringlet visitors from a small but thriving colony within an undeveloped corner of the adjacent Beckenham Cemetery. A small sister colony was established in the park just beyond the boundary culvert with the cemetery. Following the landscaping in 2002 of this neglected cemetery corner, Ringlet numbers fell sharply. Now the species survives, just, within the country park.

I first saw a Ringlet in the cemetery in 1999. I was standing by the grave of that famous Yorkshireman and sanitary engineer, Sir Thomas Crapper. Sadly Sir Thomas is no longer blessed with Ringlets "dancing" on his grave, but elsewhere, happily, the opposite is true. Indeed two of south London's older cemeteries, West Norwood and Nunhead, support recently established colonies.

Collins (1995) noted that the Ringlet was quite widely distributed in Surrey, but virtually absent from the London area. He suggested that the Ringlet could have benefited from the increase of scrubby, ungrazed grasslands following the 1950s onset of myxomatosis.

The species was adversely affected by hot, dry summers such as 1976 and, to a lesser extent, 1996. However a sequence of cooler, damper summers enabled numbers to recover over three or four years.

In the closing years of the last century the Ringlet, shadowing the progress of the Gatekeeper, was recorded from several of south London's commons but, inexplicably, this range increase faltered. Colonies such as the one at the southern edge of Wimbledon Common (Beverley Meads) failed whereas the Gatekeeper consolidated its gains and its numbers increased. In recent years the Ringlet has recovered its momentum and is now seen in increasing numbers on all of the major commons of south London. A thriving colony is now established in Richmond Park.

Phenology trend	**1990-2012**	earlier by one week	
Best transect day 2000-12	Jul 1, 2009	Park Downs	412
Transects abundance	**1990-2012** gain 5%	**2000-2012** loss 49%	
UK transects abundance	**1976-2012** gain 312%	**10-year trend** gain 14%	
UK 4,361 10k squares	**2005-09** 1,970 = 45%	**10-year trend** gain 8%	

Ringlet female. **KW**

Ringlet

weekly transect counts

Hutchinson's Bank, New Addington TQ380617 **Martin Wills**

	WEEK	2000	2001	2002	2003	2004	2005	2006	2007	2008	2009	2010	2011	2012
10 June	11	5	-	-	1	-	30	-	10	1	1	-	3	-
17	12	8	-	1	61	21	34	1	42	40	51	1	30	-
24	13	**203**	3	**136**	172	34		35	**48**	68	77	17	47	6
1 July	14	132	64		178	**70**	28	65	19	**145**	**140**	61	45	44
8	15	68	**147**	67	**188**	40	**42**	**94**	8	70	56	**74**	**50**	39
15	16	81	94	71	74	21	1	15	4	26	42	27	15	**49**
22	17	36	58	37	20	18	-	18	2	23	10	14	10	25
29	18	26	23	15	9	9		-	-	17	3	11	4	15
5 August	19	4	4	1	2	-		-	1	-	-		-	3
12	20	-	1	-	-	-					-	-	-	2
19	21	-	1	-	-	-					-	-	-	-
Abundance index		563	395	430	705	179	170	265	134	411	362	218	208	181
Weeks recorded		**9**	**9**	**7**	**9**	**7**	**5**	**6**	**8**	**8**	**8**	**7**	**8**	**8**

Glanville Fritillary *Melitaea cinxia* **Malcolm Bridge**

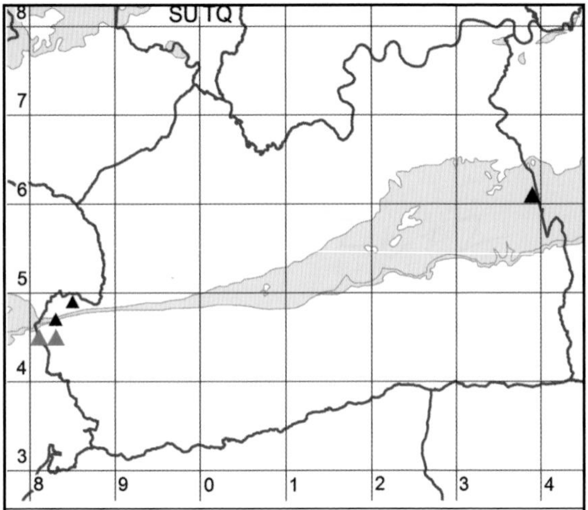

Surrey status: unofficially introduced in 2001 to Alton Road (A31) Sandpit, Wrecclesham, south-west of Farnham; natural British resident only on south coast of Isle of Wight.

Flies: from mid-May throughout June, peaking in early June; 2012 emergence was in early June, but the last week of May is more typical.

Conservation: protected from sale; UK Biodiversity Action Plan priority species;
BC 2010 Red List: endangered.

Surrey 2000-12 5 (0.9%) of 558 tetrads (2km sq)
● **STABLE** ....0 High counts ......green
▲ **GAIN** ....5 Low counts ......small

MAP NOTE: Hutchinson's Bank (TQ380617) 2012 transect records of 1-5-6-3 from June wk2 to Jul wk1 were the result of a translocation of a larval web from Wrecclesham in 2011.

The Wrecclesham site: private, with no public access, but widely used by local children and dog walkers.
A public footpath that runs along the north-west boundary is best accessed via Wrecclesham Recreation Ground on Riverdale, off the A325, or via Willey Mill on the A31.
In 2002 RMC Aggregates (acquired by Cemex in 2005) were given planning permission until March 2014 to extract sand and clay, and then fill with non-hazardous waste followed by comprehensive restoration. However, the 36.2ha site, which is officially in an Area of Great Landscape Value, has been unworked since 2004. Health and safety are monitored by the Quarries National Inspection Team and future permissions are in the hands of Surrey County Council. The sandpit's limited accessibility, via a small road from the A31 under the Farnham-Alton railway line, suggests it is safe from major development. Surrey Wildlife Trust, Surrey CC and Waverley BC have all been alerted to its high level of biodiversity, which includes several rare insects.

Trends: dispersing from Wrecclesham and recorded some 6km to the north-east (Farnham) and south-west (Bentley, Hants). Areas around the sandpit, especially to the east, and also north of the railway line, have been colonised for some years. Numbers at the core site vary, with April weather being significant. .

Wingspan: male 38-46mm, female 44-52mm.

Identification: upperside has chequered pattern of black and orange-brown; outer edge of hindwing has a submarginal row of black spots surrounded by orange; larger female is often darker.

Glanville Fritillary males on germander speedwell, Wrecclesham. **BH**

Confusion species: Heath Fritillary (subject of a less-successful release at Wrecclesham) is confined to the south-west of England, and woodland glades in Kent and Essex; it lacks the submarginal row of c. 5 dark spots on hindwing.

Habitat: warm areas of disturbed ground supporting a profusion of ribwort plantain. In NE Spain I have encountered it on almost any dry and scrubby patch with the foodplant, conditions which are characteristic of the Wrecclesham site.

Life cycle: univoltine; winters as larva. Males patrol to find a female, which then lays a batch of 50-100 eggs on the underside of a young plantain leaf in a warm, sheltered spot. The white eggs soon turn primrose yellow and hatch after 2-3 weeks.

In June and July the conspicuous larvae live gregariously in a dense web of white silk, on which they bask. They feed in short bursts when body temperature exceeds 30ºC and Thomas has suggested that by huddling together in a black mass the larval community can maximise the warmth of the sun. After the fourth moult, and still less than 1cm long, they move to taller vegetation and spin a much denser nest within which they hibernate in smaller groups. For a few weeks in early autumn these webs are easily located but are soon concealed in a tangle of wind-blown stems.

On a sunny March day the larvae will swarm out and spin a new web over fresh plantain, often in the shorter sward alongside footpaths. They drop into the safety of dense vegetation at the approach of hiking boots! During April the larvae moult twice more and scatter for their 2-3 weeks pupation.

Larval foodplants: ribwort plantain; also buck's-horn plantain on Isle of Wight.

Flight weeks (all records) ▲High counts △Middle ^Low

Apr					May				Jun				Jul					Aug				Sep			
1	8	15	22	29	6	13	20	27	3	10	17	24	1	8	15	22	29	5	12	19	26	2	9	16	23
						△	▲	▲	▲	▲	▲	△	^												

Glanville Fritillary *continued* — **Malcolm Bridge**

THIS fritillary, like other species (e.g. Swallowtail), had a wider distribution in the 18th century, as an earlier name of Lincolnshire Fritillary would suggest. Eleanor Glanville reported the butterfly from that county and it was later renamed in her honour. It was also known as the Dullidge Fritillary, an older spelling of Dulwich, so the species has a historic link with our area. This was severed in the early 19th century when it retreated from the mainland to the Isle of Wight.

In that sense the events of 2001 could be termed a reintroduction, when a Wrecclesham professional breeder with surplus Glanville larvae noted that the sandpit close to his allotment had an abundance of ribwort plantain, disturbed, sandy cliffs, and a warm microclimate, similar to the Isle of Wight sites. He scattered some final-instar larvae among the plantains and a few butterflies emerged some weeks later.

In 2002 and 2003 there was no evidence that the colony had survived its first year and in April 2004 he repeated the exercise, but as he spread the new larvae among the foodplants, he noticed webs with basking larvae. The colony of 2001 had survived!

Introductions are contentious, even when rarely approved by Natural England or Butterfly Conservation. The significance of the second introduction is a matter of conjecture but in 2004, as county recorder, I received the first Glanville record from Ian Cunningham, who scours the more obscure parts of the county and had stumbled upon the colony quite by chance. Subsequent records include photos of a larval web from Farnham Park in April 2007, and of adults in West Street Cemetery, Farnham, in 2008.

Larvae can become so numerous in favourable years that they completely defoliate extensive areas of their foodplant. It is not known whether the population-controlling braconid parasitic wasp *Cotesia melitaearum* is present in the Surrey colony. The adult feeds on thrift on the Isle of Wight. In Surrey, bird's-foot-trefoil is favoured.

Glanville Fritillary — weeks with English transect record

	WEEK	2000	2001	2002	2003	2004	2005	2006	2007	2008	2009	2010	2011	2012
29 April	5												✓	
6 May	6												✓	
13	7	✓							✓	✓			✓	
20	8	✓							✓	✓	✓	✓	✓	✓
27	9	✓							✓	✓	✓	✓	✓	✓
3 June	10	✓								✓	✓	✓	✓	✓
10	11	✓						✓		✓	✓	✓	✓	✓
17	12	✓					✓	✓		✓	✓	✓	✓	✓
24	13	✓						✓			✓	✓		✓
1 July	14													✓
Weeks recorded		7						3	3	6	6	6	8	7

Surrey trends	insufficient data	
UK 4,361 10k squares	**2005-09** 11 = 0.25%	**10-year trend** gain 22%

RARE MIGRANTS 1995-2010

Continental Swallowtail *Papilio machaon gorganus*

Jun 28, 1995	1	Leigh	TQ2246	Bill Gerrard, Gail Jeffcoate
Jun 13, 1996	1	Wisley RHS Gardens	TQ0658	Alan Reid
Aug 3, 2003	1	Hindhead	SU8835	S. J. Patton

GENUINE records are likely to be subsp. *gorganus*, which has attempted to breed in Britain. British Swallowtail, subsp. *britannicus*, occurs only in the Norfolk Broads.

Pale/Berger's Clouded Yellow *Colias hyale/alfacariensis*

Apr 16, 2007	1	Denbies Hillside	TQ1350	Ken Willmott

RELATIVES of the Clouded Yellow, difficult to separate and usually bracketed together.

Bath White *Pontia daplidice*..............................not seen since four records in 1945-46.

Long-tailed Blue *Lampides boeticus*

Jul 16, 2003	1	Wrecclesham	SU8244	(*suspected release*) Jeremy Gates
Aug 19, 2003	4	Denbies Carriageway	TQ135499	Gail Jeffcoate, Ken Willmott
July 2008	1	Denbies Carriageway	TQ135499	Malcolm Bridge

VISITOR from southern Europe. In August 2003, Gail Jeffcoate spotted a Long-tailed Blue on Denbies Hillside Carriageway, where everlasting-pea has become abundant. Three days later I found eggs on the unopened flower buds and watched a laying female. A few weeks later I collected a single larva, reared it through to pupa, and released it on the original site, where it emerged in early November.

The exact number seen during 2003 is uncertain: both sexes were recorded and eggs were found some distance apart along the Carriageway.

The 2003 records coincided with immigrations to other counties. A 2008 butterfly from the same site is an isolated record and therefore more likely to have been imported accidentally with leguminous vegetables, at whatever life stage, as has happened in other counties. A 2006 influx to other counties was not evident in Surrey. **KW**

Large Tortoiseshell *Nymphalis polychloros*

Jun 25, 1995	1	Merstham	TQ2954	S. Gibson
Jul 1, 1995	1	Merstham	TQ25	Jean Bates
Oct 31, 1995	1	Holmwood	TQ165455	Steve Jeffcoate
Aug 7, 2006	1	Worplesdon	SU9754	David Smith
Apr 22, 2007	1	Denbies Hillside	TQ1350	Mike Weller
May 1, 2007	1	Chiddingfold, Triangle Meadow	SU984339	Ken Willmott, Mike Weller
May 2, 2007	2	Botany Bay	SU9834	anon, per Nick Bowles
Apr 6, 2008	1	Oaken Wood	SU9833	Stephen Hibbard
Sep 15, 2009	1	Chobham, Burr Hill Lane	SU975626	Sylvia O'Neill

INTERMITTENT resident to 1940s. Goss (1902) noted that this species was generally distributed but, considering the amount of elm, it ought to have been more plentiful.

In 1917-20 and 1947-50, several adults were seen, but not the feeding webs, which are quite findable; 1972-73 yielded several adults in the Chobham area. There have been regular, albeit sporadic, sightings of singletons since, some four or five each decade, with spring being the most likely period following the seven-month hibernation.

This species lends itself to captive breeding and sightings may be the consequence of such activity. In June 2011 at the allotment of a well-known Surrey breeder I noted many Large Tortoiseshell larvae in a netted pot feeding on elm.

Given the butterfly's recent decline in Western Europe, and the problems associated with its foodplant, a breeding return to Surrey is not imminent, although there are an increasing number of records from the Isle of Wight. **MB**.

Camberwell Beauty *Nymphalis antiopa.*

May 13, 1996 1 Coulsdon Common TQ326571 Roger Hawkins
Jul 22, 1996 1 Ashtead Common TQ1759 Stephen Price
Aug 15, 1996 1 Addington, Croydon TQ3764 J.D. Sims
Aug 22, 1996 1 Croydon TQ3265 anon
Aug 29, 1996 1 Roehampton TQ2273 W. Matthews
Aug 11, 2006 1 nr Godalming SU9743 J. Hindley
Aug 17, 2006 1 Westcott TQ1448 Lyn Boyce
Aug 22, 2006 1 nr Aldershot SU84/85 N. Irvine
Jul 8, 2007 1 Mid-Surrey Golf Club, Kew TQ1775 Cally Harris
Apr 2, 2008 1 Gangers Hill TQ373540 Howard Whiting

IN 1995 about 300 were seen nationally, 13 of them in Surrey. Subsequent records may include successful hibernators and fresh immigrants. There are also records of three in mid-March 1997 from ill-defined localities in the Woldingham area.

Queen of Spain Fritillary *Issoria lathonia*

Jul 1 & 3, 2008 1 Sheepleas TQ0851 Harry Eve
Aug 11, 2009 1 Holmbury St Mary TQ1144 Alan Waters

IN 2009 there was a small late-summer migration into Sussex. The Holmbury St Mary record was an egg-laying female in the village churchyard.

Monarch *Danaus plexippus*

Oct 9, 1995 1 Haslemere SU9032 L. Richardson
Oct 5, 2001 1 Farncombe SU9745 C. & I. Hacker

ANY record likely to be an escape but 2001 had a genuine immigration into a number of southern counties, either from North America or populations established in Canary Islands and Spain. Unable to breed in Britain due to lack of foodplant.

EXTINCTION since 1990s, now rare vagrant

Wall *Lasiommata megera*

May 27, 2001 5 Wingate Hill TQ266524 Howard Whiting
Oct 15, 2003 1 Box Hill Lower Viewpoint TQ181509 Graham Revill
Jul 16, 2011 1 fem, British Wildlife Centre, Newchapel TQ3643 Ken Noble
Aug 1, 2011 1 Box Hill Dukes TQ185510 Peter Creasey
Aug 5, 2011 1 Ewhurst Brickworks TQ111376 Martin Gray

Lost from Surrey (clockwise from top left): Small Pearl-bordered Fritillary pair; Pearl-bordered Fritillary; Wall male; Duke of Burgundy female on cowslip. **All BH**.

THE Wall, or Wall Brown, is one of a small number of formerly common and widespread butterflies that have undergone a major range contraction for no apparent reason. Since 1997-98, when none were reported in Surrey, the Wall has been classed as no longer resident in the county. It was virtually lost in the latter half of the 1980s but odd sightings, usually from the border, offered hope of recovery. Scattered records from Box Hill suggest human interference rather than a natural occurrence, given how well this area is worked each year, but the status of rare vagrant could be justified.

Goss (1902) said it was common everywhere by roadsides. Evans & Evans (1973) noted it was generally distributed and often common from downs, meadows, lanes and rough, open spaces. Thereafter a decline set in and Collins (1995) reported it as restricted and uncommon and that it had seriously declined in the county.

The decline has been felt throughout south and central England, from where the Wall, formerly widely distributed and locally common, has disappeared from most of its inland sites. Coastal colonies seem to have escaped the worst ravages and its range has increased recently to include northern counties and southern Scotland. Historically the Wall has shown major range contraction and subsequent recolonisation, so perhaps for Surrey all is not lost. There are populations on the South Downs in Sussex. Kent colonies include a few on the North Downs no farther west than Wye, and along the Thames Estuary at places such as Cliffe and Grain. **MB**

OTHER EXTINCTIONS since 1990s

Duke of Burgundy *Hamearis lucina* ....Last records 1997

May 17, 1997 Colekitchen Hole TQ092487; Hackhurst Downs TQ093485

ONE of the most endangered species. Since the 1980s at least 260 English colonies have become extinct, a 62% decrease. Only about 130 colonies remain, 19 classed as large, in 15 counties. Strongholds are on the South Downs, Tytherley Woods landscape on the Hants/Wilts border, Salisbury Plain and the Cotswolds.

The Duke was last recorded at Colekitchen Hole and the adjacent Hackhurst Downs. Further east at Wholecombe Down (TQ120489), a colony was monitored for over a decade before its eventual demise. In May 1992 there were 10 male territories. In 1993 a female was seen laying on cowslips. In June 1994 a single male territory persisted, the last record on Wholecombe Down.

Last record at Fetcham Downs (TQ1554) on the Norbury Park Estate was in 1986. Egg counts on cowslip leaves included: 72 – May 19, 1976: 31 – Jun 8, 1978; 28 – Jun 4, 1979. During 1980 it was recorded from two woodland areas within the Chiddingfold Forest complex, both probably released specimens, on an unlikely site.

Insufficient or over-zealous management of scrub is suspected to be the main reason for the Duke's loss. Scrub thinning, to create sunny, sheltered clearings, is the preferred management regime. Problems were exacerbated in the early 1990s by drought and large rabbit populations affecting cowslips. Butterfly Conservation's "Dukes on the Edge" project, 2011-2014, is having great success in Kent, Sussex and Tytherley Woods. **KW**

Small Pearl-bordered Fritillary *Boloria selene* ....Last bred 1996

2004-2008 Chiddingfold: presumed release
Jun 2011 Chiddingfold: presumed release

THE stronghold was always Chiddingfold Forest, where the final sighting was a single male in Fisherlane Wood (SU980323) in 1997. An unrecorded reintroduction was made in 2004, persisting until 2008.

On May 25, 2004, in Triangle Meadow (SU98413387) I watched a newly-emerged female, in the process of hardening her wings, being found and mated by a patrolling male. Only odd individuals, mostly males, were recorded in the next few years. The reintroduction was doomed because the habitat was drying out as the young conifer plantations matured and the drainage ditches did their job. The species thrives on damp sites in the north of England, Wales and Scotland, where the larvae feed on marsh violet.

Other former Surrey sites include the woods around Cranleigh (late 1970s), Ashtead Common (1970s), Prince's Coverts at Oxshott (possible releases), and Thursley Common (1986-1992). Nearest current site: Park Corner Heath, East Sussex. **KW**

Pearl-bordered Fritillary *Boloria euphrosyne* ....Last bred 2006

2006 probably the last year of breeding success
2007 one male at Chiddingfold
2011-2012 Chiddingfold, presumed releases

TRIANGLE MEADOW (SU98413387) became the PBF's final refuge in Chiddingfold

Forest, but my sighting of a single male on bugle on May 1, 2007, was the last. Four males were recorded there on May 19 the previous year.

The species survived in a maturing Corsican pine plantation in Sidney Wood (TQ026348) from 1994 to 2002. On May 7, 2003, a vagrant was seen in a younger Corsican pine plantation elsewhere in the wood.

Ashpark Wood (SU992319), nearby in West Sussex, was colonised after a Corsican pine plantation was devastated by the Great Storm of 1987, but the last record was a single male on May 26, 2005. The area was left open, as it remains today, but the site was too small and, despite much effort by Butterfly Conservation volunteers, the PBF could not survive in isolation. It needs a metapopulation structure, of waxing and waning habitats, which Chiddingfold Forest complex no longer provides. After three barren years, odd individuals were seen in 2011-2012. These sudden appearances in a well-watched location were presumably the result of indiscriminate releases.

PBF was introduced to Prince's Coverts, Oxshott, in the 1970s, but failed despite the woodland being thinned. It was also found in woodlands around Cranleigh, especially Canfold Woods (TQ080400). Nearest current site: Verdley Wood, West Sussex. **KW**

OLDER EXTINCTIONS

Black-veined White *Aporia crataegi* .... 19th-century records; extinct GB since 1920s

Black Hairstreak *Satyrium pruni* .... introduction lasted 1952-1980

A COLONY thrived in the Cranleigh area after 1952 introduction by schoolmaster A E Collier, but died out after habitat destroyed for development. Last record: Jun 25, 1980.

High Brown Fritillary *Argynnis adippe* .... lost 1960s or early 1970s

Jul 1, 1980 Botany Bay, presumed release

DECLINED terminally in the 1960s due to changing woodland management.

Marsh Fritillary *Euphydryas aurinia* .... Last bred early 1970s

LAST natural record was probably in 1973 at Littlefield Common (SU9552), north-west of Guildford. Subsequent reintroductions have failed, including one at Chiddingfold that lasted from 1982 to 1986. The species has contracted westwards in response to loss of its damp grassland habitat.

Suspect records, escapes, introductions

Chequered Skipper *Carterocephalus palaemon* .... suspect record c. 1905
Mallow Skipper *Carcharodus alceae* .... accidental introduction 1923
Southern Festoon *Zerynthia polyxena* .... one record of probable escape 2003
Mazarine Blue *Polyommatus semiargus* .... suspect records in 19th century
Map Butterfly *Araschnia levana* .... one record of probable escape 1982
Weaver's Fritillary *Clossiana dia* .... one suspect record in 19th century
Heath Fritillary *Melitaea athalia* .... a few failed introductions
Woodland Grayling *Hipparchia fagi* .... accidental introduction 1946
False Grayling *Arethusana arethusa* .... probable accidental introduction 1974

DAY-FLYING MOTHS

Malcolm Bridge

THE insect order Lepidoptera has 42 regular butterfly species in Surrey but more than 500 larger moths and 1,100 micro-moths. There are more day-flying, colourful moths than butterflies and the division can seem arbitrary. Skippers look much like moths but are classed as butterflies.

Burnets have butterfly-style antennae, albeit with a slight hook at the tip. Surrey's three species have warning colours of scarlet spots on a deep blue-black forewing, and scarlet hindwings edged with black. The **Six-spot Burnet** and **Narrow-bordered Five-spot Burnet** are widespread; the **Five-spot Burnet** is confined to patches of the North Downs (notably Denbies Hillside) but helpfully flies some weeks before the other two.

Larvae of the Geometers, or earth-measurers, lack sucker feet on the central segments and are thus obliged to progress in a series of loops. Adults are slim, with a fluttering flight, but the varied styles of antennae confirm their status.

Two small Geometers are **Speckled Yellow** in spring woodland, and **Yellow Shell**, a more widespread moth of high summer. A small, largely white moth, **Lace Border**, is an exquisite speciality of the North Downs in late spring and again in late summer. **Common Carpet** flies at the same time throughout the county, even on dull days. It is the little pied moth that is so readily disturbed.

Latticed Heath, found almost anywhere, behaves like a butterfly, landing and perching with wings part-raised rather than flattened. Its wings are traversed with a lattice of brown and speckled-yellow bands. A much larger moth with a latticed appearance and longish wings is the **Grass Wave**, mostly on heathland.

Brown Silver-line, grey-brown with pale lines, is common among bracken and one of the few moths to use it as a larval foodplant. While Burnets are true day-flyers, most Geometers fly only when disturbed; a few, like the Speckled Yellow, are genuinely diurnal.

Hawk-moths are represented during the day by the **Humming-bird Hawk-moth,** which resembles a tiny humming bird as it nectars in a blur of hovering flight. It is a regular migrant to areas with an abundance of nectar-rich flowers, including gardens. It starts early – look out for it during breakfast.

The main differences between butterflies and moths, but all have exceptions:

	Butterfly	*Moth*
Time of day	diurnal	*nocturnal*
Antennae	knob or clubby hook on the tip	*plumose (feathery) or straight*
Wings	large and colourful	*many are small and drab*
At rest	wings raised over back	*wings open flat or to sides*
Body	slim and smooth	*thick and furry*

Clockwise from above:
Cinnabar. **BH**
Burnet Companion. **FK**
Five-spot Burnet and cocoon with empty pupal shell. **BH**
Speckled Yellow. **MB**

Since the turn of the century, the **Jersey Tiger** has spread across south London from the railway embankments between New Cross Gate and Forest Hill. This colourful moth, which flutters weakly in August sunshine, is the "butterfly" that draws tourists to the Valley of the Butterflies on the island of Rhodes.

The male **Vapourer** can resemble Brown Hairstreak in August but is very active and has a more gyrating flight. The wingless females are entirely blameless of creating this confusion. The red and black **Cinnabar** has yellow- and black-hooped larvae, which are found commonly on ragwort. The colouring of adult and larva warn that they are poisonous with toxins sequestered from the foodplant.

Burnet Companion resembles the less colourful Dingy Skipper. Both use bird's-foot-trefoil for nectaring and for larval foodplant, and both fly in late spring, but the butterfly is restricted mainly to calcareous soils whereas the moth occurs in many grassy habitats. Records of Dingy Skipper away from its known distribution usually prove to be Burnet Companion. Flying alongside the Burnet Companion is the **Mother Shipton**, a grey-brown moth with the pattern of a witch's face etched in white on each forewing.

Another grassland species, the **Antler**, ranges from dull brown to rich chestnut but the white antler design picked out along two veins is characteristic. Common on downland in late summer is **Dusky Sallow**, tawny/olive-brown and straw patterned. **Clouded Buff** is found on the western heaths and along the scarp slope of the North Downs. It is a larger moth, the yellow males contrasting with the orange females. **Straw Dot**, a small pale yellow moth, rests in characteristic flat-winged, delta-shaped pose.

Beautiful Yellow Underwing skips across the heaths in two generations from May to August. An even smaller species, **Purple-bordered Gold** – no description necessary – is a distinctive rarity of wet heaths. **Common Heath** and the migrant **Silver Y** are two other moths commonly disturbed.

Larger Moths of Surrey (Collins, 1997) and *Smaller Moths of Surrey* (Palmer, Porter & Collins, 2012) offer further reading.

Key sites: species checklist

	Bookham	*Box Hill*	*Denbies*	*Heaths*	*Hutch B*	*Oaken W*	*Pewley*
Adonis Blue		▲	▲				△
Brimstone	▲	▲	▲	▲	▲	▲	▲
Brown Argus	△	▲	▲		▲	△	▲
Brown Hairstreak	▲	▲	▲		△	▲	▲
Chalkhill Blue		▲	▲		△		▲
Clouded Yellow	**M**	**M**	**M**	**M**	**M**	**M**	**M**
Comma	▲	▲	▲	▲	▲	▲	▲
Common Blue	▲	▲	▲	▲	▲	▲	▲
Dark Green Frit		▲	△		▲		△
Dingy Skipper		▲	▲		▲	▲	▲
Essex Skipper	▲	▲	▲	▲	▲	▲	▲
Gatekeeper	▲	▲	▲	▲	▲	▲	▲
Grayling				▲			
Green Hairstreak		▲	▲	▲	▲	▲	▲
Green-vnd White	▲	▲	▲	▲	▲	▲	▲
Grizzled Skipper		▲	▲		▲	▲	▲
Holly Blue	▲	▲	▲	▲	▲	▲	▲
Large Skipper	▲	▲	▲	▲	▲	▲	▲
Large White	▲	▲	▲	▲	▲	▲	▲
Marbled White	△	▲	▲		▲	▲	▲
Meadow Brown	▲	▲	▲	▲	▲	▲	▲
Orange-tip	▲	▲	▲	▲	▲	▲	▲
Painted Lady	**M**	**M**	**M**	**M**	**M**	**M**	**M**
Peacock	▲	▲	▲	▲	▲	▲	▲
Purple Emperor	▲	▲	△			▲	
Purple Hairstreak	▲	▲		▲	△	▲	
Red Admiral	▲	▲	▲	▲	▲	▲	▲
Ringlet	▲	▲	▲	▲	▲	▲	▲
Silver-spotted Skip		▲	▲				
Silver-stud Blue				▲			
Silver-washed Frit	▲	▲	△		△	▲	
Small Blue		▲			▲		▲
Small Copper	▲	▲	▲	▲	▲	▲	▲
Small Heath	▲	▲	▲	▲	▲	▲	▲
Small Skipper	▲	▲	▲	▲	▲	▲	▲
Small Tortoiseshell	▲	▲	▲	▲	▲	▲	▲
Small White	▲	▲	▲	▲	▲	▲	▲
Speckled Wood	▲	▲	▲	▲	▲	▲	▲
White Admiral	▲	▲			△	▲	
W-letter Hairstreak		▲			△		
Wood White						▲	
REGULAR TOTAL	**27**	**38**	**31**	**26**	**29**	**32**	**30**

▲Regular △Occasional **M**-Regular Migrant in good years

KEY SITES

BOOKHAM COMMON — Ken Willmott

BOOKHAM COMMON, including Banks Common, is 182ha of deciduous high forest, rough grassland and scrub, managed by the National Trust. Two-thirds is woodland, dominated by oak, ash, holly, willows and, to a lesser extent, hornbeam. It is on London Clay, and has many damp areas.

The London Natural History Society has studied the site since 1941, and it was declared a Site of Special Scientific Interest in 1961. The Common has 27 regular butterfly species and two occasional (Brown Argus, Marbled White), two I have not seen for 10+ years (Grizzled Skipper, White-letter Hairstreak) and two I have not given up hope of discovering (Dingy Skipper, Green Hairstreak). NT maps, available in the main car parks, show the locations mentioned in the following notes:

Small Skipper: a newly opened glade in Hill House Wood is a good site; follow the footpath NE from opposite Merritts Cottage TQ12485634.

Large Skipper: search Broadway, between Tunnel and Mark Oak car parks.

Brimstone: I recorded a female laying on buckthorn near South-east Pond, north of Tunnel car park.

Green-veined White: the commonest White, due to the damp nature of the habitat.

Brown Hairstreak: mostly confined to the blackthorn of Central and Bayfield Plains but in 2012 eggs were located on the edge of Banks Meadow and the species now probably frequents most blackthorn areas. In spring 2012 I found an egg on a cherry plum tree near the railway bridge at Tunnel car park, where I first discovered eggs on the Common in March, 2005.

Purple Hairstreak: thought to be confined to English oaks, but I have found eggs on Turkey oak near Mark Oak car park; best observed on any oak, 5-7pm in July.

Small Copper: prefers open areas such as Bayfield and Central Plains. Look for their larval foodplants, dock and sorrel, in places that have recently been cleared, and anticipate the butterfly's arrival. They seem to survive summer cattle-grazing on the Plains, which helps egg-laying females to locate the exposed foodplants.

Brown Argus: more associated with downland and rock-rose, but occasionally turns up on the Commons, where the female lays on cranesbills. On July 9, 2010, both sexes appeared in a woodland scallop along High Point Path, but there were no larval foodplants, and no reappearance the next year. Both sexes were near the Tunnel car park in August, 2013.

Common Blue: open areas like Bayfield, Central and Eastern Plains, plus the clearing in Hill House Wood; like the Small Copper, it appears to survive summer cattle-grazing, which exposes its larval foodplants.

Holly Blue: an aged hawthorn growing beneath the Purple Emperor Hill Farm master trees is a reliable male territory in July.

White Admiral: butterfly-watching at Bookham is at its best from mid-June and throughout July. The White Admiral's distinctive flap-and-glide flight, sometimes at speed if a male is pursuing a female, is unbeatable viewing along the wider woodland rides, such as Broadway, High Point Path, Central, Eastern, Hill House and Kelsey's Woods, where early stages can be located on semi-shaded honeysuckle.
Purple Emperor: the ultimate attraction; usually emerges shortly after midsummer day. Most reliable of the three known territories is east of Hundred Pound Bridge car park, close to Hill Farm: walk beyond the crest of the first slope on High Point Path to TQ12315673 from midday and look up at the canopy. If no sighting within 15 minutes you are too early! The other locations are close to Mark Oak car park: TQ13335683 is a small canopy gap along a shady path towards the junction of High Point Path and Broadway; TQ13335679 is a group of large Turkey oaks with open aspect, at this junction, the highest point on the Common. Look south-west from the open junction.
Red Admiral: often the earliest butterfly to be seen. A mild, sunny February day will find this species basking on the ground at Mark Oak, the common's high spot at the junction of High Point Path and Broadway. Also has an annual territory in July below the Purple Emperors at Hill Farm.
Small Tortoiseshell: the larger nettle beds, which attract this species in the spring, have declined. Work on the railway bridge near Tunnel car park eliminated regular patches of nettles on which larvae were always found. General tidying and summer cattle-grazing have contributed to the decline of this once-common butterfly.
Peacock: during April usually replaces male Commas on their March territories along sunny edges. Females utilise the nettle beds after Small Tortoiseshell, sometimes as late as early May. Has similar problems to the Small Tortoiseshell.
Comma: first nymphalid to emerge in numbers from hibernation in March and establish territories along the open rides of High Point Path, Broadway and between Central Wood and Hill House Wood. In March they usually appear shortly after midday. Females, depositing single eggs, have a wide choice of suitable nettles and are thus faring better on the Common than the Peacock and Small Tortoiseshell, which lay eggs in batches.
Silver-washed Fritillary: from Mark Oak car park, walk south along Broadway to its junction with High Point Path. Turn right down the gentle slope, left at the major fork and continue along the hardcore road to an open area and Merritts Cottage. You will see Silver-washed Fritillaries on this route during July. Look out for females fluttering against oak trunks in the semi-shade, laying on moss or in bark crevices.
Marbled White: thought to be a release; recorded in ones and twos, mainly in the open areas of Central and Bayfield Plain; my last record, in July 2011, was a male in the grassy ride at the southern end of Broadway. The Common's grass foodplants may not be suitable to sustain a stable population.
Ringlet: not as common as Meadow Brown but more tolerant of damper areas and prefers meadow edges.

Small Heath: not common; mainly associated with finer-leaved grasses on Bayfield and Central Plains.
Grizzled Skipper: last recorded on May 2, 1997, on Central Plain.
White-letter Hairstreak: formerly common on English or wych elm; declined drastically after the 1970s outbreak of Dutch elm disease; my last record was July 12, 2003 – a female laying on an English elm sucker. BC member Graham Revill recorded one on July 20, 2009, nectaring on creeping thistle on High Point Path.

ACCESS

NT car parks – Tunnel, east of station TQ12995568.
The Approach, west of station TQ12535581.
Mark Oak, Cobham Rd TQ13355690.
Hundred Pound Bridge, Bookham Rd TQ12105672.
Railway station: Bookham (Waterloo to Guildford via Epsom).
Bus: 622 from Epsom; 479 from Epsom, Guildford & Leatherhead.
Website: *www.nationaltrust.org.uk/bookham-commons*

BOX HILL — Mike Weller

BOX HILL, north-east of Dorking, is named after the box trees that grow beneath the larger trees and on The Whites, the steep chalk slope that descends to the River Mole on the west side. The core of the estate was given to the National Trust by Leopold Salomon in 1914 and it has been enlarged over time to 485ha, including as yet butterfly-unfriendly farmland.

The hill rises to 224m overlooking the southern end of the gap in the North Downs eroded by the Mole as it flows north to the Thames. The dense woodland (growing on Clay-with-flints, a deposit resting on the Late Cretaceous Chalk) is of limited interest to the lepidopterist. More important are the substantial areas of chalk grassland, where the height and density of the sward influences the success or failure of different species of flora and fauna, in particular ants and butterflies, some of which are near the northern limit of their European range.

BEST AREAS: the field south of the Viewpoint (TQ17975117), much less trampled lower down, and The Dukes fields to the east, are both interesting parts of the south-facing scarp slope (gradient about 30%).

The remaining areas of grassland follow the three hill spurs and two dry valleys on the north side of the hill. They include Burford Spur (TQ17245218), Military Road and Little Alp to Broadwood's Folly (a flint tower at TQ17665229), including Zig Zag Road; and Juniper Top and Bottom.

KEY SPECIES: hosts 38 of Surrey's 42 regular butterflies.
Adonis & Chalkhill Blue, Silver-spotted Skipper
....Dukes (especially the lower track) TQ18435112
Dark Green Fritillary ....Burford Spur TQ17655155
Small Blue .... Little Alp TQ17755186
Silver-washed Fritillary, White Admiral, White-letter Hairstreak
....Juniper Bottom (Happy Valley) TQ18045266

PERSONAL HIGHLIGHTS: BC field trips enjoying 100s of Silver-spotted Skippers on the Dukes in 2010-2012; double-figure Dark Green Fritillaries on Burford Spur & Little Alp in 2011; Purple Emperor at Broadwood's Folly.

CONSERVATION CONCERNS: encroachment by scrub and yew into the grassland, especially along Juniper Bottom, and increasing shade from trees growing ever taller along the sides of this valley; increased trampling by viewers of cycling events, especially up the Zigzag.

ACCESS

NT car parks TQ177514, 180513, 182514, 171513, 177529, 176520.
Burford Bridge council car park at TQ171520.
Railway stations: Box Hill & Westhumble (the nearest), Dorking Main (North), Dorking Deepdene.
Bus stops: Burford Bridge TQ171520, Juniper Hall TQ172528,
A24 near Westhumble Street TQ171517, Stepping Stones TQ171513.
On foot from Boxhill Bridge, off A25 Reigate Road (TQ184503);
Fredley (TQ171524); and from the North Downs Way.
Visitor centre: TQ17835135
Website: *www.nationaltrust.org.uk/box-hill*

DENBIES HILLSIDE — Mike Weller

DENBIES HILLSIDE, named after a 17th century farmer and owned since 1963 by the National Trust, is 3km west of Dorking and the jewel in a larger area of chalk grassland. The hillside is part of the south-facing scarp slope of the North Downs (gradient about 30%), and at 190m affords a beautiful view across the Holmesdale valley to Leith Hill.

BEST AREAS: from Ranmore Common Road car park (east), enter Steer's Field and explore its southern steeper part, and western and southern hedge and fence lines. Pass through the gate in the south-west corner into the lower fields and the Big Field (TQ135500) to the west. Beyond the lowest fence line is the old carriageway (a sanctuary in cool or windy weather for butterflies and observers). Fields south of the carriageway and east of the lower field are also productive, particularly for Silver-spotted Skipper. Other good areas are The Brow, east of Steer's Field at 146502, and Secretary's Field, further east at 149501.

Denbies Hillside from the west: Big Field is on the left; Ranmore Common church is behind Steer's Field. **MB**

KEY SPECIES: Adonis, Chalkhill & Common Blue; Silver-spotted, Grizzled & Dingy Skipper; Brown Argus, Small Heath, Green & Brown Hairstreak; Small Copper, Marbled White, Dark Green Fritillary.

PERSONAL HIGHLIGHTS: former abundance of Adonis Blue and the variation in their wing pattern; past healthy numbers of Dark Green Fritillary; emergences in late October of six Clouded Yellows and their survival until a frosty night in early November; fleeting view of a Large Tortoiseshell in April 2007; aberrant Brown Argus with white instead of red spots; visit by a female Purple Emperor to the car park at the start of a field trip in 2012; clouds of Chalkhill Blue in recent Augusts, estimated at over 100,000 in 2012.

CONSERVATION CONCERNS: grazing over most of the lower field, to improve the habitat for Blues and Silver-spotted Skipper, has gone against the Dark Green Fritillary, which was once common but now struggles on the short turf. Adonis Blue has had poor years in 2011-12 due to wet summers, in contrast to the huge success of the single-brooded Chalkhill Blue.

NEARBY: Further west is White Downs, part of the Wotton Estate open to the public by agreement between the Evelyn family (the owners) and Surrey County Council. It is managed by Surrey Wildlife Trust and the National Trust.

Specific localities from west to east along the escarpment:

Blatchford Down 103487, Old Simms Field 105486, Old Plantation 107486, Chalk Quarry 114486, Great Down 117488, Chalkpit Field 119489, Wholecombe Down 121492, Lamb's Leys 124494, The Ranges 126495.

ACCESS

NT car park off Ranmore Common Road, TQ142504.

Railway stations: Dorking West, Dorking Main (North), Dorking Deepdene. Also Box Hill & Westhumble for access from the east via the North Downs Way.

By foot along the old Denbies carriageways from Dorking or Westcott, or from the North Downs Way, TQ133500.

Website: *www.nationaltrust.org.uk/denbies-hillside*

HEATHS — Howard Street

SURREY has 3,000ha of the UK's 95,116ha of lowland heath, which is 20% of the world's total. In 1988, Surrey County Council and the Nature Conservancy Council identified that Surrey had lost over 85% of its heathland since the late 18th century.

The key areas, which support the specialist butterflies Grayling and Silver-studded Blue, are the Thames Basin heaths (c 2,000ha) in the north-west of the county and the Lower Greensand heaths in the south-west.

STATUS: more than half of Surrey's heathland is owned by the Ministry of Defence (MoD), including Ash Ranges (between Ash and Pirbright), Pirbright Ranges (between Bisley and Camberley, no access) and Barossa (north of Camberley, partly in Berks). Access to most MoD sites is allowed after 4pm and on non-firing days. The rest is largely owned by Surrey CC with some in trust or private ownership.

All have SSSI (Site of Special Scientific Interest) status and many are within the Thames Basin Heaths SPA (Special Protection Area), designated specifically to protect three heathland birds: Nightjar, Woodlark and Dartford Warbler. Two of the largest (non-military) sites, Chobham Common and Thursley Common, are National Nature Reserves (NNRs).

MANAGEMENT: from 2002 to 2008 the Surrey Heathland Project, supported by Natural England (then English Nature) and the Heritage Lottery Fund, restored a number of sites across the north-east of the county. From 2006 Surrey Wildlife Trust, also supported by Natural England via Higher Level Stewardship funding, took on the conservation management of the military ranges. Fences with gates and grids were installed to allow extensive grazing. Surrey Wildlife Trust manages the grazing stock, mainly Belted Galloway cattle because of their tolerance of low-nutritional vegetation and indifference to people.

KEY SITES: Chobham and Thursley Commons have both specialist species. But to see Silver-studded Blue and Grayling in abundance, without having to walk far, Dawney Hill SU94595648, 400 metres from Pirbright village hall, is recommended. Park at Pirbright village green SU94615608. The heath is 600m from the south exit of Brookwood Station via Brookwood cemetery. SSB fly in maximum numbers from mid-June to mid-July, and will overlap Grayling, which are at their best from mid-July to mid-August.

Dawney Hill is a good example of the effectiveness of heathland restoration. This gently-sloping area of 5.8ha was stripped of vegetation in 1948, but was later planted with Corsican pine by the MoD. By the start of the Surrey Heathland Project the plantation was at least 20 years old and contained two small areas of heath which were probably the result of fires early in the life of the plantation. In 2003 the plantation was felled and chipped, the stumps mulched and the ground stripped and rotovated. By the following summer, ling and bell heather had grown from old buried seed. It soon became apparent that the surviving patches of heath had supported small numbers of Silver-studded Blue, which within a few years spread across the entire area. In 2009 SSB numbers were estimated at 5,000+. Grayling has also established a significant colony. The butterflies are more difficult to track down on the vast military ranges.

FIELD TRIPS: Surrey branch of Butterfly Conservation have regular field trips to heathland at Brentmoor SU938613, Fairmile TQ119618, Whitmoor SU984535, Chobham SU966650 and Dawney Hill. As well as the two key butterflies, over 20 other species frequent heathland and its surrounds.

Websites: *www.surreycc.gov.uk* (search heathland)
www.surreywildlifetrust.org/conservation/habitat/2
www.surreywildlifetrust.org/reserves (search Chobham)
www.naturalengland.org.uk (search Thursley)

HUTCHINSON'S BANK — Malcolm Bridge

HUTCHINSON'S BANK (HB) Local Nature Reserve occupies a steep south-west-facing slope above the dry valley of Featherbed Lane and crested by the plateau of New Addington, a satellite of Croydon developed from the 1930s.

The site is some 900m long but generally less than 100m wide, and shows mostly surface chalk but with Clay-with-flints along the valley bottom. These deeper soils were cultivated for arable as recently as 1950 but the upper slopes have never been ploughed and were farmed for rabbits from the 13th century.

HISTORY: The onset of myxomatosis in the early 1950s dramatically altered the open-downland-with-light-scrub character, and by the 1980s the chalk slopes had largely disappeared under heavy scrub and secondary woodland. The London Borough of Croydon had bought the site (Fishers Farm) and surrounding lands as part of the development of New Addington, but work at the northern end, Farleigh Dean Crescent, was interrupted by WW2. The crescent was scheduled to occupy the whole of the current reserve but remained incomplete after the war, with the concrete footprint of the planned route running halfway through the reserve being a visible reminder.

In 1985 a young London Wildlife Trust was alerted by Martin Wills and with its lively Croydon local group sought to save HB from further development. An agreement was signed the following year for LWT to manage the reserve.

MANAGEMENT: Miraculously the butterflies that depend on herb-rich downland had survived the decades of neglect, and a recent introduction of Marbled White had succeeded from the outset. LWT collaborated with the newly created Downlands Countryside Management Project, which enabled the reserve to be part-fenced to allow for winter sheep-grazing as part of Countryside Stewardship.

Subsequent plans have emphasised the need for a variety of grazing regimes but the initial burden was borne by sheep and goats, although the latter suffered from dog attacks and were withdrawn. The long-term aim for ponies or cattle to tackle dominant post-clearance grasses such as false-brome (which sheep largely ignore), has now been realised thanks to the introduction of piped water and self-filling drinking troughs in each of the five large paddocks. These were created in 2008-11 with mainly Lottery and Landfill Tax funds and are intended to be the main areas of downland, with light scrub cover, and a few trees to provide livestock shelter.

HB is intended to be c. 70% open downland with light scrub cover and a scattering of mature shrubs (buckthorn for Brimstone) and trees such as field maple. The remainder will be secondary woodland with heavy scrub.

The reserve is traversed along its length by a lower path, the bridleway; a middle path, the nature trail; and an upper path. These provide more grassland with scrub and are key main breeding habitats.

SMALL BLUE: Management since 2008 has targeted the Small Blue, which survived in only two small areas where its foodplant, kidney vetch, persisted. Scrapes are created each winter as older ones become less kidney-vetch-friendly. Butterfly Conservation has recognised the importance of the site and funded the costs of JCB hire to create large (10-30 sq m) scrapes, which volunteers have seeded and plug-planted with kidney vetch. Ground disturbance by fencing contractors has created further favourable conditions for the plant.

The areas of kidney vetch have allowed the Small Blue to spread over a substantial part of the reserve, and 2011 produced a best-ever transect index of 297. The index averaged 25 from 2007-10. The terrible summer of 2012 inevitably produced a lower index of 33, but correct management gives the butterfly every chance of bouncing back.

CONSERVATION CONCERNS: Dark Green Fritillary is still present in small numbers. Individuals were recorded in four separate weeks during 2012 transect walks. Hairy violet, its larval foodplant, is scattered throughout and it is difficult to assess whether the decline mirrors a countywide one (the species has retreated to its core areas close to Dorking since 1999) or is a consequence of the extensive works which have taken place over the last decade.

It is very special to have such a gem of a reserve so close to suburbia. Moths are also well recorded, thanks to the presence close by of one of the country's foremost experts, Bernard Skinner. The future is bright despite worries about future funding sources.

KEY SPECIES: Dingy & Grizzled Skipper, Green Hairstreak, Small Blue, Marbled White, Dark Green Fritillary. Chapel Bank, a LWT reserve immediately to the south, has regular Silver-Washed Fritillary, White Admiral and White-letter Hairstreak.

ACCESS

TQ377620, Farleigh Dean Crescent, off Featherbed Lane. CR0 9AD.
Tram: New Addington Tramstop, Route 3. **Bus**: numbers 64, 130, 314, 464, T31, T32. 5 mins walk down footpath. **Website**: *www.wildlondon.org.uk*

OAKEN WOOD Malcolm Bridge

OAKEN WOOD is Butterfly Conservation's 8.9ha reserve in the south-west of the county, 2.6km south of Dunsfold, and a similar distance north of the Sussex village of Plaistow. It is a part of the Forestry Commission's 324ha Chiddingfold Forest.

The reserve is largely oak woodland, mostly planted by FC in the 1920s, with a birch understorey. There are stands of blackthorn and hazel and the ground cover is dominated by bramble and bracken. A large area of open grassland occupies the western third of the reserve and a small pond in the north-west corner was created in 1989 by blocking a drainage ditch. The following year four rides were created, radiating N, S, E and W from a large glade, which was named Berkeley Square in recognition of the annual arrival of nightingales.

HISTORY: the reserve was the brainchild of Peter Beale BEM, an FC Conservation Officer who in 1983 recognised the significance of Oaken Wood. In 1987 he was allowed to manage the site, with help from local enthusiasts.

Peter's retirement in 1995 coincided with the emergence of a new Butterfly Conservation branch for Surrey, which adopted the Peter Beale Reserve. Branch chairman Stephen Jeffcoate became reserve manager, with Pearl and Small Pearl-bordered Fritillary being the priority species.

From a peak in 1997, the fritillaries declined after three years of cool, wet springs restricted larval feeding. In 2006 the colony at nearby Triangle Meadow (SU98413387) petered out, as key habitat become overgrown. So too did the one in Ashpark Wood, just over the Sussex border. Chiddingfold Forest had lost its two small woodland fritillaries.

CURRENT ERA: In 2003, which coincided with record numbers of Wood White, now Chiddingfold's key species, I became manager, assisted along the way by Howard Whiting (passed away in Jan 2013), Mike Weller, Peter Webster, John Buckley, David Gardner, Philip Underwood, John Rees and Michael Friend.

The last Pearl-bordered breeding area was re-coppiced in the winters of 2009-2011. Now 200 hazel whips have been planted in the meadow area to create new areas of coppice wood over the next 20 years.

The ditches which criss-cross Oaken Wood, mostly FC-created to prevent adjacent Corsican pine crops from waterlogging, support an abundance of violet, bugle, primrose and stitchwort. Betony and devil's-bit scabious prefer the rides, with marsh thistle enjoying the many wet parts, and wood sage everywhere. Bracken is a useful component of this woodland habitat. It provides ideal litter for violets, foodplant of the lost fritillaries, so control, not eradication, is the policy. A future reintroduction of Pearl-bordered Fritillary, 20 years or more distant, is the long-term aim.

■ *Information board at the entrance to Oaken Wood: page 239*

CONSERVATION CONCERNS: **Betony Case-bearer** is a tiny brown moth. Chiddingfold Forest is the only UK site for this rarity and the core breeding area is along the reserve's western boundary, where betony grows among birch and aspen. A number of trial management regimes will be developed in 2013-2015 in an attempt to unravel the mystery of its requirements.

Although the future of FC is unclear, the work of Butterfly Conservation at Oaken Wood should ensure that, whatever the political outcome, the reserve will be preserved as a wildlife hot-spot for future generations.

KEY SPECIES: Wood White, Dingy & Grizzled Skipper, Silver-washed Fritillary, White Admiral. Marbled White was successfully introduced by Peter Beale.

ACCESS

Entrance SU99303379, via track (usually no vehicular access) running west from Plaistow Rd at SU99433381; GU8 4PG. Parking for only one or two cars at the track junction.

Western (Botany Bay) entrance to Chiddingfold Forest is off High Street at SU9783734815, GU8 4YA; parking here is slightly easier but beware the roadside ditches! Distance to Oaken Wood is 1.6 miles.

Websites: *www.butterfly-conservation.org; www.surreybutterflies.org*

PEWLEY DOWN — Peter Curnock

PEWLEY DOWN is a Local Nature Reserve less than 1.6km south-east of Guildford town centre and within the Surrey Hills Area of Outstanding Natural Beauty. It is 75-120m high and covers 8ha, over half being chalk grassland. The steep scarp slope faces south.

HISTORY: The Down has been owned by Guildford Borough Council since 1919. Photographs during 1945-50 show extensive scrub, management having probably ceased during WW2. Pewley Down Conservation Volunteers was formed in March 2003, working under the direction of the council.

MANAGEMENT: In 2007 a large area was fenced and a water main extended to allow winter cattle-grazing from 2008. Funding was provided by the Old Surrey Downs project.

MAIN AREAS

1 Flat plateau: heavy public use and little botanical interest. Hedgerow on northern boundary is good for Holly Blue, Green and Brown Hairstreak.

2 Woodland: Speckled Wood.

3 Slope west of the disused chalk pit (now wooded) and just east of the Fort Road and Northdown Lane entrances. This is the least interesting slope but has Chalkhill Blue colonies; Brown Argus and Small Blue have also been seen here.

4 The Paddock: below the Mile Path, a diagonal track and associated hedge from the top of the Down to the Chantries. All the key downland species can be seen here, particularly at the eastern end and near the southern hedge and fence line. Currently

overrun with tor-grass and butterfly numbers are reduced.

5 Slope above Mile Path: currently the best area, particularly the eastern end.

SPECIES: **Small Blue** numbers are stable but distribution seems to be increasingly restricted.

Brown Argus presence and numbers are puzzling as its main larval foodplant, rock-rose, is surprisingly absent. Cranesbills, its alternative foodplants, are scarce.

Small Heath numbers have risen inexplicably from only one sighting in 2005 to the third commonest butterfly on my 2012 transect.

Dark Green Fritillary was seen in 2007-08, 2011-12.

Small Heath pair, female above: numbers have risen on Pewley Down. **KW**

Adonis Blue was introduced during the 1970s but had become extinct by 1987. Seen again in 2004-2007, with reasonable numbers in 2006. No records 2008-2011; males recorded in May 2012 (one) and June 2013 (two). These later sightings are suspected to have originated from an unauthorised introduction.

OTHER KEY SPECIES: Grizzled (declining) & Dingy Skippers, Marbled White.

CONSERVATION CONCERNS: cattle-grazing in the Paddock has failed to check the spread of tor-grass. It is hoped to improve the timing and intensity of the grazing. The slope above Mile Path is managed by brush-cutting (or mowing) and raking. This is labour-intensive and relies on the large volunteer force. In the long term, consideration will need to be given to either enclosing and grazing the area or finding a more mechanised way of controlling the vegetation.

ACCESS

West (town): Pewley Hill GU1 3SW, TQ00544906; limited street parking; less parking at Fort Road and Pewley Way. There is a path from Northdown Lane off Warwick's Bench Road.

East: path from Longdown Road GU4 8PR, TQ02004910.

South-east: up Mile Path from Chantries/St Martha's car park off Halfpenny Lane GU4 8PZ, TQ02184842.

North: an attractive option is the one mile walk from the large car park next to Guildford Golf Club at GU1 2QP, TQ02194996; walk up Merrow Down (look out for Small Blues in late May, June and early August), west along Warren Road, and take the path opposite Rosetrees at GU1 2HE; TQ01374956.

Website: *www.surreycommunity.info* (search Pewley Down).

Surrey transects

Red shows walked in 2012

Map ID		Grid ref	1st year	Latest
1	Ashtead Common A	TQ180594	1992	2008
2	Ashtead Common B	TQ179592	2002	2012
3	Banstead Downs	TQ257614	1986	2012
4	Bealeswood Common, Frensham	SU823409	2008	2012
5	Betchworth Quarry NR	TQ204514	2012	2012
6	Box Hill, Dukes	TQ185510	1994	2012
7	Box Hill, Viewpoint	TQ180510	1994	2012
8	Box Hill, Zig Zag	TQ177520	1994	2010
9	Brentmoor Heath, West End	SU936612	1990	2009
10	Chapel Bank, New Addington	TQ382615	1997	2004
11	Chobham Common	SU974633	2002	2012
12	Chobham Common North-East	SU977655	2004	2012
13	Colekitchen, Gomshall	TQ085488	2000	2009
14	Coulsdon Common	TQ320570	1990	2012
15	Denbies Hillside, Dorking	TQ150501	1988	2012
16	Denbies Landbarn, Dorking	TQ135498	2000	2008
17	Denbies Landbarn B, Dorking	TQ135499	2002	2012
18	Devil's Punch Bowl, Hindhead	SU891373	2008	2010
19	Earlswood Common, Reigate	TQ273486	1997	2003
20	Epsom Common	TQ189605	2009	2012
21	Fairmile Common, Cobham	TQ118617	2006	2012
22	Farnham Park	SU843480	2004	2012
23	Farthing Downs, Coulsdon	TQ300575	1990	2012
24	Farthing Downs New Hill, Coulsdon	TQ305578	2003	2012
25	Featherbed Lane, New Addington	TQ376621	1999	2007
26	Frensham (2009)	SU859415	2009	2010
27	Frensham Common (Little Pond)	SU855418	2005	2009
28	Hackhurst Down, Gomshall	TQ094484	1988	2012
29	Happy Valley, Coulsdon	TQ309567	2000	2012
30	Headley Heath, Box Hill	TQ195533	1990	2012
31	Headley Warren, Mickleham	TQ190540	2000	2010
32	Hindhead Common	SU894351	2009	2010
33	Holmwood Common	TQ177459	2012	2012
34	Horton Country Park	TQ187620	2012	2012
35	Howell Hill, Ewell	TQ239619	2002	2012
36	Hutchinson's Bank, New Addington	TQ380617	1997	2012
37	Juniper Hill, Epsom Downs	TQ222572	2000	2009
38	Kenley Common	TQ330587	1990	2012
39	Lingfield Wildlife Area	TQ387442	2002	2012
40	London Wetland Centre, Barnes	TQ228770	1996	2012
41	Mitcham Common A	TQ285680	1994	2012
42	Mitcham Common B	TQ296676	1994	2012
43	Mynthurst, Leigh (Reigate)	TQ228454	2000	2000

Map ID		Grid ref	1st year	Latest
44	Nore Hill, Woldingham	TQ377573	2000	2012
45	Nower Wood, Headley	TQ195547	2010	2012
46	Oaken Wood, Chiddingfold	SU990338	1995	2012
47	Oxted Downs, Whistlers Steep	TQ385542	2000	2011
48	Oxted Downs, Grangers Hill	TQ375542	2000	2009
49	Park Downs, Banstead	TQ265585	1998	2012
50	Pewley Down, Guildford	TQ009489	2005	2012
51	Prey Heath, Worplesdon	SU993554	2006	2012
52	Quarry Hangers NR, Caterham	TQ319536	2008	2012
53	Richmond Park	TQ190730	2003	2012
54	Riddlesdown, Kenley	TQ330601	1990	2012
55	Riddlesdown Quarry, Kenley	TQ338594	2000	2012
56	Roundshaw Downs, Sth Croydon	TQ309629	2007	2012
57	Sheepleas, West Horsley	TQ088515	1992	2006
58	Smarts Heath, Worplesdon	SU983555	2006	2012
59	South Norwood CP	TQ352684	1998	2012
60	Swan Barn Farm, Haslemere	SU913327	2002	2012
61	Sydenham Hill Wood LNR	TQ340724	2010	2012
62	Wallis Wood, Ockley	TQ121388	2000	2001
63	Wandsworth Common Woodland	TQ272734	1999	2003
64	White Down, Gomshall	TQ103487	1988	2006
65	Wimbledon Common	TQ220720	2005	2012
66	Wingate Hill, Reigate	TQ266524	2000	2009
67	Witley Common	SU928405	2005	2012

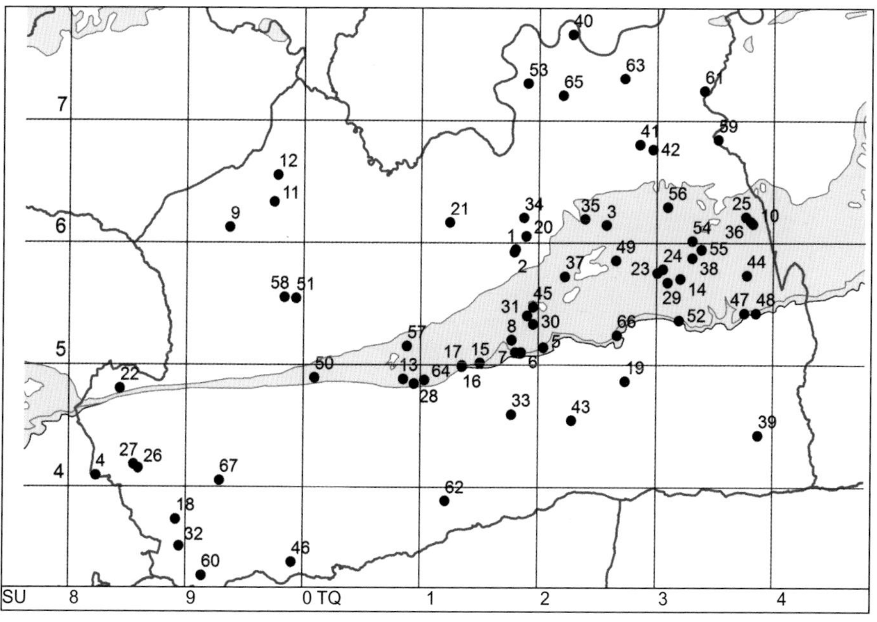

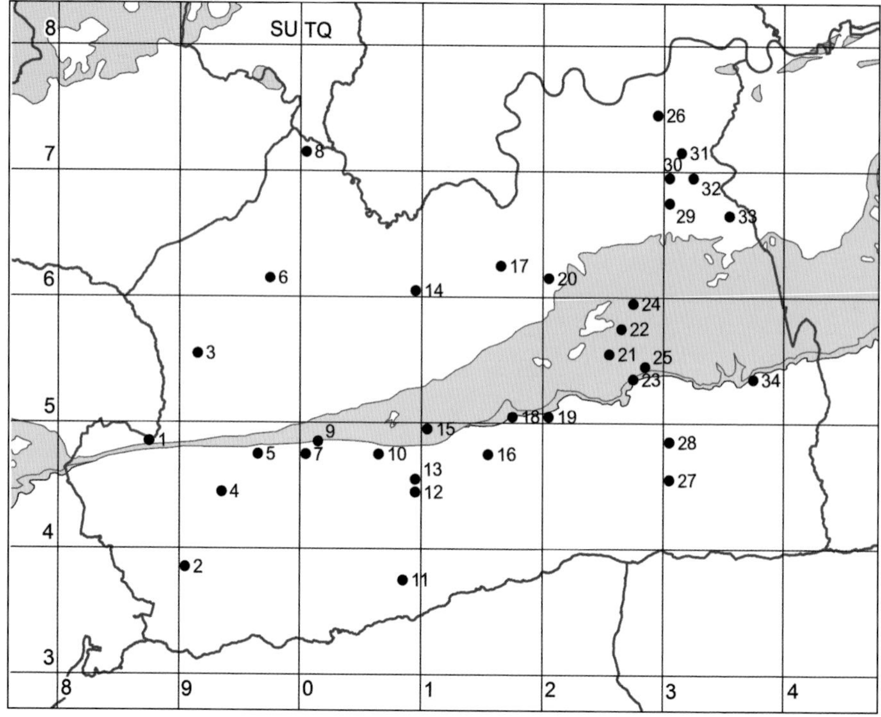

Wider Countryside Butterfly Survey: Surrey 1km squares (monads) in WCBS, commenced in 2009 between BC, Centre for Ecology & Hydrology, and British Trust for Ornithology. Supplements BMS transect records. *www.ukbms.org/wcbs.aspx*

1 **Badshot Lea, Tice's Meadow** SU8748
2 **Bowlhead Green**............................SU9038
3 **Ash Ranges**...................................SU9155
4 **Peper Harrow**...............................SU9344
5 **Compton**..SU9647
6 **Chobham** SU9761
7 **Shalford** TQ0047
8 **Egham**...TQ0071
9 **The Chantries** TQ0148
10 **Albury Park**.................................TQ0647
11 **Cranleigh** TQ0837
12 **Hurtwood, Peaslake** TQ0944
13 **Peaslake** TQ0945
14 **Painshill, Cobham** TQ0960
15 **White Down** TQ1049
16 **Westcott** TQ1547
17 **Claygate** TQ1662
18 **NE Dorking** TQ1750
19 **Brockham**......................................TQ2050
20 **Epsom**...TQ2061
21 **Kingswood** TQ2555
22 **Banstead Wood** TQ2657
23 **Gatton**...TQ2753
24 **Woodmansterne**............................TQ2759
25 **Marsham** TQ2854
26 **Clapham**...TQ2974
27 **Outwood**..TQ3045
28 **South Nutfield** TQ3048
29 **Thornton Heath**.............................TQ3067
30 **Norbury** TQ3069
31 **Streatham**......................................TQ3171
32 **Thornton Heath**.............................TQ3269
33 **Shirley**...TQ3566
34 **Gangers Hill**..................................TQ3753

Key sites on the Chalk		
west to east		*Managed*
TQ005490	Pewley Down	*Guildford Borough & Pewley Down Volunteers*
TQ022500	Merrow Common	*Guildford Borough*
TQ042492	Newlands Corner & Albury Downs	*SWT*
TQ084588	Colekitchen Down	*SWT*
TQ084514	Sheepleas	*SWT*
TQ096487	Hackhurst Down	*SWT*
TQ112491	White Down	*SWT & NT*
TQ142503	Denbies Hillside	*NT*
TQ163552	Norbury Park	*SWT*
TQ178514	Box Hill	*NT*
TQ198509	Brockham Limeworks	*SWT*
TQ222579	Epsom & Walton Downs	*Epsom & Walton Downs Conservators*
TQ238618	Howell Hill	*SWT*
TQ255610	Banstead Downs	*Banstead Commons Conservators*
TQ262523	Reigate Hill & Colley Hill	*NT*
TQ265585	Park Downs	*Banstead Commons Conservators*
TQ272583	Chipstead Downs	*Reigate & Banstead Borough & Surrey CC*
TQ274563	Shabden Park	*SWT*
TQ275612	Oaks Park & Carshalton Rd Pastures	*Sutton Borough*
TQ301571	Farthing Down, Happy Valley & New Hill	*City of London Corporation & Croydon Borough*
TQ305628	Roundshaw Down	*Sutton & Croydon Boroughs*
TQ315538	Quarry Hangers & Park Ham	*Surrey CC & SWT*
TQ316583	Dollypers Hill	*Croydon Borough*
TQ325604	Riddlesdown	*City of London Corporation*
TQ341586	The Dobbin	*Tandridge District*
TQ343534	Caterham Viewpoint	*Tandridge District*
TQ344571	Manor Park	*Tandridge District*
TQ374541	Woldingham Down	*Woodland Trust & NT*
TQ383547	Oxted Down	*Woodland Trust & NT*
TQ383614	Hutchinson's Bank & Chapel Bank	*London WT*
TQ407609	Saltbox Hill	*London WT*
TQ423560	Hill Park, Tatsfield	*SWT*

BUTTERFLIES AND THE WEATHER

David Gradidge

BUTTERFLIES are sensitive to the weather on two distinct levels: firstly, the effect of the short-term meteorological conditions of the day-to-day weather in a specific place or area; secondly, the effect of changes in climate, the long-term prevalent weather conditions of a region.

We are only too aware of the short term effects of a cold spring or a wet summer, as in 2012 and 2013. However, we are becoming increasingly aware of the long-term effects of climate change. This change proceeds almost imperceptibly, year by year, but its significance can only be appreciated by considering past records over periods of perhaps tens of years. Here we are primarily concerned with the more immediate, seasonal and year-to-year impact of the weather on our butterflies.

Weather trends

To assess trends in our weather I have considered sunshine, rainfall and temperature since 1960, using data for the South East and Central Southern region from the Meteorological (Met) Office database:
www.metoffice.gov.uk/climate/uk/datasets

Trends in this data become more obvious after year-to-year variations are smoothed out. I have done this by

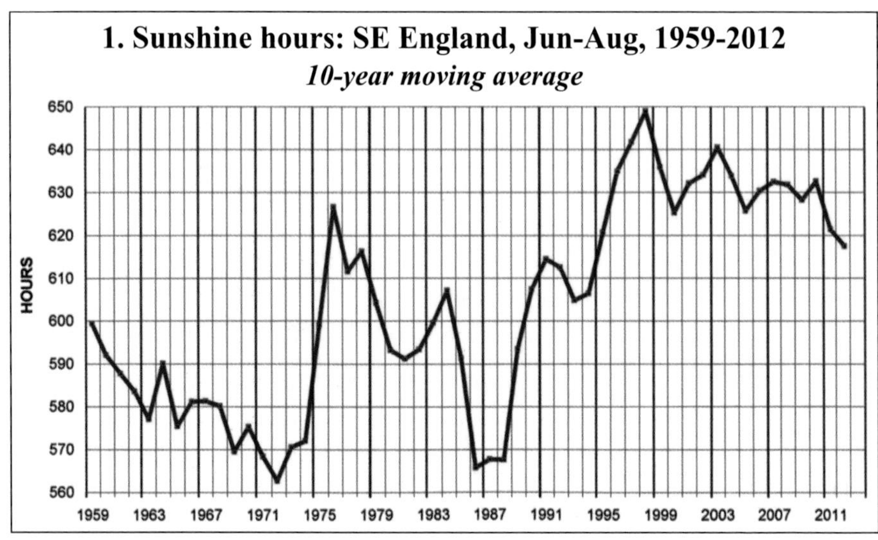

compiling 10-year moving averages (averaging over 10 years, up to and including the designated year). For statistical purposes, the Met Office divides the year into four periods of three months roughly corresponding to the seasons. Since butterflies are most numerous and diverse in the summer, I have used the June - August data to illustrate seasonal trends in sunshine, rainfall and temperature in charts 1 to 3.

Annual sunshine has trended upwards significantly from a low point of 1,491 hours in the 1960s to 1,696 hours in the 10 years to 2011, an increase of 14%. All four seasons show an increase, but none more than winter with an astonishing 39% from 150 to 208 hours. Summer sunshine (**chart 1**) peaked in the 1990s, but has trended downwards since then and especially so in 2011 and 2012. The summer of 1976 remains the sunniest on record by a large margin.

Annual rainfall trended downwards from a peak of 809mm in the 1960s to a dry point of 722mm in the 10 years to 1997. Since then it has peaked at 838mm in the 10 years to 2002. By season, only summer shows an obvious trend (**chart 2**). The generally poor summers in the 10 years to 1960 peaked at 200mm, followed by a fall to 138 mm in the 10 years to 1984 with four notably dry summers. It has become wetter in the last 10 years, reaching 187mm, with 2007 and 2012 being two of the wettest on record.

The trends in annual temperature are the most interesting. Following an earlier, relatively warm decade up to 1950, averaging 9.98°C, temperatures trended downwards to a low point of 9.38°C in the 10 years to 1971. After that there was no discernible trend to 1988, before temperatures rose sharply through the 1990s and peaked at 10.82°C in the 10 years to 2007. In reality there has been no obvious trend in the last 10 years, and 1995 is still the warmest year, with 1989 and 2007 close

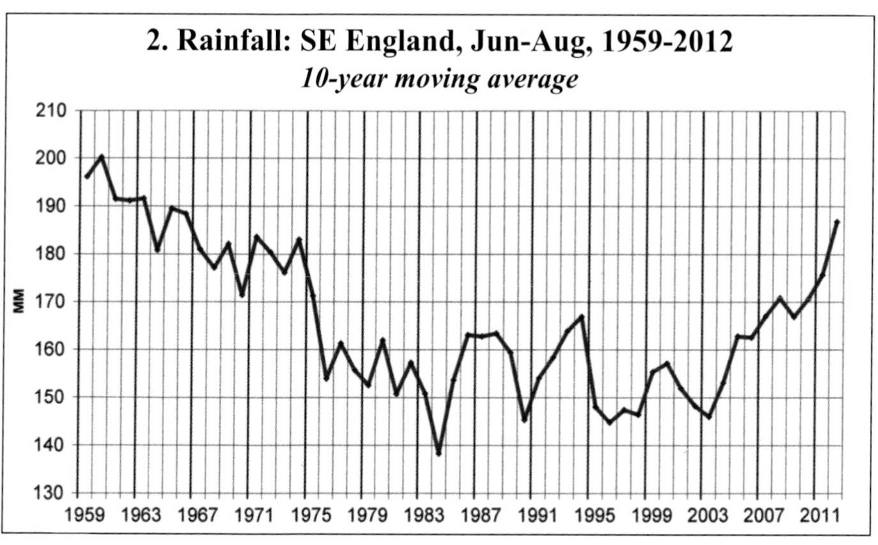

behind. These increases are apparent in all seasons, with winter, spring, summer and autumn temperatures peaking in the 10 years ending 2007, 2011, 2006 and 2011 respectively. This upward trend has faltered over the last few years (there has been a dramatic increase in snow events more reminiscent of the late 70s and early 80s) and 2006 was the last really warm summer. The trend in summer temperatures (**chart 3**) is broadly similar to the annual picture; also, from the late 1970s to the early 1990s there were dramatic fluctuations in the upward trend.

Relationship between butterflies and the weather

The Butterfly Monitoring Scheme (BMS) has ranked each butterfly year going back to 1976, based on transect data covering the UK. This composite picture of our annual butterfly population gives 1992 as the "best" year and this correlates well with Surrey transect data. One thing that does seem quite clear is that butterflies have not really benefited from the warmer conditions in recent years as much as one might have expected. In fact the best six years all occurred before 1998, and the last "good" year was 2005.

In that best year, 1992, the driest winter on record was followed by the second warmest, third sunniest May. Also, May and June were significantly dry. Overall though, the summer was rather wet, going downhill rapidly in July and August. It was on the warm side, but sunless. The following year was poor.

The second-worst year in the BMS rankings was 1981 (superior only to the disastrous 2012). May 1981 was wet, cold and the second dullest in 80 years; June and July were dull but dry; and while August was very good, this improvement came too late to have any real effect. The following year, 1982, was surprisingly good.

Looking at the top six butterfly years, a sunny May followed by a warm June and a dry summer appears to give the best results. Overall a hot July is far less

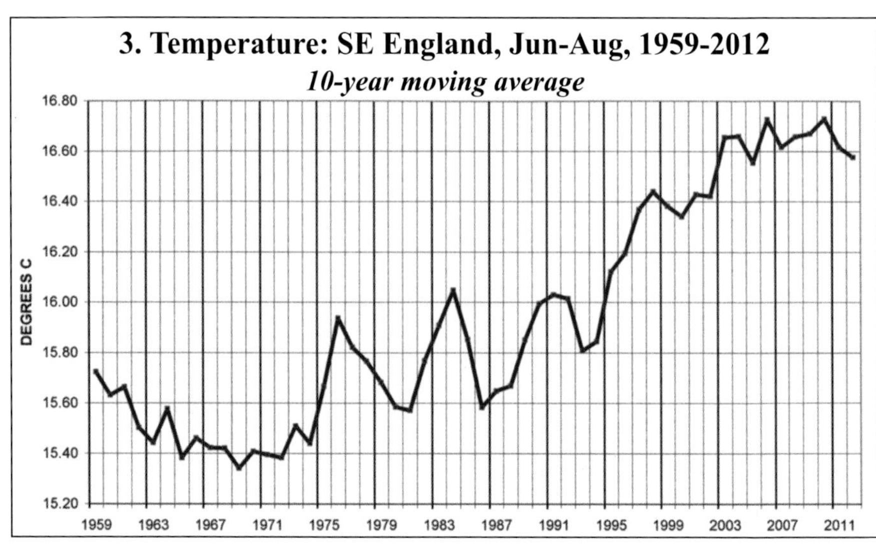

important. However, it is not clear what makes a bad year.

The years with the two coldest Mays since 1976 came out third and fourth in the BMS ranking, while the years with the fifth and sixth wettest summers in the same period came first and second for butterflies! A dull summer appears to be the most important factor, with a cold summer not far behind. The five hottest summers in this period have been 1976, 1983, 1995, 2003 and 2006, and three of these registered in the top ten. However, the year following a hot summer is not necessarily good for butterflies. Three of the following years (1984, 1996, 2004) were classed as good, but 1977 and 2007 were awful.

Pursuing the idea that a sunny May, a warm June and a dry summer are important for a good butterfly year (and one might well have suspected this), I ranked the years from 1976 on the basis of these three aspects of the weather. Numbering the years from 1 (best) to 37 (worst), I compared them with the corresponding 37 butterfly years in the BMS ranking. One could hardly expect a perfect fit between the two data sets, particularly as I used regional weather data against national butterfly data, but this comparison, shown graphically in **chart 4**, gives some surprising results. There is a remarkably close fit from 1976 to 1983 and to a slightly lesser extent from 1999 to 2012, but from 1984 to 1998 the fit is generally poor. It is perhaps significant that in this last period there was considerable fluctuation in the summer sunshine, rainfall and temperature data.

Although the outcome of this comparative study is not entirely satisfactory, it does confirm the complex nature of the relationship between the weather and annual butterfly numbers; the most significant feature common to both is their bewildering variability.

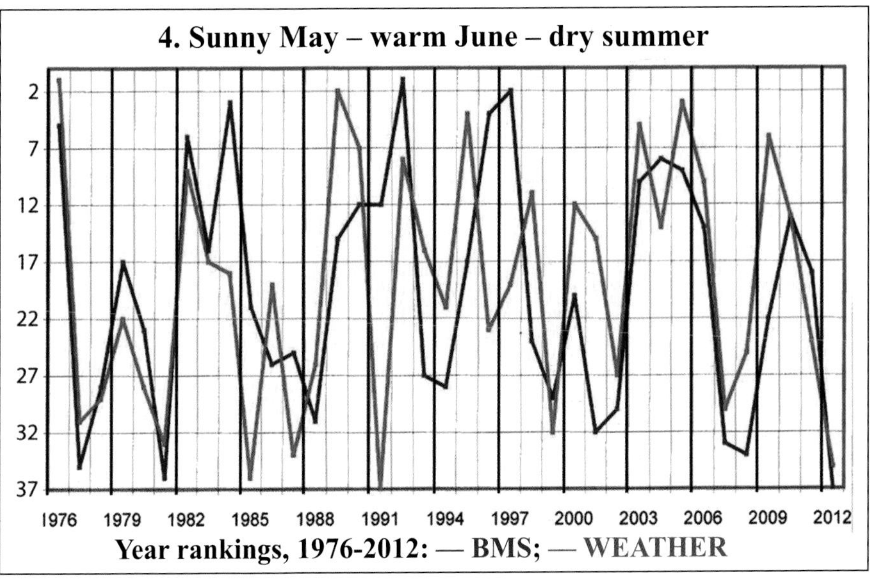

BUTTERFLY GARDENING

Harry Eve

THERE is a growing realisation that our gardens have a valuable role to play in providing suitable habitat for wildlife. Nowhere is this truer than in the densely populated south-east, where land is in demand for all manner of uses that effectively exclude our native biodiversity.

Large open spaces that are rich in species can be condemned to a sterile future at the whim of those who govern us. Even open spaces such as public parks and roadside verges are sometimes so over-managed that they might as well be concrete from the point of view of butterflies. All the more important then, that in the one place where we are in charge – our gardens – we do our best to conserve the plants and creatures that we cherish and adopt a more sympathetic approach to gardening.

My first wildlife garden was in suburban Orpington (not far from Surrey) with countryside nearby. Despite the garden being small and surrounded by more conventional plots with manicured lawns and bare-earth flower borders (the standard approach for the respectable citizen of the day) I was surprised by the number of butterfly species that turned up – about 18 in 14 years – and, in some cases, laid eggs.

What you can expect from your garden does depend on where it is located. In my current garden, on the dip slope of the North Downs east of Guildford, I have recorded 35 species over 19 years. Some of these were just passing through, but many have found it suitable for colonisation. However, enabling a rarely-visiting Common Blue to find somewhere safe to lay its eggs in my former garden – a small oasis in a desert of housing and lawns – was more satisfying than catching a glimpse of a local rarity passing by my current home.

Butterflies vary widely in the distance they will travel to form new colonies. Individuals will disperse to some degree and reach new locations that are suitable, provided such places are not too thinly spread. Suitably-managed gardens can help mobile species by providing stepping stones through an urban or intensive agricultural landscape. A number of such gardens, reasonably close together, can form a large fragmented habitat and the closer the stepping stones the greater the benefit to butterflies in colonising and moving through an area. If a stepping stone is lost, through change of ownership and attitude, it matters less if it is replaced by another nearby.

The Small Blue, a Surrey conservation priority, may colonise and persist in gardens on chalk if they are managed appropriately. It has suffered a serious decline in our county through habitat loss and changes in land management. These diminutive butterflies can survive in a surprisingly small area and, if newly-provided habitat is not too far from the remaining known sites, it is quite likely that it will be colonised. It is even possible that the existence of suitable gardens could help to bridge the gap between the remaining sites and former strongholds.

The foodplant – kidney vetch – will grow on exposed chalk or in thin soil overlying

Small Blue female choosing egg-laying sites on kidney vetch. **FK**

chalk. I used the spoil from the excavation of a wildlife pond to create a south-facing chalk bank in my garden many years ago and kidney vetch thrives on this and in a former lawn. To my delight, the Small Blue colonised within a few years.

A garden that will help to conserve butterflies should have:

- **Plants for larvae to feed on**
- **Places to pupate**
- **Flowers chosen to provide nectar, as well as for our own enjoyment**
- **The right mix of sunlight and shelter for the species concerned**

The garden should be maintained in a way that avoids disturbance during the vulnerable early stages and hibernation (e.g. avoid mowing or dead-heading or digging up plants that may harbour eggs, larvae or pupae.

It follows that studying the requirements of those species that are likely to occur is the best guide to the decisions you make in carrying out work in your garden. For example, excluding stinging nettles will prevent some of our most colourful butterflies from breeding in your garden. Management techniques required for each species can be deduced from the accounts in this book and elsewhere.

It is important when introducing larval foodplants to ensure the seeds or plants are derived from native UK stock (of local origin where possible) – not from imported stock propagated in the UK.

A garden for wildlife is not an unmanaged wilderness "left to nature". It is an environment managed in such a way as to keep it suspended in a state of high biodiversity where the choices made over techniques and planting reflect our desire to share our space with our fellow creatures.

Your garden can extend the habitat available to butterflies and other wildlife rather than exclude them. It will be progress if the youngsters of today are able to tell a future generation that there are more butterflies around than there used to be in their childhood.

BUTTERFLY PHOTOGRAPHY

Barry Hilling Associate of the Royal Photographic Society

HOW to get close enough to the subject: cool days, early mornings and evenings are best for approaching butterflies. They are more torpid at these times but the downside is that they are inactive and more difficult to find. Behaviour shots, such as feeding, courtship, mating and egg-laying are most likely to be encountered on sunny days, so bright spells, with cooler, cloudy periods, is probably the best combination.

Set up your camera, possibly in close-up (macro) mode. You may want to set the aperture manually, as this will give control of how much is in focus behind and in front of the subject. An out-of-focus background for example, achieved with a lower aperture number (f-stop), usually makes for a better picture.

Plan your angle of approach so that your shadow does not disturb the butterfly. When you get near the insect's tolerance distance, which can vary between species, move directly towards it, ever more stealthily, often with each step taking seconds. Crouching and keeping low helps; no jerky movements – use fluid motion. A tuft of grass or maybe a small bush can be used to hide your approach. In blustery weather, the insect is less likely to be aware of you if it is being buffeted by wind.

Once in position, check the image on the screen or viewfinder. Final adjustments should be kept to a minimum so as not to spook the butterfly. It is best to be totally square on to the subject otherwise parts of it may be out of focus.

After all this preparation you may notice that the butterfly is worn, faded or damaged. Maybe it has changed position, requiring a different camera angle. Perhaps only one in 20 approaches will result in a worthy photograph of an undamaged subject with good composition

For the best photographs, check the background and foreground for distractions. A blade of grass behind or, worse still, in front of the butterfly, can spoil a good photograph. Although digital images can be manipulated and distractions removed with editing programs such as Photoshop, it is better to get it right with the camera.

COMPOSITION: there is often little time to compose the picture and many photographers are content with properly exposed and sharp images. However, the best pictures have good composition and artistic appeal.

Having the butterfly in the centre of the photograph can be lifeless and uninteresting. It is better if the subject is looking into the picture, with more space in front of the butterfly's head than behind. This directs the viewer's eye into the picture.

Consider whether to use the camera in vertical (portrait) or horizontal (landscape) position. For example, if the butterfly is on an orchid or tall plant, maybe a better composition could be achieved by turning the camera through 90 degrees and using a vertical picture frame.

Common Blues roosting. **BH**

A branch that is more diagonal, rather than horizontal or vertical, can create a more appealing composition.

Also, consider the size of the butterfly in the picture. If the subject fills the frame, with no breathing space around it, the photo may have great impact and show much fine detail, but will not reveal anything about the insect's size, behaviour or environment.

That said, there is a place for some large images to show close-up detail. A butterfly that is too small in the picture will lack impact and tell the viewer little about the actual butterfly but may show the habitat.

Generally, the best pictures have the butterfly in about one third of the frame, thereby showing the habitat, what the butterfly is settled on and its surroundings, together with good detail of the butterfly itself. However a collection of photos with butterflies all the same size can be rather dull.

Careful framing produces better compositions and a slight change in the position or orientation of the camera can improve a picture. For example, if a snapped-off twig behind a perched butterfly spoils the composition, carefully moving the camera can keep it out of view. An out-of-focus bright object behind the butterfly, such as a blurred buttercup, may be an issue. Again, a slight change of camera angle can solve the problem.

Artists, architects and photographers have long used the rule of thirds to produce aesthetically pleasing compositions. To do this, mentally divide the viewfinder or focusing screen with four lines at 1/3rd distances – two horizontal and two vertical.

Many digital cameras give the option to display this grid. Placing the subject near to any one of the four points where the lines cross can produce a strong composition.

These suggestions are aids rather than strict rules. A photo can be further improved by cropping on a computer or with slide film, by masking.

LEARN About Your Subject: knowing your subject and its often complex behaviour will give you more success in photographing it. Prior research will pay dividends as it will help you to know the butterfly's habitat preference, flight periods and behaviour. Knowledge accumulated in the field will also improve your success rate.

Many species frequent a limited number of sites at specific times of year, and require particular plants for egg-laying. Most butterflies seek nectar from a limited number of plants. For example the Gatekeeper's proboscis is just 6mm long and it is unable to penetrate the deep corollas of teasels and other tubular flowers and therefore feeds only on flat flowers. However the Brimstone's 15mm proboscis can access the nectar in tubular flowers.

Some species prefer honeydew; others, like the Purple Emperor, require mineral salts from the soil or from animal excrement. Knowing such details will give you more opportunities. Perched butterflies will usually close their wings when cloud covers the sun and the temperature drops, reopening them when the sun reappears. Wings open or closed will require a different camera position so looking at the sky prior to approach will help you to anticipate the butterfly's action and to position the camera accordingly.

FINAL tips: avoid bright clothes as these will emphasise your movements. Be aware that dangling camera straps may spook the butterfly. Look at your successes and failures and analyse what you did right or wrong. Incorporate what you did right into your technique. It pays to plan ahead and don't forget that other life stages can also make good photographs.

MY Surrey butterfly year: often starts on Denbies Hillside in early April, when careful searching can reveal Adonis Blue caterpillars attended by ants. Early fliers include Orange-tip, Green Hairstreak, Grizzled and Dingy Skippers, followed by the first brood of Adonis Blue around the middle of May.

Howell Hill is a gem and one could imagine being miles away from London rather than just a mile or so from Cheam or Ewell. This chalk grassland site in June is possibly the best place in Surrey for Small Blue, with a good range of other species.

Bookham Common from late June gives opportunities for Purple Emperor, Silver-washed Fritillary, White Admiral and Purple Hairstreak. The same species are in Chiddingfold Forest, which also supports the dainty Wood White.

In July at Pewley Down, near Guildford, it is a joy to see Marbled Whites and Chalkhill Blues in good numbers. A bonus for the photographer in the late afternoon and early evening is the chance to take pictures of these lovely species when they settle down for the night to roost.

Choice of camera and equipment, exposure and lighting, depth of field, focusing, processing the images on a computer and many other technical matters are too large a subject to be covered here.

■ *Recommended books on photography, page 235.*

SPECIES RICHNESS MAP

Species richness varies across the county, due in some degree to recording effort but mainly to habitat. More species are found on chalk downland than on the heaths.

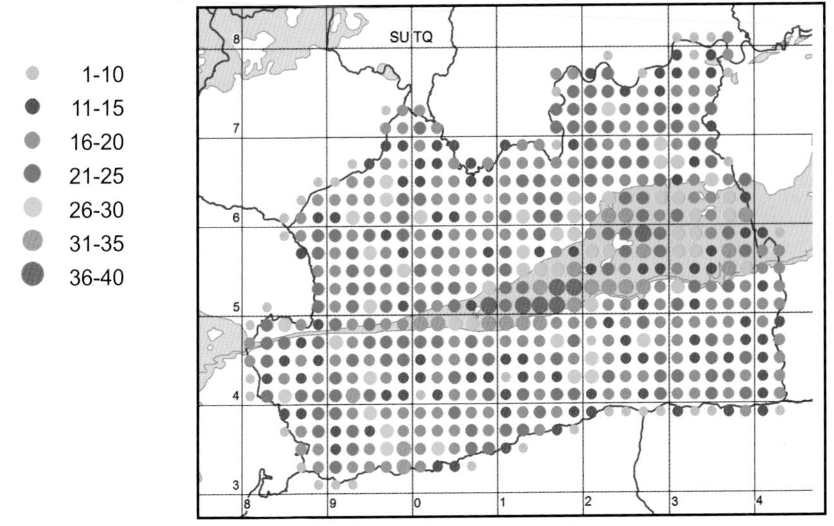

Surrey's 42 regular species by family (and subfamily)

Skippers ....Hesperiidae (Hesperiinae, Pyrginae).....................................6
Whites & Yellows ....Pieridae (Dismorphiinae, Coliadinae, Pierinae) 7
Hairstreaks ....Lycaenidae (Theclinae) 4
Copper.............................Lycaenidae (Lycaeninae)..1
Blues ....Lycaenidae (Polyommatinae) 7
Vanessids (Admirals etc)..Nymphalidae (Limenitinae, Apaturinae, Nymphalinae)..........7
Fritillaries ....Nymphalidae (Argynninae, Melitaeinae) 3
Browns ....Nymphalidae (Satyrinae) 7

Additional 17 British & Irish species

South etc — Large Blue, Duke of Burgundy; Heath, Marsh, Small Pearl-bordered, Pearl-bordered & High Brown Fritillary; Wall 8
Dorset — Lulworth Skipper 1
Norfolk — Swallowtail (subsp. *britannicus*) 1
Midlands — Black Hairstreak..1
North — Northern Brown Argus, Mountain Ringlet, Scotch Argus, Large Heath 4
Scotland — Chequered Skipper...1
Ireland — Cryptic Wood White..1

GB/IRE total 59

UK's 4,361 hectads				Transect abundance trends	
	Recorded 2005-2009		Change	1976-2012	2003-12
Green-veined White	**2,594**	59%	-3%	-13%	-16%
Peacock	**2,492**	57%	17%	15%	-30%
Small Tortoiseshell	**2,470**	57%	-3%	-74%	-77%
Meadow Brown	**2,441**	56%	-2%	5%	-31%
Painted Lady	**2,419**	55%	10%	224%	-94%
Red Admiral	**2,402**	55%	-2%	318%	-25%
Orange-tip	**2,192**	50%	0%	20%	59%
Common Blue	**2,147**	49%	-6%	-15%	-52%
Large White	**2,126**	49%	-8%	-36%	-40%
Small White	**2,060**	47%	-4%	-29%	-55%
Ringlet	**1,970**	45%	8%	312%	14%
Small Heath	**1,934**	44%	-9%	-54%	-22%
Speckled Wood	**1,932**	44%	20%	128%	-20%
Small Copper	**1,927**	44%	-6%	-23%	-16%
Comma	**1,599**	37%	8%	262%	-39%
Large Skipper	**1,442**	33%	-8%	-21%	-18%
Small Skipper	**1,422**	33%	-3%	-73%	-66%
Holly Blue	**1,409**	32%	-3%	145%	-23%
Gatekeeper	**1,372**	31%	-2%	-37%	-62%
Brimstone	**1,232**	28%	-1%	9%	-30%
Clouded Yellow	**1,143**	26%	-1%	367%	-98%
Green Hairstreak	**1,002**	23%	6%	-43%	-26%
Dark Green Fritillary	**931**	21%	-1%	153%	12%
Purple Hairstreak	**847**	19%	-16%	-8%	-8%
Brown Argus	**795**	18%	10%	6%	-35%
White-letter Hairstreak	**756**	17%	32%	-86%	-69%
Essex Skipper	**687**	16%	8%	-64%	-91%
Marbled White	**668**	15%	2%	46%	-28%
Silver-washed Fritillary	**586**	13%	12%	106%	-2%
Dingy Skipper	**547**	13%	-5%	-28%	49%
Grayling	**489**	11%	-18%	-60%	18%
White Admiral	**428**	10%	14%	-57%	-44%
Grizzled Skipper	**320**	7%	-17%	-31%	63%
Small Blue	**238**	5%	-4%	21%	0%
Chalkhill Blue	**208**	5%	-1%	14%	13%
Brown Hairstreak	**136**	3%	1%	-11%	-75%
Purple Emperor	**131**	3%	44%	43%	-55%
Adonis Blue	**125**	3%	30%	168%	-46%
Silver-studded Blue	**91**	2%	-3%	5%	-40%
Wood White	**63**	1.4%	-23%	-84%	-59%
Silver-spotted Skipper	**42**	1.0%	35%	854%	-55%
Glanville Fritillary	**11**	0.3%	22%	-34%	4,957%

Surrey's 558 tetrads							Transect abundance trends	
Recorded 2000-2012			Stable	Gain	Loss	Change	1990-2012	2000-12
Small White	**546**	98%	486	60	6	11%	3%	-21%
Speckled Wood	**538**	96%	485	53	10	9%	4%	-25%
Large White	**534**	96%	476	58	14	9%	-58%	-49%
Meadow Brown	**533**	96%	515	18	15	0.6%	-34%	-30%
Gatekeeper	**520**	93%	481	39	21	4%	-37%	-46%
Green-veined White	**516**	92%	470	46	29	3%	-24%	-56%
Comma	**505**	91%	403	102	21	19%	13%	-38%
Peacock	**492**	88%	445	47	41	1.2%	-65%	-75%
Red Admiral	**487**	87%	365	122	30	23%	-3%	-39%
Brimstone	**451**	81%	359	92	43	12%	-35%	-37%
Holly Blue	**446**	80%	365	81	64	4%	-27%	-14%
Small Tortoiseshell	**423**	76%	381	42	94	-11%	-96%	-71%
Common Blue	**415**	74%	294	121	54	19%	-32%	-34%
Orange-tip	**409**	73%	318	91	73	5%	-22%	19%
Small/Essex Skipper	**407**	73%	344	63	98	-8%	-71%	-62%
Large Skipper	**402**	72%	288	114	72	12%	-50%	-31%
Ringlet	**394**	71%	264	130	55	24%	5%	-49%
Painted Lady	**383**	69%	224	159	73	29%	42%	75%
Small Copper	**364**	65%	254	110	73	11%	4%	27%
Purple Hairstreak	**266**	48%	178	88	111	-8%	-6%	117%
Essex Skipper	**248**	44%	181	67	150	-25%	-	-76%
Small Heath	**201**	36%	126	75	71	2%	-46%	23%
Silver-washed Frit	**168**	30%	92	76	42	25%	38%	-26%
Marbled White	**139**	25%	58	81	18	83%	-41%	4%
Brown Argus	**132**	24%	62	70	52	16%	-34%	-31%
Clouded Yellow	**119**	21%	54	65	46	19%	-17%	-88%
White Admiral	**105**	19%	62	43	53	-9%	-13%	252%
Green Hairstreak	**96**	17%	53	43	32	13%	-4%	3%
Brown Hairstreak	**73**	13%	31	42	18	49%	-	-31%
Grizzled Skipper	**62**	11%	46	16	24	-11%	-54%	22%
White-letter Hstreak	**59**	11%	34	25	59	-37%	-74%	-92%
Dingy Skipper	**55**	10%	45	10	24	-20%	116%	28%
Grayling	**55**	10%	44	11	7	8%	285%	73%
Purple Emperor	**55**	10%	17	38	23	38%	-	-
Silver-studded Blue	**41**	7%	33	8	10	-5%	4%	58%
Chalkhill Blue	**38**	7%	30	8	15	-16%	2,838%	466%
Dark Green Fritillary	**31**	6%	22	9	17	-21%	417%	15%
Small Blue	**26**	5%	22	4	10	-19%	679%	85%
Silver-spotted Skip	**25**	4%	19	6	4	9%	73%	-43%
Wood White	**15**	3%	6	9	1	114%	11%	-31%
Adonis Blue	**11**	2%	9	2	6	-27%	201%	-14%
Glanville Fritillary	**5**	0.9%	0	5	0	-	-	-

Flight weeks ▲High transect counts, △Middle, ^Low

	Ap 1	8	15	22	29	My 6	13	20	27	Jn 3	10	17	24
Brimstone	△	△	▲	▲	▲	▲	▲	▲	▲	△	△	△	^
Peacock	▲	▲	▲	▲	▲	▲	△	△	△	△	△	^	^
Small Tortoisehell	▲	▲	△	▲	△	△	△	^	△	^	△	▲	▲
Comma	▲	▲	△	△	△	^	^	△	^	^	^	△	▲
Orange-tip	△	△	△	▲	▲	▲	△	△	△	△	^	^	
Red Admiral	△	^	^	^	^	^	△	^	^	△	△	△	△
Grizzled Skipper	^	△	△	△	▲	▲	▲	△	▲	△	△	△	△
Green Hairstreak		^	△	▲	▲	△	▲	△	△	△	△	△	^
Dingy Skipper		^	△	△	▲	▲	▲	▲	▲	△	△	△	△
Holly Blue	^	^	△	△	△	△	△	△	△	△	^	^	^
Green-veined White	^	^	^	△	△	△	△	△	△	△	^	△	△
Small White	^	^	^	△	△	△	△	△	^	^	^	△	△
Speckled Wood	^	^	^	△	△	△	△	^	△	△	△	△	^
Wood White		^	^	△	△	△	▲	▲	▲	△	△	^	△
Adonis Blue					△	△	△	▲	▲	▲	△	△	^
Large White	^	^	^	^	△	△	△	△	△	△	△	^	^
Brown Argus					^	△	△	▲	▲	△	△	△	△
Small Heath			^	^	^	△	△	△	▲	▲	▲	▲	▲
Small Copper	^	^	^	^	^	△	△	△	△	^	△	^	△
Glanville Frit+							△	▲	▲	▲	▲	▲	△
Common Blue			^	^	^	^	△	△	▲	△	△	△	△
Painted Lady		^	^	^		^	^	▲	▲	△	△	▲	△
Small Blue					^	^	^	△	▲	▲	▲	▲	▲
Clouded Yellow				^		^		△	△	△	^	△	△
Large Skipper						^	^	△	△	△	△	▲	▲
Silver-studded Blue								^	^	△	△	▲	▲
Marbled White									^	△	△	△	▲
Ringlet								^	^	△	△	△	▲
Small Skipper									^	△	△	△	▲
White Admiral									^	△	△	△	▲
Dark Green Frit									^	^	^	△	△
Essex Skipper										^	^	△	△
Meadow Brown							^	^	^	^	^	△	△
Purple Hairstreak+											^	△	△
Silver-washed Frit										^	^	△	△
W-letter Hairstreak+											^	△	△
Purple Emperor+												^	△
Gatekeeper												^	^
Chalkhill Blue											^	^	^
Grayling													^
S-spotted Skipper													
Brown Hairstreak+													

General (non-transect) records also used for the five species with +													
Jy 1	*8*	*15*	*22*	*29*	*Au 5*	*12*	*19*	*26*	*Se 2*	*9*	*16*	*23*	
^	△	△	△	△	△	△	△	^	^	^	^	^	Brimstone
△	△	△	△	▲	△	△	△	^	^	^	^	^	Peacock
▲	△	△	△	△	▲	△	△	^	^	^	^	^	Small Tortoisehell
▲	▲	▲	▲	△	^	△	△	△	△	△	△	^	Comma
	^												Orange-tip
▲	▲	▲	▲	▲	△	△	△	△	△	△	▲	▲	Red Admiral
^	△	^									^		Grizzled Skipper
^													Green Hairstreak
^	^	^	△	△		^							Dingy Skipper
△	▲	▲	▲	▲	▲	▲	△	△	△	△	^		Holly Blue
△	▲	▲	▲	▲	▲	▲	▲	△	△	^	^	^	Green-veined White
△	▲	▲	▲	▲	▲	▲	▲	△	△	△	△	^	Small White
^	△	△	▲	▲	▲	▲	▲	▲	▲	△	△	^	Speckled Wood
^	^	△	△	▲	▲	△	△						Wood White
^		^	△	^	△	△	▲	▲	△	△	△	^	Adonis Blue
△	▲	▲	▲	▲	▲	▲	▲	△	△	△	△	^	Large White
^	^	^	△	△	▲	▲	▲	▲	△	△	^	^	Brown Argus
▲	△	△	△	△	△	▲	▲	▲	▲	△	△	△	Small Heath
△	▲	▲	▲	△	△	△	△	△	▲	▲	▲	▲	Small Copper
^													Glanville Frit+
△	^	△	△	▲	▲	▲	▲	▲	△	△	△	^	Common Blue
△	△	△	△	▲	▲	△	▲	△	△	△	△	^	Painted Lady
△	△	△	△	△	△	△	△	^	^				Small Blue
^	△	△	△	△	▲	▲	▲	▲	△	▲	△	△	Clouded Yellow
▲	▲	▲	△	△	△	△	△	^	^				Large Skipper
▲	△	▲	△	△	^	^	^						Silver-studded Blue
▲	▲	△	△	△	△	^	^						Marbled White
▲	▲	▲	△	△	△	△	△	△	^				Ringlet
△	▲	▲	▲	△	△	△	^	^					Small Skipper
▲	△	▲	△	△	△				^				White Admiral
▲	▲	▲	▲	△	△	△	△	^	^				Dark Green Frit
▲	▲	△	▲	△	△	^							Essex Skipper
△	▲	▲	▲	▲	▲	△	△	△	△	△	△	△	Meadow Brown
△	▲	▲	▲	△	△	△	△	^	^				Purple Hairstreak+
△	▲	▲	▲	▲	△	△	△	△	^	^			Silver-washed Frit
▲	▲	▲	▲	▲	▲	△	^	^					W-letter Hairstreak+
▲	▲	▲	▲	△	△	^							Purple Emperor+
△	△	▲	▲	▲	▲	△	△	△	△	△	^	^	Gatekeeper
△	△	△	▲	▲	▲	▲	△	△	△	△	△	^	Chalkhill Blue
^	^	△	△	△	△	▲	▲	▲	▲	△	△	^	Grayling
		^	△	△	▲	▲	▲	△	△	△	^		S-spotted Skipper
	^	^	^	△	△	▲	▲	▲	▲	▲	△	△	Brown Hairstreak+

Top one-day counts

Transects 2000-2012	*Date*	*Site*	*Count*
Chalkhill Blue	2012, Aug 8	Denbies Landbarn B	1,681
Meadow Brown	2004, Aug 7	Sheepleas	846
Adonis Blue	2005, May 27	Denbies Landbarn B	600
Small/Essex Skipper	2008, Jul 15	Richmond Park	450
Ringlet	2009, Jul 1	Park Downs	412
Silver-studded Blue	2010, Jul 2	Fairmile Common	268
Gatekeeper	2006, Jul 18	Fairmile Common	222
Marbled White	2009, Jul 2	Pewley Down	190
Small Skipper	2010, Jul 10	Roundshaw Downs	156
Painted Lady	2009, May 28	London Wetland Centre	148
Large White	2003, Jul 24	Sheepleas	147
Small Blue	2004, Jun 6	Howell Hill	129
Common Blue	2003, Aug 5	Sheepleas	127
Small Heath	2005, Jun 24	Richmond Park	123
Silver-spotted Skipper	2003, Aug 19	Colekitchen	99
Small White	2004, Jul 15	Mitcham Common B	82
Speckled Wood	2001, Jul 23	Wandsworth Common	79
Brown Argus	2004, Aug 14	Sheepleas	67
Essex Skipper	2008, Jul 10	Richmond Park	66
Small Copper	2006, Jul 12	Fairmile Common	61
Grayling	2006, Aug 5	Chobham Common NE	56
Large Skipper	2003, Jun 24	Wandsworth Common	54
Dingy Skipper	2005, May 11	Denbies Landbarn B	53
Small Tortoiseshell	2003, Aug 5	Sheepleas	47
Brimstone	2000, May 5	Park Downs	42
Green-veined White	2000, Jul 29	South Norwood	41
Silver-washed Fritillary	2006, Jul 11	Sheepleas	40
Peacock	2000, Aug 11	Happy Valley	32
Dark Green Fritillary	2006, Jul 12	Box Hill, Zig Zag	19
White Admiral	2010, Jul 4	Epsom Common	19
Holly Blue	2004, Aug 14	Sheepleas	18
Purple Hairstreak	2008, Jul 21	Mitcham Common B	18
Wood White	2003, Aug 2	Oaken Wood	18
Orange-tip	2012, May 20	Bealeswood Common	17
Green Hairstreak	2011, May 1	Nore Hill	16
Comma	2009, Jul 15	Wimbledon Common	15
Grizzled Skipper	2011, Apr 25	Headley Heath	12
Red Admiral	2003, Jul 13	Sheepleas	12
Clouded Yellow	2000, Sep 4	Headley Warren	8
Glanville Fritillary	2012, Jun 26	Hutchinson's Bank	6
White-letter Hairstreak	2000, Jul 17	Wingate Hill	3
Brown Hairstreak	2010, Sep 12	Howell Hill	2
Purple Emperor	2011, Jul 2	Chobham Common NE	2

Wintering strategies

Larval moults pre-winter		winters	later moults	Total
Brimstone	4	adult		4
Comma	4	adult		4
Peacock	4	adult		4
Red Admiral	4	adult/migrant		4
Small Tortoiseshell	4	adult		4
Green Hairstreak	3	pupa		3
Green-veined White	4	pupa		4
Grizzled Skipper	4	pupa		4
Holly Blue	3	pupa		3
Large White	4	pupa		4
Orange-tip	4	pupa		4
Small White	4	pupa		4
Wood White	4	pupa		4
Speckled Wood	2-3	pupa or larva	0-1	3
Adonis Blue	1-2	larva	2-3	4
Brown Argus	1-2	larva	2-3	4
Common Blue	2	larva	2	4
Dark Green Fritillary	0	larva	5	5
Dingy Skipper	4	larva	0	4
Gatekeeper	1	larva	3	4
Glanville Fritillary	4	larva	2	6
Grayling	2	larva	2	4
Large Skipper	4	larva	2	6
Marbled White	0	larva	3	3
Meadow Brown	3	larva	2	5
Purple Emperor	2	larva	2	4
Ringlet	2	larva	2	4
Silver-washed Fritillary	0	larva	4	4
Small Blue	3	larva	0	3
Small Copper	2-3	larva	1-2	4
Small Heath	2-3	larva	1-2	4
Small Skipper	0	larva	4	4
White Admiral	2	larva	2	4
Brown Hairstreak		egg	3	3
Chalkhill Blue		egg	4	4
Essex Skipper		egg	4	4
Purple Hairstreak		egg	3	3
Silver-spotted Skipper		egg	4	4
Silver-studded Blue		egg	4	4
White-letter Hairstreak		egg	3	3
Clouded Yellow	4	migrant		4
Painted Lady	4	migrant		4

PRIMARY LARVAL FOODPLANTS

Scientific Name	Common Name	
Agrimonia eupatoria	**Agrimony**	Grizzled Skipper
Agrostis curtisii	**Bristle bent**	Grayling
Agrostis stolonifera	**Creeping bent**	Gatekeeper, Small Heath
Aira praecox	**Early hair-grass**	Grayling
Alliaria petiolata	**Garlic mustard**	Green-veined White, Orange-tip
Anthyllis vulneraria	**Kidney vetch**	Small Blue
Brachypodium pinnatum	**Tor-grass**	Grayling
Brachypodium sylvaticum	**False-brome**	Essex Skipper, Meadow Brown, Grayling Ringlet, Speckled Wood
Brassica oleracea	**Cabbage**	Large White, Small White
Calluna vulgaris	**Heather or Ling**	Silver-studded Blue
Cardamine amara	**Large bitter-cress**	Green-veined White
Cardamine hirsuta	**Hairy bitter-cress**	Green-veined White
Cardamine pratensis	**Cuckooflower**	Green-veined White, Orange-tip
Carduus crispus	**Welted thistle**	Painted Lady
Carduus nutans	**Musk thistle**	Painted Lady
Cirsium arvense	**Creeping thistle**	Painted Lady
Cirsium palustre	**Marsh thistle**	Painted Lady
Cirsium vulgare	**Spear thistle**	Painted Lady
Cytisus scoparius	**Broom**	Green Hairstreak
Dactylis glomerata	**Cock's-foot**	Essex Skipper, Gatekeeper Large Skipper, Meadow Brown, Ringlet, Speckled Wood
Deschampsia cespitosa	**Tufted hair-grass**	Grayling, Ringlet
Elytrigia repens	**Common couch**	Meadow Brown, Ringlet, Speckled Wood
Erica cinerea	**Bell heather**	Silver-studded Blue
Festuca ovina	**Sheep's-fescue**	Gatekeeper, Silver-spotted Skipper, Small Heath
Festuca rubra	**Red fescue**	Marbled White, Small Heath
Fragaria vesca	**Wild strawberry**	Grizzled Skipper
Frangula alnus	**Alder buckthorn**	Brimstone
Genista tinctoria	**Dyer's greenweed**	Green Hairstreak
Geranium dissecta	**Cut-leaved crane's-bill**	Brown Argus
Hedera helix	**Ivy**	Holly Blue
Helianthemum nummularium	**Common rock-rose**	Brown Argus, Green Hairstreak
Hippocrepis comosa	**Horseshoe vetch**	Adonis Blue, Chalkhill Blue
Holcus lanatus	**Yorkshire-fog**	Small Skipper
Holcus mollis	**Creeping soft-grass**	Essex Skipper
Ilex aquifolium	**Holly**	Holly Blue
Lathyrus linifolius	**Bitter-vetch**	Wood White
Lathyrus pratensis	**Meadow vetchling**	Wood White
Lolium perenne	**Perennial rye-grass**	Gatekeeper
Lonicera periclymenum	**Honeysuckle**	White Admiral

Lotus corniculatus	**Common bird's-foot-trefoil**	Common Blue, Dingy Skipper, Green Hairstreak, Wood White
Lotus pedunculatus	**Greater bird's-foot-trefoil**	Wood White
Medicago sativa subsp. *sativa*	**Lucerne**	Clouded Yellow
Molinia caerulea	**Purple moor-grass**	Large Skipper
Nasturtium officinale	**Water-cress**	Green-veined White, Small White
Plantago lanceolata	**Ribwort plantain**	Glanville Fritillary
Poa annua	**Annual meadow-grass**	Gatekeeper
Poa nemoralis	**Wood meadow-grass**	Meadow Brown
Poa pratensis	**Smooth meadow-grass**	Small Heath
Poa trivialis	**Rough meadow-grass**	Gatekeeper
Potentilla reptans	**Creeping cinquefoil**	Grizzled Skipper
Prunus spinosa	**Blackthorn**	Brown Hairstreak
Quercus petraea	**Sessile oak**	Purple Hairstreak
Quercus robur	**Pedunculate oak**	Purple Hairstreak
Rhamnus cathartica	**Buckthorn**	Brimstone
Rumex acetosa	**Common sorrel**	Small Copper
Rumex acetosella	**Sheep's sorrel**	Small Copper
Salix caprea	**Goat willow**	Purple Emperor
Salix cinerea	**Grey willow**	Purple Emperor
Sisymbrium officinale	**Hedge mustard**	Green-veined White
Trifolium pratense	**Red clover**	Clouded Yellow
Trifolium repens	**White clover**	Clouded Yellow
Ulex europaeus	**Gorse**	Green Hairstreak, Silver-studded Blue
Ulmus glabra	**Wych elm**	Comma, White-letter Hairstreak
Ulmus procera	**English elm**	Comma, White-letter Hairstreak
Urtica dioica	**Common nettle**	Comma, Peacock, Red Admiral, Small Tortoiseshell
Urtica urens	**Small nettle**	Small Tortoiseshell
Vaccinium myrtillus	**Bilberry**	Green Hairstreak
Vicia cracca	**Tufted vetch**	Wood White
Viola hirta	**Hairy violet**	Dark Green Fritillary
Viola riviniana	**Common dog-violet**	Dark Green Fritillary, Silver-washed Fritillary
Vulpia myuros	**Rat's-tail fescue**	Grayling

NECTAR SOURCES

Achillea millefolium	**Yarrow**	Silver-spotted Skipper
Ajuga reptans	**Bugle**	Dingy Skipper, Grizzled Skipper, Wood White
Alliaria petiolata	**Garlic mustard**	Orange-tip
Angelica sylvestris	**Wild angelica**	Brown Hairstreak
Anthriscus sylvestris	**Cow parsley**	Essex Skipper
Anthyllis vulneraria	**Kidney vetch**	Brown Argus, Glanville Fritillary, Small Blue
Armoracia rusticana	**Horse-radish**	Small White
Aster x salignus	**Common Michaelmas-daisy**	Brimstone, Comma, Clouded Yellow, Large White, Painted Lady, Peacock, Red Admiral, Small Copper, Small Tortoiseshell, Speckled Wood
Aubrieta deltoidea	**Aubretia**	Brimstone, Green-veined White, Large White, Orange-tip, Peacock, Small Tortoiseshell
Bellis perennis	**Daisy**	Grizzled Skipper, Small Heath
Betonica officinalis	**Betony**	White Admiral
Brassica rapa	**Turnip**	Silver-studded Blue
Buddleja davidii	**Buddleia**	Brimstone, Comma, Clouded Yellow, Common Blue, Dark Green Fritillary, Essex Skipper, Gatekeeper, Grayling, Green-veined White, Holly Blue, Large Skipper, Large White, Marbled White, Meadow Brown, Painted Lady, Peacock, Purple Emperor, Purple Hairstreak, Red Admiral, Ringlet, Silver-washed Fritillary, Small Copper, Small Skipper, Small Tortoiseshell, Small White, Speckled Wood, White Admiral
Calluna vulgaris	**Heather or Ling**	Common Blue, Dingy Skipper, Gatekeeper, Grayling, Green Hairstreak, Grizzled Skipper, Ringlet, Silver-washed Fritillary, Small Copper, Small Heath
Cardamine pratensis	**Cuckooflower**	Orange-tip
Carlina vulgaris	**Carline thistle**	Chalkhill Blue
Castanea sativa	**Sweet chestnut**	Purple Emperor
Centaurea nigra	**Common knapweed**	Adonis Blue, Chalkhill Blue, Clouded Yellow, Dark Green Fritillary, Essex Skipper, Grayling, Marbled White, Meadow Brown, Painted Lady, Silver-spotted Skipper, Silver-washed Fritillary, Small Skipper, Wood White
Centaurea scabiosa	**Greater knapweed**	Chalkhill Blue, Marbled White, Silver-washed Fritillary, Small Skipper
Centranthus ruber	**Red valerian**	Brimstone, Comma, Dark Green Fritillary, Grayling, Green-veined White, Large Skipper, Large White, Meadow Brown, Painted Lady, Peacock, Red Admiral, Silver-washed Fritillary, Small White
Chamerion angustifolium	**Rosebay willowherb**	White-letter Hairstreak
Cirsium acaule	**Dwarf thistle**	Silver-spotted Skipper

Cirsium arvense	**Creeping thistle**	Brown Argus, Brown Hairstreak, Comma Essex Skipper, Gatekeeper, Green-veined White Large Skipper, Marbled White, Meadow Brown Painted Lady, Peacock, Ringlet Silver-washed Fritillary, Small Skipper Small Tortoiseshell, Small White White Admiral, White-letter Hairstreak
Cirsium palustre	**Marsh thistle**	Clouded Yellow, Essex Skipper Dark Green Fritillary, Small Heath
Cirsium vulgare	**Spear thistle**	Brown Argus, Dark Green Fritillary, Grayling Marbled White, Silver-washed Fritillary Small Copper, White-letter Hairstreak
Cruciata laevipes	**Crosswort**	Glanville Fritillary
Diplotaxis tenuifolia	**Perennial wall-rocket**	Peacock
Dipsacus fullonum	**Wild teasel**	Brimstone, Grayling
Epilobium hirsutum	**Great willowherb**	Green-veined White
Erica cinerea	**Bell heather**	Grayling, Silver-studded Blue
Erysimum cheiri	**Wallflower**	Brimstone, Orange-tip
Eupatorium cannabinum	**Hemp-agrimony**	Adonis Blue, Brown Argus Brown Hairstreak, Dark Green Fritillary, Gatekeeper Holly Blue, Peacock, Meadow Brown Purple Hairstreak, Red Admiral, Ringlet Silver-washed Fritillary, Small Tortoiseshell Speckled Wood, White-letter Hairstreak
Euphorbia amygdaloides	**Wood spurge**	Glanville Fritillary
Fragaria vesca	**Wild strawberry**	Brown Argus, Grizzled Skipper
Frangula alnus	**Alder buckthorn**	Purple Hairstreak, White Admiral
Galium verum	**Lady's bedstraw**	Silver-studded Blue
Gentianella amarella	**Autumn gentian**	Silver-spotted Skipper
Geranium robertianum	**Herb-Robert**	Wood White
Glechoma hederacea	**Ground-ivy**	Brimstone, Dingy Skipper Grizzled Skipper, Wood White
Hedera helix	**Ivy**	Comma, Holly Blue, Red Admiral, Speckled Wood
Helianthemum nummularium	**Common rock-rose**	Silver-studded Blue
Heracleum sphondylium	**Hogweed**	Brown Hairstreak, Purple Hairstreak White Admiral
Hesperis matronalis	**Dame's-violet**	Green-veined White, Large White Orange-tip, Small White
Hippocrepis comosa	**Horseshoe vetch**	Adonis Blue, Glanville Fritillary, Small Blue
Hyacinthoides hispanica	**Spanish bluebell**	Orange-tip
Hyacinthoides non-scripta	**Bluebell**	Green Hairstreak
Ilex aquifolium	**Holly**	Holly Blue
Knautia arvensis	**Field scabious**	Adonis Blue, Chalkhill Blue, Marbled White Silver-spotted Skipper
Lathyrus linifolius	**Bitter-vetch**	Wood White
Lathyrus pratensis	**Meadow vetchling**	Wood White

Lavandula x intermedia	**Lavender** ......Common Blue, Gatekeeper, Green-veined White Holly Blue, Large Skipper, Large White Marbled White, Meadow Brown, Red Admiral Small Copper, Small White
Leontodon hispidus	**Rough hawkbit** ....Silver-spotted Skipper
Leontodon saxatilis	**Lesser hawkbit** ....Clouded Yellow, Glanville Fritillary Silver-spotted Skipper
Leucanthemum vulgare	**Oxeye daisy** ....Dingy Skipper
Leucanthemum x superbum	**Shasta daisy** ....White-letter Hairstreak
Ligustrum ovalifolium	**Garden privet** ....Silver-studded Blue, White Admiral White-letter Hairstreak
Ligustrum vulgare	**Wild privet**........Green Hairstreak, Small Blue, White Admiral White-letter Hairstreak
Lobularia maritima	**Sweet Alison** ....Orange-tip
Lonicera periclymenum	**Honeysuckle** ....White Admiral
Lotus corniculatus	**Common bird's-foot-trefoil** ....Adonis Blue, Chalkhill Blue Clouded Yellow, Common Blue, Dingy Skipper Essex Skipper, Glanville Fritillary, Green Hairstreak Grizzled Skipper, Large Skipper, Ringlet Silver-spotted Skipper, Silver-studded Blue Small Blue, Small Skipper, Wood White
Lunaria annua	**Honesty** ....Brimstone, Green-veined White Large White, Orange-tip
Lythrum salicaria	**Purple-loosestrife** ....Purple Hairstreak
Medicago sativa subsp. *sativa*	**Lucerne** ..Clouded Yellow, Essex Skipper, Small Tortoiseshell
Myosotis arvensis	**Field forget-me-not** ....Brown Argus, Grizzled Skipper
Ononis repens	**Common restharrow** ....Glanville Fritillary
Origanum vulgare	**Wild marjoram** ....Adonis Blue, Brown Argus, Chalkhill Blue Comma, Common Blue, Gatekeeper Holly Blue, Marbled White, Meadow Brown Purple Hairstreak, Ringlet, Small Copper Small Heath, Small White Speckled Wood, White-letter Hairstreak
Pilosella officinarum	**Mouse-ear-hawkweed** ....Adonis Blue, Dingy Skipper
Prunella vulgaris	**Selfheal** ....Dingy Skipper, Small Skipper, Wood White
Pulicaria dysenterica	**Common fleabane** ....Brown Argus, Brown Hairstreak Clouded Yellow, Common Blue, Peacock Purple Hairstreak, Ringlet, Small Copper
Ranunculus spp.	**Buttercups**.............................Brown Argus, Green Hairstreak, Grizzled Skipper, Small Heath
Rubus fruticosus agg.	**Bramble** ....Adonis Blue, Brown Argus, Brown Hairstreak Chalkhill Blue, Comma, Dark Green Fritillary, Gatekeeper Grayling, Green-veined White, Holly Blue, Large Skipper Marbled White, Meadow Brown, Painted Lady Purple Hairstreak, Ringlet, Silver-studded Blue Silver-washed Fritillary, Small Heath, Small White Speckled Wood, White Admiral, White-letter Hairstreak

Salix cinerea	**Grey willow**	Green Hairstreak
Scabiosa columbaria	**Small scabious**	Chalkhill Blue, Silver-studded Blue
Sedum spectabile	**Butterfly stonecrop**	Comma, Large White, Painted Lady Peacock, Red Admiral, Small Copper Small Tortoiseshell, Speckled Wood
Senecio aquaticus	**Marsh ragwort**	Painted Lady, Purple Hairstreak
Senecio jacobaea	**Common ragwort**	Adonis Blue, Brown Argus Brown Hairstreak, Chalkhill Blue, Common Blue Dark Green Fritillary, Essex Skipper, Gatekeeper Grayling, Meadow Brown, Ringlet Silver-washed Fritillary, Small Copper, Small Heath Small Skipper, Small Tortoiseshell Speckled Wood, White-letter Hairstreak
Silene coronaria	**Rose campion**	Purple Hairstreak
Silene flos-cuculi	**Ragged-robin**	Dingy Skipper
Stellaria holostea	**Greater stitchwort**	Green Hairstreak
Stellaria media	**Common chickweed**	Dingy Skipper, Small Heath
Succisa pratensis	**Devil's-bit scabious**	Chalkhill Blue, Common Blue Meadow Brown, Small Heath
Taraxacum spp.	**Dandelions**	Brimstone, Clouded Yellow, Glanville Fritillary Green-veined White, Grizzled Skipper, Orange-tip Peacock, Small Tortoiseshell, Small White, Speckled Wood
Thymus polytrichus	**Wild thyme**	Adonis Blue, Gatekeeper Grayling, Silver-studded Blue
Torilis japonica	**Upright hedge-parsley**	White Admiral
Trifolium dubium	**Lesser trefoil**	Common Blue
Trifolium pratense	**Red clover**	Clouded Yellow, Dark Green Fritillary Essex Skipper, Grizzled Skipper, Large Skipper Marbled White, Small Skipper
Trifolium repens	**White clover**	Brown Argus, Common Blue Ringlet, Small Heath
Ulex europaeus	**Gorse**	Brown Argus, Green Hairstreak
Vaccinium myrtillus	**Bilberry**	Green Hairstreak
Viburnum opulus	**Guelder-rose**	Green Hairstreak
Vicia cracca	**Tufted vetch**	Large Skipper, Small Skipper, Wood White
Vicia sativa	**Common vetch**	Wood White

Surrey species of greatest concern						
	BC Endangered	*BC Vulnerable*	*BC Near Threatened*	*JNCC Priority*	*Protected from sale*	*Surrey BAP*
Glanville Frit	▲			▲	▲	
White-letter Hs	▲			▲	▲	
Wood White	▲			▲	▲	
Brown Hs		▲		▲	▲	
Silver-stud Blue		▲		▲	▲	
Dingy Skipper		▲		▲		
Grayling		▲		▲		
Grizzled Skip		▲		▲		
White Admiral		▲		▲		
Small Blue			▲	▲	▲	▲
Small Heath			▲	▲		
Adonis Blue			▲		▲	
Chalkhill Blue			▲		▲	
Purple Emperor			▲		▲	
Silver-sp Skip			▲		▲	

Butterfly Conservation

www.butterfly-conservation.org/files/red-list-of-british-butterflies.pdf

BC's 2010 Red List of threatened GB species has six categories:
Regionally Extinct, Critically Endangered, Endangered (3 Surrey species), Vulnerable (6), Near Threatened (6), Least Concern (27).

Joint Nature Conservation Committee

www.jncc.defra.gov.uk/page-5717; www.nhm.ac.uk

PRIORITY butterflies, including 11 Surrey species, are described in JNCC's 2007 UK Biodiversity Action Plan as:
Of principal importance for the purpose of conserving biodiversity, covered under section 41 (England) of the NERC Act (2006) and therefore need to be taken into consideration by a public body when performing any of its functions with a view to conserving biodiversity.

Protected species

www.jncc.defra.gov.uk/page-3614

PROTECTION levels under the Wildlife and Countryside Act 1981, section 9:
1 Fully protected: no Surrey species.
2 Protected from sale (excludes captive-breds): 10 Surrey species.

Surrey Biodiversity Partnership

www.surreybiodiversitypartnership.org
www.surreycc.gov.uk (search biodiversity)

Surrey Biodiversity Action Plan species: **Small Blue**.

GLOSSARY

The following terms are considered to require explanation; other terms (usually occurring only once) are explained in the text where convenient.

Androconia (androconial scales): on the forewing or body of male, specialised scales that release pheromones.

Apex (apical): tip of the wing.

Aurelians: name applied to early butterfly collectors.

Bivoltine: produces two generations per year.

Brassicaceae (brassicas, crucifers): plant family of mustards and cabbages.

Calcareous: lime (calcium)-rich, as in alkaline soils associated with limestones, e.g. the Chalk.

Costal: associated with front margin of wing.

Diapause: period of suspended growth or development, e.g. wintering as an egg, larva or pupa.

Dimorphism (dimorphic): difference in form or colour between individuals of the same species; may be seasonal, sexual or geographic.

Diurnal: active during the day; opposite of nocturnal.

Downland: short-grass habitat on limestone hills in southern England formed of the Chalk, e.g. North and South Downs, Wessex Downs, Chilterns.

Emergence: period during which the new adult generation of a butterfly species takes to the wing.

Frass: larval excrement.

Front margin: leading edge of wing.

Glucosinolates: class of organic compounds found in cruciferous plants, containing sulphur and nitrogen, and derived from glucose and an amino acid.

Hectad: 10km square (100 monads).

Hibernaculum: location for overwintering.

Inner angle: angle between inner and outer margins of wing.

Inner margin: edge of wing from behind where it joins the body, to the outer margin.

Instar: larval stage; newly-hatched larva is first instar; each instar (total ranges from 3-6 depending on species) is followed by a moult; final moult produces the pupa.

Jizz: combination of characteristics (including shape, flight style, behaviour) that serves to identify a particular species. This term is used routinely by birdwatchers.

Melanism (melanistic): abnormal or unusual darkening.

Metapopulation: group of spatially separated, interacting populations of the same species.

Monad: one kilometre square.

Multivoltine: produces more than three generations per year.

Outer margin: edge of wing furthest from where it joins the body.

Parasite: organism that obtains nourishment from a host without benefiting or killing it.

Parasitoid: organism that obtains nourishment from a host and eventually kills it.

Phenology: study of the times of recurring natural phenomena, especially in relation to climate; e.g. the emergence of adult butterflies from pupation.

Pheromone: substance secreted by the male of a species to sexually attract the female.

Pieridae (pierids): the family of Whites.

Pierinae (pierines): a subfamily of Whites, which in Britain includes Large, Small, Green-veined and Orange-tip.

Quartile: in statistics, each of the three values that divide a sequence of numbers into four groups; can also refer to an individual group. Reference is commonly made to the upper and lower quartiles. For example, there are Brimstone records in 451 tetrads; 173 are in the upper quartile with a count of 5+; 162 are in the lower quartile with a count of one.

Tetrad: 2km square (4 monads).

Translocation: deliberate, artificial transfer of a species from an established location to a new one.

Trivoltine: produces three generations per year.

Univoltine: produces one generation per year.

ORGANISATIONS, ABBREVIATIONS & WEBSITES

AES Amateur Entomologists' Society .... *www.amentsoc.org*

AONB Area of Outstanding Natural Beauty, designated by Natural England; e.g. Surrey Hills

BC Butterfly Conservation .... *www.butterfly-conservation.org*
Surrey & SW London branch .... *www.surreybutterflies.org*

BIS Department for Business, Innovation and Skills: see NERC .... *www.bis.gov.uk*

BMS UK Butterfly Monitoring Scheme: begun in1976 and now a partnership between CEH, BC and JNCC, funded by Defra;
database, based at CEH, is managed by BRC. .... *www.ukbms.org*

BNM Butterflies for the New Millennium: BC recording scheme, initially from 1995-1999, which resulted in landmark 2001 Millennium Atlas.

BRC Biological Records Centre .... *www.brc.ac.uk*

British Butterflies independent website .... *www.britishbutterflies.co.uk*

BSBI Botanical Society of the British Isles .... *www.bsbi.org.uk*

BTO British Trust for Ornithology .... *www.bto.org*

CEH Centre for Ecology & Hydrology: one of NERC's six research centres; based at Wallingford, Oxon. .... *www.ceh.ac.uk*

City of London Corporation .... *www.cityoflondon.gov.uk*

Defra Department of the Environment, Food and Rural Affairs .... *www.defra.gov.uk*

Downlands Project .... *www.surreycc.gov.uk (search downlands project)*

ECN UK Environmental Change Network .... *www.ecn.ac.uk*

Fauna Europaea database of scientific names .... *www.faunaeur.org*

FC Forestry Commission land .... *www.forestry.gov.uk*

FE Forestry Enterprise agencies: manage FC land .... *www.forestry.gov.uk*

IUCN International Union for Conservation of Nature .... *www.iucn.org*

JNCC Joint Nature Conservation Committee: advises government on nature conservation *www.jncc.defra.gov.uk*

Learn about Butterflies independent website .... *www.learnaboutbutterflies.com*

LNR Local Nature Reserve: 1,500+, designated by Natural England

LWT London Wildlife Trust .... *www.wildlondon.org.uk*

MOD Ministry of Defence (access & recreation*)* .... *www.mod.uk*

NBN National Biodiversity Network Gateway .... *www.nbn.org.uk*

NE Natural England: advises government on the natural environment *www.naturalengland.org.uk*

NERC National Environment Research Council: funding agency of BIS .... *www.nerc.ac.uk*

NNR National Nature Reserve, designated by Natural England; Surrey has three: Ashtead, Chobham & Thursley Commons

NT National Trust .... *www.nationaltrust.org.uk*

RES Royal Entomological Society (F=Fellow) .... *www.royensoc.co.uk*

RPS Royal Photographic Society (A=Associate) .... *www.rps.org*

RSPB Royal Society for the Protection of Birds .... *www.rspb.org.uk*

SAC Special Area of Conservation, designated by Natural England

SBIC Surrey Biodiversity Information Centre .... *www.surreywildlifetrust.org/sbic*
www.surreybiodiversitypartnership.org

SCC Surrey County Council .... *www.surreycc.gov.uk*

SPA Special Protection Area (for birds), designated by Natural England:
e.g. Thames Basin & Wealden Heaths

SSSI Site of Special Scientific Interest: 4,000+, designated by Natural England

Surrey Heathland Project .... *www.surreycc.gov.uk (search heathland project)*

Surrey Hills Area of Outstanding Natural Beauty .... *www.surreyhills.org*

Surrey Insight .... *www.surreyi.gov.uk*

Surrey Tourism .... *www.visitsurrey.com*

SWT Surrey Wildlife Trust .... *www.surreywildlifetrust.org*

UK Butterflies independent website .... *www.ukbutterflies.co.uk*

WCBS Wider Countryside Butterfly Survey: recording scheme rolled out in 2009
between BC, CEH and BTO... *www.ukbms.org/wcbs.aspx*

WWT Wildfowl & Wetlands Trust .... *www.wwt.org.uk*

LANDOWNERS & MANAGERS

Butterfly Conservation: Oaken Wood, Chiddingfold.

City of London Corporation: manages seven open spaces, known as the City Commons, on the borders of south London and Surrey:
Ashtead, Coulsdon, Farthing Downs and New Hill, Kenley, Riddlesdown, Spring Park, West Wickham (the last two being just inside VC16 West Kent).

Downlands Project

Forestry Commission

London Borough Councils: Croydon, Kingston upon Thames, Lambeth, Merton, Richmond upon Thames, Southwark, Sutton, Wandsworth.

London Wildlife Trust

Ministry of Defence

National Trust

RSPB: Farnham Heath.

Surrey Borough Councils: Elmbridge, Epsom & Ewell, Guildford, Reigate & Banstead, Runnymede, Spelthorne, Surrey Heath, Waverley, Woking.

Surrey County Council

Surrey District Councils: Mole Valley, Tandridge.

Surrey Heathland Project

Surrey Wildlife Trust: largest land manager in Surrey, including partnership with Surrey County Council and Ministry of Defence.

Wildfowl & Wetlands Trust: London Wetland Centre.

RECORDERS

Sincere thanks to the following recorders, who all contributed at least 10 records in 2000-12, and to everyone else who has submitted a record.

Mary Adler
Gary Aldridge
Dianne Allcock
Barbara Allison
Alastair Angus
Vanessa Ansell
Maria Ashdown-Ford
Janet Atkinson
John Austin
Graham Avison
Lea Bacon
Andy Bailey
Ray Baker
Neil Banks
Matthew Banner
John Bannister
Sue Barker
Luke Barley
Richard Bartlett
Sarah Barton
Ralph Batchelor
Sue Beale
Dick Beasley
Jim Bennett
Mark Bennett
Will Bermingham
Tony Bertenshaw
Steve Bolton
Vicky Booth
Martin Boyle
Matt Bramich
Keith Brandwood
James Bray
Peter Brewer
Malcolm Bridge
Mary Bridge
Tim Bright
Spike Brooker
Andy Brown
Gordon Brown
Lizzie Bruce
Lucy Bryce
Jessica Buckle
John Buckley
Graham Bugg
Richard Bullock
Enid Burman
Gerry Burman
Neil Burnett
Peter Camber
Gay Carr
John Carr
Rebecca Cash
Catherine Castree
Helen Cavilla
Geoffrey Chandler
James Chapman
R Charles
Steve Chastell
Ken Cheeseman
Janet Cheney
Peter Churchill
John Clark
Cathy Clarke
Harry E Clarke
M Clifford
Sarah Clift
Stewart Cocker
Sarah Cockhead
Derek A Coleman
Graham Collins
David Cooling
Lindsay Coomber
Sue Cooper
Celia Couzins
Robert Cramp
John Cranham
Peter Creasey
Heather Crooke
Robin Crowther
Ian Cunningham
Peter Curnock
D Curry
David Dancey
T Daniels
Angus Davies
John Davis
Rosey Davy
Stephen Daws
Donna Dawson
Peter De Jong
Michael De Saulles
Bridget De Whalley
Lawrence De Whalley
Tom De Whalley
M Dixon
Scott Dodd
Richard Donovan
Bill Downey
Mathew Drew
Carol Driver
Don Dunkin
G Durbin
Daniel Duthie
Geoff Eaton
Debbie Edwards
Julia Edwards
Piers Eley
Daniel Elger
Dave Elliott
Martin Ellis
Mike Enfield
Valerie Esplen
Angela Evans
Harry Eve
Pat Ewin
Peter Farrant
L Farrell
Teresa Farrell
Elitta Fell
Jim Ferguson
Stuart Fisher
Gillian Flinn
Gordon Flower
Rachael Forsyth
Ted Forsyth
John Foulsham
Richard Fox
Peter Frost
Emily Funnell
Pauline Gabriel
Tim Gabriel
Steve Gallis
David Gardner
Una Garland
Raymond Garrett
G J Geiger
Jim Giles
Alison Gilry
David Gittins
Allan Goddard
Rosemary Gooding
Elizabeth Goodyear
K Gosling
David Gough
Brenda Grabaskey
David Gradidge
Sally Graham
Martin Gray
Daniel Greenwood
Louise Greenwood
Duncan Greig
Clare Grindrod
Peter Grove
Barry Gutteridge
Catherine Hadler
Lucy Halahan
Oliver Halford
Jill Hall
Philippa Hall
Kay Halley
Friederike Hammer
Gill Hanson
Pandora Harbury
P Harding
D M Hardy
Kathleen Harman
Kaye Harman
Richard Harris
Sue Harris
Pauline Harrison
R Harvey
David Havenhand
Gavin Hawgood
Roger Hawkins
Fiona Haynes
Peter Haynes
John Hemmings
Rob Hewer
James Hewitt
Geoff Hewlett
Barbara Higginbotham
Maurice Higginbotham
Barry Hilling
Vivienne Hilling
Ron Hills
Dan Hoare
Tony Hoare
Celia Hodges
Julian Holliday
Peter Holliday
Deborah Holttum
Terry Hotten
S Howard
K Howland
Simon Humphreys
Alan Hunt
Lee Hurrell
Peter Ireland
Nigel Jackman
Derek Jackson
Cynthia James
Gail Jeffcoate
Steve Jeffcoate
Diana Jeffrey
Lee Jennings
Matt Johnson
Melanie Johnson
Pete Johnson
Jos Johnston
Eileen Jones
Gwilym Jones
Rosy Jones
Sam Jones
Hendryk Jurk
Andy Keay
Francis Kelly
D King
Sonia King-Hele
David Knapp
David Knight
Chris Lamsdell
Gill Langridge
Dave Law
William Laws
Sophie Leguil
Andrea Leonard
Tony Leveson-Gower
Carol Lewis
Val Lewis
Andrew Loader
Morag Loader
John Lobb
Neil Lodge

Paul Losse
Jane Lowe
Joan Lowe
Alex Macdonald
John Madden
Steve Mansfield
Joan Martin
Sheila Mason
Chris Maynard
Ailsa McCluskey
Amanda McCormick
Simon Meek
Monica Meeneghan
Helen Middlemas
Dave Miller
Hugh Millman
Les Mitchell
Dennis Moore
Tony Moore
Paul Moorhouse
Nicholas Morgan
Sheila Morley
Charles Morris
Audrey Moss
David Moss
Maureen Moss
Maurice Moss
Will Mouger
Edwin Mullins
Graham Mytton
Dennis Newland
Enid Newland
A Nicholson
Louise Niekirk
Kenneth Noble
Dominic North
Susan Oestel
Heather Ogborn
Ray Ogborn
David Olliver
Giles Osbourne
Joanne Osmond
Dave Page
J R Page
Michael Paling
R Palmer
Bryan Parnell
Gordon Parry
Neil Parsons
Nigel Parsons
Gill Peachey
Mike Pearce
Lee Peters
B A Petrie
John Petts
Peter Phillips
Gary Pocklington
Jim Porter
Nick Press
Sally Priestley
Steve Prowse
John Rees
Nigel Reeve
Alan Reid
Graham Revill
John Richardson
Christine Ridley
Martin Ripper
Mark Roberts
J Rogers
Kim Van Rooyen
Graham Rowbotham
Gill Sanders
Lorna Sandford
Bryan Saull
Clive Saunders
Andrew Scott
Valerie Searle
Relton Shakespeare
Marjorie Shattock
Abigail Shaw
Alan Shelley
Neil Sibley
Sue Simpson
Chris Skinner
Thelma Smalley
Andrew Smith
C Smith
David Smith
Bob Snellgrove
Adam Sobey
G Sparks
Henry Stapleton
John Stather
Timothy Staton
Ian Stone
Richard Stone
William Straker
Howard Street
Phil Strugnell
Keith Sturridge
G R Style
David Taylor
Geoffrey Taylor
Kim Taylor
Mark Taylor
Lene Tegldal
Brian Thomas
Marian Thomas
Rachael Thornley
Stephen Thorpe
Mike Thurner
Graham Titchmarsh
Margaret Tomsett
Peter Trew
Matthew Tugwell
Cheryl Turkington
Adrian Turner
Lone Le Vay
John Vetterlein
Neil Vigar
Gordon Voller
Shaun Waddell
June Wakefield
Peter Wakeham
Dave Warburton
Michael Ward
Derek Washington
Maggie Washington
Don Weatherill
Sue Webber
Joy Webster
Peter Webster
Anne Wedd
Mike Weller
Chris Whaley
Gloria Whaley
Kerry Wheeler
Paul Wheeler
Ashley White
Geoff White
Howard Whiting
Gareth Wilkins
Katie Wilkinson
Penny Williams
Ken Willmott
Martin Wills
Danial Winchester
Alan Wingrove
Matthew Wise
Geoff Woodcock
P Woodhead
Muriel Woolven
Lizzie Worth
David Wraith
Ian Wright
David Wynn

TOP RECORDERS

Ian Cunningham 14,082
Malcolm Bridge 5,739
Gail Jeffcoate 5,605
Howard Whiting 4,826
Richard Donovan 3,670
Alan Wingrove 3,519
June Wakefield 3,337
Derek A Coleman 3,112
Martin Wills 3,100
Alan Shelley 2,975
Jill Hall 2,705
Andrew Scott 2,705
Richard Bullock 2,636
Paul Wheeler....................2,617
Martin Ellis......................2,280
Mike Enfield....................2,183
Graham Revill..................1,894
Mary Adler 1,875
Gay Carr 1,866
Donna Dawson 1,830
Martin Boyle....................1,776
Duncan Greig 1,770
Peter Curnock 1,759
Marian Thomas................1,724
David Smith 1,704
Harry Eve 1,580
Sue Harris 1,540
John Buckley 1,347
Paul Moorhouse 1,345
Dominic North 1,322
Gill Peachey 1,311
Matt Bramich 1,294
Howard Street..................1,069
Alan Hunt 1,063
Peter Churchill 1,006
Neil Lodge 1,004
Peter Creasey 959
Peter Farrant 950
Peter Webster.......................936
Lawrence De Whalley 845
Andy Bailey.........................832
Joan Lowe 829
David Moss 828
Piers Eley............................809
John Madden 766
Raymond Garrett 735
David Havenhand 723
James Hewitt 723
Mike Weller 721
Richard Stone 655
Roger Hawkins 654
Shaun Waddell....................652
Martin Gray 621
Graham Collins 610
Graham Bugg......................599
Peter Grove 597

REFERENCES

This list includes references formally cited in the text plus others considered useful for additional, background information. The latter category also includes the references listed separately for Geology and Photography.

Asher J, Warren M, Fox R, Harding P, Jeffcoate G & Jeffcoate S, 2001
The millennium atlas of butterflies in Britain and Ireland. Oxford University Press, Oxford.

Bright P M & Leeds H A, 1938
A monograph of the British aberrations of the Chalk-hill Blue butterfly Lysandra coridon *(Poda, 1761).* Richmond Hill, Bournemouth.

Buckler W, 1886
The larvae of the British butterflies and moths, Vol. 1. The butterflies.
The Ray Society, London.

Chew F S, 1995
From weeds to crops: changing habitats of pierid butterflies (Lepidoptera, Pieridae)
Journal of the Lepidopterists' Society **49**: 285-303.

Chew F S & Renwick J A A, 1995
Host plant choice in *Pieris* butterflies *in* **Eisner T & Meinwald J (eds),**
Chemical Ecology of Insects 2. Chapman and Hall, New York.

Collins G A, 1995
Butterflies of Surrey. Surrey Wildlife Trust, Pirbright.

Collins G A, 1997
Larger moths of Surrey. Surrey Wildlife Trust, Pirbright.

Cook L M, Dennis R L H & Hardy P B, 2001
Butterfly-hostplant fidelity, vagrancy and measuring mobility from distribution maps.
Ecography **24**: 497-504.

Dennis R L H, 2010
A resource-based habitat view for conservation: butterflies in the British landscape.
Wiley-Blackwell, Oxford.

Eaton G, 2011a
Attack and defence: observations of behaviour in the Grayling *Hipparchia semele* (L.).
Atropos **43**: 50-53.

Eaton G, 2011b
In search of the "Blind Peacock", an aberrant form of *Inachis io* (L.). *Atropos* **44**: 37-40.

Eaton G, 2012
A tale of three Grayling *Hipparchia semele* (L.). *Atropos* **47**: 55-57.

Emmet A M & Heath J (eds), 1989
The moths and butterflies of Great Britain and Ireland, Vol. 7, Part 1. The butterflies.
Harley Books, Colchester.

Evans L K & Evans K G W, 1973
A survey of the macro-lepidoptera of Croydon and north-east Surrey.
Proceedings of the Croydon Natural History and Scientific Society **XIV**: 273-408.

Ford E B, 1945
Butterflies. New Naturalist Series. Collins, London.

Fox R, Asher J, Brereton T, Roy, D & Warren M, 2006
The state of butterflies in Britain and Ireland. Pisces Publications, Newbury.

Fox R, Brereton T M, Asher J, Botham M S, Middlebrook I, Roy D B & Warren M S, 2011
The state of the UK's butterflies 2011.
Butterfly Conservation and the Centre for Ecology and Hydrology, Wareham.

Fox R, Warren M S & Brereton T M, 2010
A new red list of British butterflies. *Species Status* 12: 1-32.
Joint Nature Conservation Committee, Peterborough.

Friedrich E, 1986
Breeding butterflies and moths: a practical handbook for British and European species.
Harley Books, Colchester.

Frohawk F W, 1924
Natural history of British butterflies. Hutchinson, London.

Goss H, 1902
Lepidoptera *in* **Malden H E (ed.),** *The Victoria history of the County of Surrey, Part 3, Zoology.* Constable, London.

Harper G W & Waller W E, 1950
Notes on breeding the first generation of *Polygonia c-album. The Entomologist* **83**: 145-148.

Hawes F W, 1890
Hesperia lineola Ochsenheimer: an addition to the list of British butterflies.
The Entomologist **23**: 3-4.

Heath J, Pollard E & Thomas J A, 1984
Atlas of butterflies in Britain and Ireland. Viking (Penguin), Harmondsworth.

Higgins L H & Riley N D, 1970
A field guide to the butterflies of Britain and Europe. Collins, London.

Jeffcoate G, Enfield M & Gerrard B, 2000
Surrey butterfly report. Butterfly Conservation (Surrey & SW London Branch), Wareham.

Newland D, Still R, Tomlinson D & Swash A, 2010
Britain's butterflies: a field guide to the butterflies of Britain and Ireland (second edition).
WILD*Guides*, Old Basing.

Newman L H, 1948
Butterfly haunts Chapman & Hall, London.

Palmer R M, Porter J & Collins G A, 2012
Smaller moths of Surrey. Surrey Wildlife Trust, Pirbright.

Pollard E & Yates T J, 1993
Monitoring butterflies for ecology and conservation. Chapman & Hall, London.

Robinson A & Brereton T, 2008
Habitat requirements of the Grayling butterfly *Hipparchia semele* on lowland heathland *in* **Botham M S, Brereton T M, Middlebrook I, Cruickshanks K L, Harrower C, Beckmann B & Roy D B,** *United Kingdom butterfly monitoring scheme report for 2008.*
Centre for Ecology & Hydrology, Wallingford.

Roy D B & Thomas J A, 2003
Seasonal variation in the niche, habitat availability and population fluctuations of a bivoltine thermophilous insect near its range margin. *Oecologia* **134**: 439-444.

Russwurm A D A, 1978
Aberrations of British butterflies. E. W. Classey, London.

Skelton M, 1999
Successful overwintering by Clouded Yellow *Colias croceus* (Geoff.) in Southern England.
Atropos **8**: 3-6.

South R, 1906
The butterflies of the British Isles (third edition, 1941). Frederick Warne, London.

Symes N & Day J C, 2003
A practical guide to the restoration and management of lowland heathland. RSPB, Sandy.

Thomas J A, 2007
Philip's guide to butterflies of Britain and Ireland. Philip's, London.

Thomas J & Lewington R, 2010
The butterflies of Britain & Ireland (revised edition). British Wildlife Publishing, Gillingham.

Tinbergen N, 1974
Curious naturalists (revised edition). Penguin Education, Harmondsworth.

Tucker M, 1997
The Red Admiral butterfly. Butterfly Conservation, Colchester.

Vallin A, Jakobsson S, Lind J & Wiklund C, 2006
Crypsis versus intimidation - anti-predation defence in three closely related butterflies.
Behavioral Ecology & Sociobiology **59**: 455-459.

Wiklund C, Kaitala A, Lindfors V & Abenius J, 1993
Polyandry and its effect on female reproduction in the Green-veined White butterfly
(*Pieris napi* L.). *Behavioral Ecology & Sociobiology* **33**: 25-33.

Willmott K, 1990
The Purple Emperor butterfly.
The British Butterfly Conservation Society Limited, Loughborough.

Willmott K, 1999
The Holly Blue butterfly. Butterfly Conservation, Colchester.

Wilson R, 2003
Silver-spotted Skipper survey 2002 *in* **Bridge M,** *Annual butterfly & moth report of the Surrey/SW London branch of Butterfly Conservation for the year 2002.*
Butterfly Conservation (Surrey/SW London Branch), Wareham.

Worms C G M de, 1950
The butterflies of London and its surroundings. *The London Naturalist* **29**: 46-80.

GEOLOGY

Batten D J (ed.), 2011
English Wealden fossils. Palaeontological Association field guides to fossils: No. 14.
The Palaeontological Association, London.

Brenchley P J & Rawson P F (eds), 2006
The geology of England and Wales (second edition). The Geological Society, London.

Ellison R A, Williamson I T & Humpage A J, 2002
Geology of the Guildford district - a brief explanation of the geological map.
Sheet Explanation of the British Geological Survey.
1:50,000 Sheet 285 Guildford (England and Wales).
British Geological Survey, Keyworth, Nottingham.

Ellison R A, Woods M A, Allen D J, Forster A, Pharoah T C & King C, 2004
Geology of London. *Memoir of the British Geological Survey,*
Sheets 256 (North London), 257 (Romford), 270 (South London), 271 (Dartford)
British Geological Survey, Keyworth, Nottingham.

Fortey R, 2010
The hidden landscape: a journey into the geological past (second edition).
The Bodley Head, London.

Stevens A J, 1976
Geology and soils *in* **Lousley J E,** *Flora of Surrey.* David and Charles, Newton Abbot.

PHOTOGRAPHY

Bebbington J, 2012
Insect photography: art and techniques. Crowood Press, Marlborough.

Davies A, 2010
Close-up and macro photography. Focal Press, Oxford.

Harcourt Davies P, 1998
The complete guide to close-up and macro photography. David and Charles, Newton Abbot.

Hicks P, 1997
Photographing butterflies and other insects. Fountain Press, Kingston-upon-Thames.

Thompson R, 2002
Close-up on insects: a photographer's guide. Guild of Master Craftsman Publications, Lewes.

Thompson R, 2007
Close-up and macro: a photographer's guide. David and Charles, Newton Abbot.

SURREY BUTTERFLIES BY WINGSPAN

	mm min	*max*
Purple Emperor	70	92
Silver-washed Fritillary	69	80
Red Admiral	64	78
Peacock	63	75
Brimstone	60	74
Painted Lady	58	74
Dark Green Fritillary	58	68
White Admiral	54	66
Comma	50	64
Large White	58	63
Clouded Yellow	52	62
Grayling	51	62
Small Tortoiseshell	45	62
Meadow Brown	40	60
Marbled White	53	58
Small White	38	57
Speckled Wood	46	56
Ringlet	42	52
Green-veined White	40	52
Orange-tip	40	52
Glanville Fritillary	38	52

	mm min	*max*
Gatekeeper	37	48
Brown Hairstreak	36	45
Wood White	30	42
Chalkhill Blue	33	40
Purple Hairstreak	31	40
Adonis Blue	30	40
Small Copper	26	40
Common Blue	29	38
Silver-spotted Skipper	29	37
Small Heath	29	37
Large Skipper	29	36
White-letter Hairstreak	25	36
Dingy Skipper	27	34
Green Hairstreak	27	34
Small Skipper	27	34
Holly Blue	26	34
Silver-studded Blue	25	32
Brown Argus	25	31
Essex Skipper	26	30
Grizzled Skipper	23	29
Small Blue	18	25

SPECIES INDEX: LATIN

SPECIES INDEX: ENGLISH

THE SURREY WILDLIFE ATLAS SERIES

published by Surrey Wildlife Trust

"An outstanding monument . . . I am delighted to have them on my shelves."
– Sir David Attenborough

". . . great testament to the remarkable skills of great British naturalists."
– Chris Packham

Dragonflies of Surrey **by Peter Follett**

"Well produced, well written . . . at a sensible price." – ENTOMOLOGIST'S RECORD

Larger Moths of Surrey **by Graham A. Collins**

". . . a much-needed, thorough and extremely well-researched book." – ATROPOS

Hoverflies of Surrey **by Roger K. A. Morris**

"It should be, as the publishers hope, a model of its kind." – BRITISH WILDLIFE

Grasshoppers and Crickets of Surrey **by David W. Baldock**

". . . without doubt, the best County Orthoptera to be published to date."
– BIOLOGICAL RECORDS CENTRE ORTHOPTERA RECORDING SCHEME

Ladybirds of Surrey **by Roger D. Hawkins**

". . . an excellent book, a mine of information, attractively produced, and easy to read." – ANTENNA

Shieldbugs of Surrey **by Roger D. Hawkins**

"Entomologists thinking of starting on the study of true bugs would be well advised to start here . . . this is natural history at its best."
– ENTOMOLOGIST'S MONTHLY MAGAZINE

Ants of Surrey **by John Pontin**

". . . relevant wherever you record in Britain . . . this is an excellent book that I would recommend to beginner and expert alike."
– BEES WASPS AND ANTS RECORDING SOCIETY (BWARS)

Water Bugs and Water Beetles of Surrey **by Jonty Denton**

". . . nicely, even joyously, written and includes excellent colour photographs of nearly every species." – BRITISH WILDLIFE

Bees of Surrey **by David W. Baldock**

". . . worth reading cover to cover . . . an inspiring piece of work that is useful far beyond the boundaries of this fine county"
– BEES WASPS AND ANTS RECORDING SOCIETY (BWARS)

Wasps of Surrey **by David W. Baldock**

". . . a fascinating depth as well as breadth of coverage and a feast of excellent photographs" – INVERTEBRATE CONSERVATION NEWS

Smaller Moths of Surrey **by Bob Palmer, Jim Porter & Graham A. Collins**

". . . very useful addition to the biodiversity inventory of Surrey . . . an inspiration to others in different counties."
– ENTOMOLOGISTS'S RECORD & JOURNAL OF VARIATION

Butterflies of Surrey Revisited (2013) **by Ken Willmott, Malcolm Bridge, Harry E. Clarke & Francis Kelly**

Also published by Surrey Wildlife Trust

THE SURREY COUNTY CHECKLIST SERIES

***Beetles of Surrey – a Checklist* by Jonty Denton**

Order via
www.surreywildlifetrust.org
(go to "Shop")

SOLD OUT

***Butterflies of Surrey* by Graham A. Collins 1995**

***Amphibians and Reptiles of Surrey* by Julia Wycherley and Richard Anstis 2001**

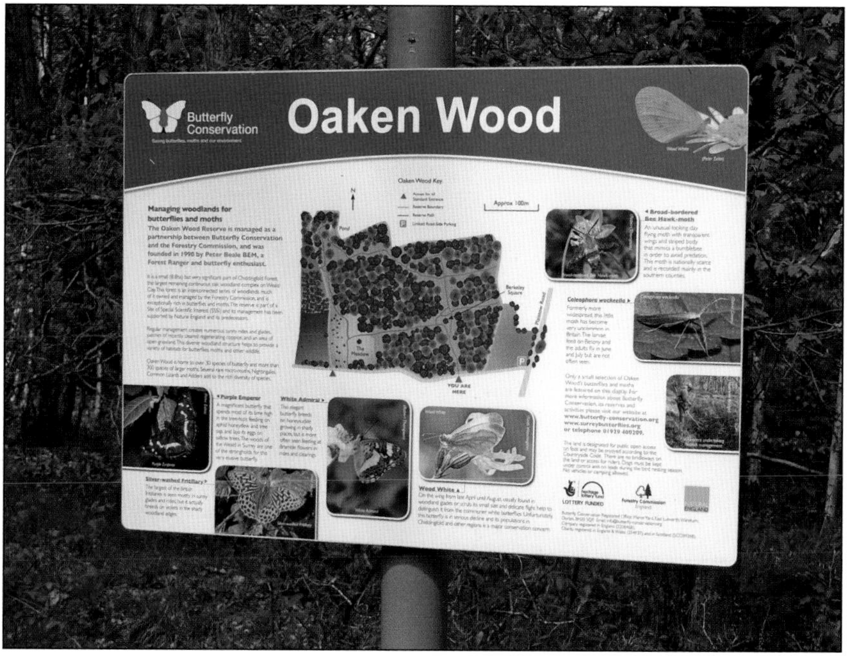

The information board at the entrance to Butterfly Conservation's Oaken Wood reserve at Chiddingfold.

SURREY WILDLIFE TRUST
Nature Reserves and Open Spaces

www.surreywildlifetrust.org/reserves

Ash Ranges (*restricted access*) SU917539
Ashtead Park TQ193585
Bagmoor Common SU926423
Barossa & Poors Allotments............SU875621
Bay Pond TQ351516
Betchworth Quarry & Lime Kilns ..TQ208518
Bisley & West End Commons SU946594
Blindley Heath Common TQ367448
Brentmoor Heath SU936612
Broadstreet, Backside & Ryde Hill Commons SU963507
Brockham Limeworks TQ197513
Brookwood Lye SU962574
Burners Heath & Swallow Pond SU948552
Chinthurst Hill TQ014462
Chitty's Common SU979524
Chobham Common.........................SU971647
Colekitchen Down TQ085488
Crooksbury Hill SU878459
Cucknells Wood TQ041430
Dawcombe (*via permit only*) TQ215525
Deepdene Terrace............................TQ174489
Dollypers Hill.................................TQ315584
Fir Tree Copse TQ023350
Fraser Down TQ212523
Glory Wood TQ171485
Gracious Pond SU987638
Graeme Hendrey Wood TQ346503
Hackhurst Downs TQ096487
Hankley & Elstead Commons SU915422
Hedgecourt.....................................TQ353403
Hill Park Estate TQ423560
Howell Hill.....................................TQ238618
Inholms Claypit TQ174471
Kitchen Copse TQ328525
Ledgers Wood TQ378593
Littlefield Common SU960526
Manor Farm TQ070608
McAlmont Reserves.......................SU956469
Middlebriars Wood.........................SU953457
Milford Green & Coxhill Green......SU981611
Milton Heath & The Nower TQ156485
Newdigate Brickworks...................TQ205427
Newlands Corner TQ044494
Norbury Park TQ158538
Nore Hill Chalk Pinnacle TQ378575
Nower Wood TQ193546
Papercourt Marshes (*via permit only*) TQ035562
Papercourt Meadows TQ032567
Park Ham & Quarry Hangers..........TQ319536
Pirbright Ranges (*no access*) SU921599
Puttenham Common........................SU910455
Rodborough Common SU934415
Runfold Wood SU869468
Seale Chalk Pit (*via permit only*) SU899482
Seccombe's Wood...........................TQ043433
Shabden Park TQ274563
Sheepleas TQ084514
Sheepwalk Lake TQ070675
Shere Woodlands TQ069489
Silent Pool TQ060485
Spynes Mere...................................TQ307524
St Martha's Hill TQ031485
Staffhurst Wood TQ414485
Stringer's Common.........................SU985534
The Forest, East Horsley TQ095552
The Moors, Redhill TQ209512
Thorpe Hay Meadow TQ030701
Thundry Meadows SU896440
Tilburstow Hill...............................TQ349501
Underdown.....................................SU832444
Vann Lake & Candy's Copse TQ157394
Wallis Wood TQ121388
Wentworth SU963666
Whippets Cant TQ181388
White Downs TQ112491
Whitmoor & Rickford Common SU985534
Wisley & Ockham Commons TQ080590
Wotton, Abinger & Broadmoor Commons TQ133441